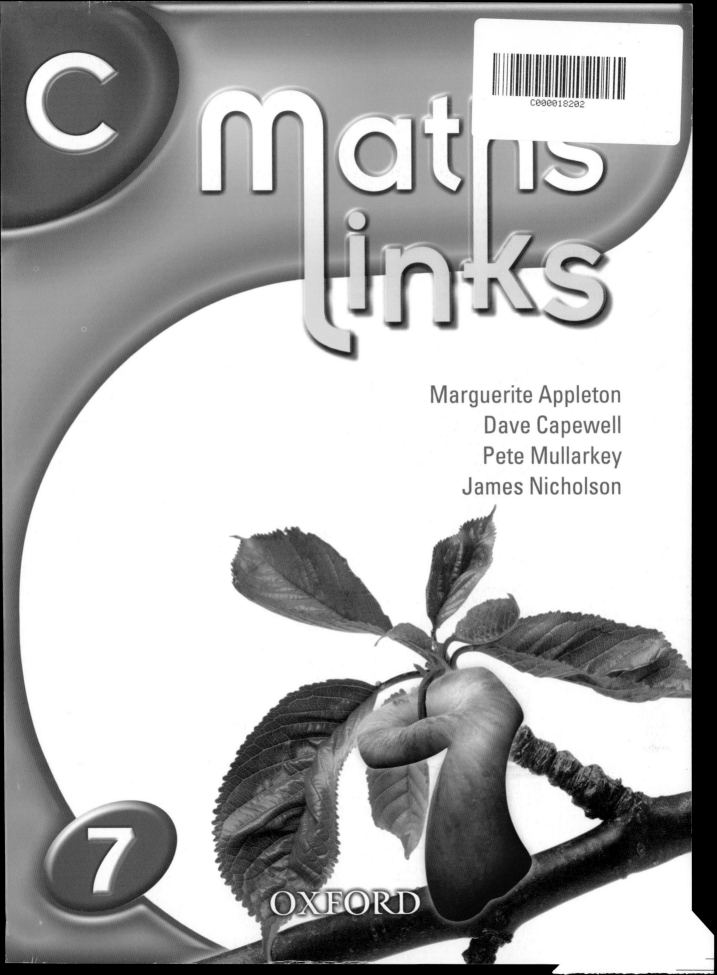

C maths links

Marguerite Appleton
Dave Capewell
Pete Mullarkey
James Nicholson

7

OXFORD

OXFORD
UNIVERSITY PRESS

Great Clarendon Street, Oxford OX2 6DP

Oxford University Press is a department of the University of Oxford.
It furthers the University's objective of excellence in research, scholarship, and
education by publishing worldwide in

Oxford   New York

Auckland   Cape Town   Dar es Salaam   Hong Kong   Karachi
Kuala Lumpur   Madrid   Melbourne   Mexico City   Nairobi
New Delhi   Shanghai   Taipei   Toronto

With offices in

Argentina   Austria   Brazil   Chile   Czech Republic   France   Greece
Guatemala   Hungary   Italy   Japan   Poland   Portugal   Singapore
South Korea   Switzerland   Thailand   Turkey   Ukraine   Vietnam

British Library Cataloguing in Publication Data

Data available

ISBN-13: 9780-19-915281-0
10 9 8 7 6 5 4 3 2

Printed in Spain by Cayfosa

Paper used in the production of this book is a natural, recyclable product made
from wood grown in sustainable forests. The manufacturing process conforms
to the environmental regulations to the country of origin.

Acknowledgments
The editors would like to thank: Stefanie Sullivan, Nottingham Shell Centre,
for her advice with the Case Studies; Mike Heylings and Jennie Golding for
their excellent reviews of this book; and Dave Capewell and Clare Plass for
their contributions to the material.

p 1 The Print Collector/Alamy; **p 3** Photography/Alamy; **p 7** OUP; **p 17** Image
100/Corbis UK Ltd.; **p 33** Picture Library/Alamy; **p 53** Nic Hamilton/Alamy; **p 61**
Tim Davis/Corbis UK Ltd.; **p 69** Pictures/Getty Images; **p 71** David Bowman/
Alamy; **p 73** Juniors Bildarchiv/Alamy; **p 75** Steve Dibblee/iStockphoto; **p 85**
Dagli Orti/Art Archive; **p 92** OUP; **p 93** OUP; **p 99** Zooid Pictures; **p 111** OUP;
p 119 Maciej Czajka/Alamy; **p 123** Gerry Penny/Epa/Corbis UK Ltd.; **p 125**
OUP; **p 173** OUP; **p 193t** PM Images/Iconica/Getty Images; **p 193c** OUP, **p 198**
OUP; **p 199** Joe Fox/Alamy; **p 201** OUP; **p 204** Roman Soumar/Corbis UK Ltd.;
p 209 Bettman/Corbis UK Ltd.; **p 219** OUP; **p 225** Juniors Bildarchiv/Alamy; **p
229** Dexter Mikami/Alamy; **p 249** Ian Waldie/Getty Images; **p 269** OUP; p 271
Dainis Derics/iStockphoto; **p 275** Adrian Sherratt/Alamy;

Figurative artworks are by:
Peter Donnelly: **p 135, 161², 169**; Ian Naylor: **p 50-1, 266-7**; The Beacon
Studio: **p 165**. All other figurative artworks are by Geo Parkin.

Contents

First page of a chapter
The first page of each chapter shows you real-life maths in context and also includes levelled Check in questions.

Consolidation
The Consolidation pages offer additional practice for each lesson in the chapter.

Lesson²
A 'squared' lesson exists outside of the running page order and either consolidates or extends a topic.

Summary
The Summary page for each chapter contains Key Indicators, a levelled worked exam-style question and levelled past KS3 exam questions.

Case Study
The Case Studies bring maths alive through engaging real-life situations and innovative design.

continued next page

Number

Algebra

Shape

1 Number

Integers and decimals

In 1843, Lady Ada Lovelace wrote what would become the first computer program when she wrote a series of instructions for one of the first 'computers', the Analytical engine. In her honour, Microsoft uses her image on its authenticity holograms.

What's the point? Computers and calculators aren't as modern as we think. People have been using these tools for generations.

 **Check in**

1 Calculate these using an appropriate written method.
    a $451 + 75$ **b** $562 - 58$ **c** $684 + 356$ **d** $504 - 237$

2 Match each of these numbers in figures with the correct number in words.

| 52080 | $502\frac{8}{10}$ | 5028000 | 520008 | $5\frac{28}{100}$ |

    a Five and twenty eight hundredths
    b Fifty-two thousand and eighty
    c Five million and twenty-eight thousand
    d Five hundred and two and eight tenths
    e Five hundred and twenty thousand and eight

3 Calculate
    a 17×10 **b** 35×100 **c** $48 \div 10$ **d** $130 \div 100$

4 Put these temperatures in order from lowest to highest:
    -6°C   -1°C   8°C   4°C   0°C

- Understand place value in decimals
- Compare the size of decimals and put them in order

Keywords
Decimals   Place value
Digit   Tenth
Hundredth   Thousandth
Order

- The value of each **digit** in a number depends upon its place in the number. This is called its **place value**.

example

What does the digit **3** represent in the number 17.08**3**?

Thousands 1000	Hundreds 100	Tens 10	Units 1	•	Tenths $\frac{1}{10}$	Hundredths $\frac{1}{100}$	Thousandths $\frac{1}{1000}$
		1	7	•	0	8	3

The number 17.083 stands for

1 ten + 7 units + 0 **tenths** + 8 **hundredths** + 3 **thousandths**.
The **3** digit represents 3 thousandths and can be written as 0.003 or $\frac{3}{1000}$.

- Fractions expressed as tenths, hundredths and thousandths can be written as decimals.

example

Write the number 4 units and 28 thousandths as a decimal.

Units 1	•	Tenths $\frac{1}{10}$	Hundredths $\frac{1}{100}$	Thousandths $\frac{1}{1000}$
4	•	0	2	8

✓

The zero in the tenths column is a placeholder.

28 thousandths are the same as 2 hundredths and 8 thousandths. You can write the number 4 units + 28 thousandths as
4 units + 0 tenths + 2 hundredths + 8 thousandths = 4.028

10 thousandths are the same as 1 hundredth.

- To **order** decimals, digits in the same position must be compared, beginning with the first non-zero digit.

example

Put these numbers in order from lowest to highest.
0.06   0.0634   0.067   0.059   0.064

Line up the numbers vertically.

Compare the hundredths digit. 5 is lowest.

Then compare the thousandths digits of the remaining numbers.

The order is 0.059, 0.06, 0.063, 0.064, 0.067.

0.06
0.063
0.067
0.059
0.064

0.06 = 0.060

Exercise 1a

1 Write each of these numbers in words.

   a 52.6   **b** 45.09   **c** 5.008   **d** 25.034   **e** 107.302

Express the digits after the decimal point as tenths, hundredths or thousandths.

2 Write each of these numbers in figures.

   a four hundred and seven thousand, and twenty-eight
   b three million, twenty-eight thousand, and seven
   c four and three hundredths
   d eight and seventeen hundredths
   e thirty-five and forty-three hundredths
   f twenty-five hundred and three thousandths
   g twelve units, and two hundred and sixty-five thousandths
   h two units, and three hundred and seventy thousandths

3 Write the value of the 4 in each of these numbers.
   Write your answer in words.

   a 2540   **b** 18 470   **c** 204 103   **d** 140 263   **e** 4 523 712
   f 71.4   **g** 83.24   **h** 81.254   **i** 7.04   **j** 21.054

Did you know?

The idea of zero as a place holder originated in 12th century India.

4 Write each list of numbers in order, starting with the smallest.

   a 4.3   4.29   4.4   4.34   4
   b 2.63   2.646   2.61   2.77   2.7
   c 0.02   0.044   0.04   0.043   0.042
   d 1.8   1.782   1.099   1.787   1.78
   e 5.305   5.3   5.318   5.2   5.31
   f 4.543   4.548   4.54   4.55   4.5

5 Place < or > between these pairs of numbers to show
   which number is the larger.

   a 0.48 ☐ 0.45   **b** 1.92 ☐ 1.91   **c** 15.284 ☐ 15.283
   d 9.25 ☐ 9.3   **e** 6.48 ☐ 6.32   **f** 1.723 ☐ 1.729
   g 12.385 ☐ 12.38   **h** 5.303 ☐ 5.31

< means less than.
> means greater than.

6 Put these measurements in order, starting with the smallest.

   a 1200 cm   1.4 km   13 m 27 cm   112.8 m
   b 3 kg   3.085 kg   2.95 kg   2905 g   2.9 kg

100 cm = 1m
1000 m = 1km
1000 g = 1kg

7 Find the number that is halfway between
   a 5.1 and 5.2   **b** 3.48 and 3.49

challenge

   a 0.85 lies exactly between two numbers.
      What could the two numbers be?
   b Given that 12.6 < y < 12.8, what possible numbers
      could y be if it has 2 decimal places?

- Multiply and divide decimals by 10, 100, 0.1 and 0.01

Keywords

Digit   Multiply

Divide   Powers

- The decimal system is based upon **powers** of 10.

1 hundred	$= 100$	$= 10 \times 10$	$= 10^2$
1 thousand	$= 1000$	$= 10 \times 10 \times 10$	$= 10^3$
10 thousand	$= 10\ 000$	$= 10 \times 10 \times 10 \times 10$	$= 10^4$

- When you **multiply** a number by a positive power of 10, all the **digits** move to the left.
- When you **divide** a number by a positive power of 10, all the digits move to the right.

example

Calculate   **a** 2.85×10^2 **b** $3290 \div 10^3$

....

a 2.85×10^2

    $= 2.85 \times 10 \times 10$

    $= 2.85 \times 100$

    $= 285$

b $3290 \div 10^3$

    $= 3290 \div 10 \div 10 \div 10$

    $= 3290 \div 1000$

    $= 3.290$

> When you multiply by 10^2 the digits move **2** places to the left.

> When you divide by 10^3 the digits move **3** places to the right.

p. 230

- Multiplying by 0.1 has the same effect as multiplying by $\frac{1}{10}$ or dividing by 10.
- Multiplying by 0.01 has the same effect as multiplying by $\frac{1}{100}$ or dividing by 100.

- Dividing by 0.1 has the same effect as dividing by $\frac{1}{10}$ or multiplying by 10.
- Dividing by 0.01 has the same effect as dividing by $\frac{1}{100}$ or multiplying by 100.

example

Calculate

a 8×0.1 **b** 6×0.01 **c** $18 \div 0.01$ **d** $35 \div 0.1$

....

a $8 \times 0.1 = 8 \times \frac{1}{10} = 8 \div 10$

                  $= 0.8$

b $6 \times 0.01 = 6 \times \frac{1}{100} = 6 \div 100$

                  $= 0.06$

c $18 \div 0.01 = 18 \div \frac{1}{100} = 18 \times 100$

                   $= 1800$

d $35 \div 0.1 = 35 \div \frac{1}{10} = 35 \times 10$

                   $= 350$

Exercise 1b

1 Calculate

  a 23 × 10   **b** 19 × 100   **c** 35 ÷ 10   **d** 470 ÷ 100

  e 38 × 10   **f** 3.9 × 10   **g** 67 ÷ 100   **h** 279 ÷ 10

  i 0.8 × 1000   **j** 1.3 × 100   **k** 3.6 ÷ 10   **l** 0.053 × 100

  m 0.0085 × 10   **n** 1.47 ÷ 100   **o** 590 ÷ 1000   **p** 0.000067 × 100

2 Calculate

  a 44×10^2 **b** 9×10^3 **c** $350 \div 10^2$ **d** $5200 \div 10^3$

  e 5.2×10^3 **f** 1.4×10^2 **g** $127 \div 10^2$ **h** $358 \div 10^2$

  i 0.75×10^3 **j** 4.87×10^3 **k** $7.6 \div 10^2$ **l** 0.061×10^2

  m 0.005×10^2 **n** $6.35 \div 10^2$ **o** $41 \div 10^3$ **p** $0.000\,041 \times 10^2$

3 Calculate

  a 270 × 0.1   **b** 95 × 0.1   **c** 6 × 0.1   **d** 0.7 × 0.1

  e 270 ÷ 0.1   **f** 95 ÷ 0.1   **g** 6 ÷ 0.1   **h** 0.7 ÷ 0.1

  i 430 × 0.01   **j** 61 × 0.01   **k** 7 × 0.01   **l** 0.3 × 0.01

  m 430 ÷ 0.01   **n** 61 ÷ 0.01   **o** 7 ÷ 0.01   **p** 0.3 ÷ 0.01

4 Calculate

  a 28 × 0.1   **b** 136 ÷ 0.1   **c** 29 × 0.01   **d** 11 ÷ 0.01

  e 64 ÷ 0.1   **f** 9 ÷ 0.01   **g** 268 × 0.1   **h** 0.7 × 0.01

  i 54 × 0.01   **j** 0.87 × 0.1   **k** 7 ÷ 0.01   **l** 0.8 ÷ 0.1

5 Here are six number cards.
Use one of the cards to complete
each of these statements.

                                 | 10 | 1000 | 100 | 1 | 0.1 | 0.01 |

  a 8 × ☐ = 80   **b** 0.4 × ☐ = 40   **c** 360 ÷ ☐ = 36   **d** 480 ÷ ☐ = 48

  e 8 ÷ ☐ = 80   **f** 0.4 ÷ ☐ = 40   **g** 360 × ☐ = 36   **h** 480 × ☐ = 48

This is a spider diagram to show different
ways of multiplying or dividing a number
by 10, 100, 1000, 0.1 and 0.01 to make a final
answer of 640.

  a Copy and complete this spider diagram.
You have to decide what numbers go
inside the empty boxes.

  b Add as many branches as you can,
and try to make some long chains
of your own.

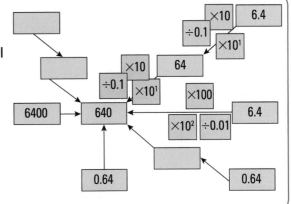

1c Negative numbers

- Combine positive and negative numbers in different ways

Keywords
Integer
Negative
Positive

- You can order **positive** and **negative** numbers using a number line.

Place these numbers in order, starting with the smallest. 0.5, -0.5, 3.2, -2.7

The correct order is -2.7, -0.5, 0.5, 3.2

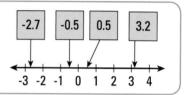

- You can use a number line to help you add or subtract from a negative **integer**.

$-9 + 8 = -1$

$1 - 8 = -7$

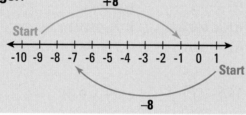

An integer is a whole number.

When adding, move up (→) the number line.

When subtracting, move down (←) the number line.

- Adding a negative integer is the same as subtracting a positive integer. Subtracting a negative integer is the same as adding a positive integer.

$-1 + -8 = -1 - 8 = -9$ $-9 - -8 = -9 + 8 = -1$

- You can multiply and divide negative integers according to these rules.

Multiply or divide	by negative integer	by positive integer
negative integer	+	−
positive integer	−	+

Calculate   **a** -4×3 **b** $-12 \div -4$

a $4 \times 3 = 12$

$- \times + = -$

$-4 \times 3 = -12$

b $12 \div 4 = 3$

$- \div - = +$

$-12 \div -4 = +3 = 3$

Exercise 1c

1 Put each of these sets of numbers in order, starting
with the smallest.

a -8	-5	3	0	-4
b -15	13	-9	-13	12
c -6	2.5	-5.5	-4	8
d -1.5	2	0	-4.5	5.5
e -3	-3.1	-4	-3.8	-3.7

2 Calculate

a -7 + 4	**b** -11 − 5	**c** -18 + 16
d 19 − 33	**e** -6 + 18	**f** -4 + 17
g -33 − 2	**h** -5 − 4 − 3	**i** -18 + 17 −16

3 Calculate

a 19 + -4	**b** 12 + -17	**c** 13 + -13
d -4 + -13	**e** -15 + -11	**f** 19 − -4
g 12 − -17	**h** 13 − -13	**i** -4 − -13
j -15 − -11	**k** -12 − -8	**l** -15 − -16
m -18 + -23	**n** 28 + -17	**o** 8 − -27

4 Calculate

a 5 × -3	**b** -6 × 8	**c** -3 × -9
d -8 × -9	**e** -7 × 9	**f** -6 × -9
g 7 × -7	**h** -8 × -8	**i** -9 × 9
j -8 × -10	**k** -20 ÷ -4	**l** -30 ÷ 6
m -56 ÷ -8	**n** -63 ÷ -7	**o** 64 ÷ -8

5 Ben's homework has been marked by his teacher. Look
at the questions he got wrong. Explain why each is wrong
and write down the correct answer.

a 3 × -5 = 15 ✗   **b** 50 ÷ -2 = -25 ✓

c -80 ÷ -8 = -10 ✗   **d** -14 × -4 = -56 ✗

e 17 × -2 = -34 ✓   **f** -72 ÷ 9 = 8 ✗

g 9 × -5 = 45 ✗   **h** 90 ÷ -5 = 18 ✗

problem

A submarine is 50 m below sea level.

It dives in four bursts of 30 m each.

It then rises twice, 15 m each time.

If there is a wrecked ship 150 m below sea level,

does the submarine avoid it?

* Add and subtract whole numbers and decimals mentally

Keywords
Compensate   Partition
Difference   Round

* You can **partition** (split) numbers into parts to make them easier to add or subtract.

---

example

Calculate $9.3 + 7.8$.

$9.3 + 7.8 = 9.3 + 7 + 0.8$ Think of 7.8 as 7 + 0.8.

$\quad\quad\quad = 16.3 + 0.8$ Add 7 to 9.3 first, then add 0.8.

$\quad\quad\quad = 17.1$

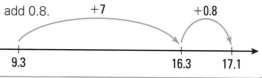

$+7$ $+0.8$

9.3   16.3   17.1

---

* You can **round** the number you need to add or subtract to make the calculation easier. You must then **compensate** for the rounding by adding or subtracting as necessary.

---

example

Calculate $14.7 - 5.9$.

$14.7 - 5.9 = 14.7 - 6$ 5.9 is nearly 6, so subtract 6.

$\quad\quad\quad = 8.7 + 0.1$ Add 0.1 to compensate

$\quad\quad\quad = 8.8$ $(6 - 5.9 = 0.1)$

-6

8.7   8.8   14.7

$+0.1$

---

* You can find the **difference** between two numbers by counting up from the smallest number to the largest number. This method is sometimes called 'shopkeeper's subtraction'.

---

example

Teri is investigating the population of Littleton.
There are 8207 people in the town, of whom 3789 are men.
How many of the people who live in Littleton are women?

Start at the lowest number, 3789, and count up in 'chunks' until you reach 8207.
Then add the 'chunks' together.

$8207 - 3789 = 11 + 200 + 4000 + 207$

$\quad\quad\quad\quad = 4418$ women

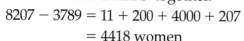

$+11$ $+200$ $+4000$ $+207$

3789 3800   4000   8000   8207

Exercise 1d

1 Calculate these using a mental method.

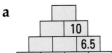

a 75 + 29   b 86 + 37   c 96 + 88   d 85 + 89

e 122 − 5   f 137 − 75   g 5.3 + 6.8   h 8.1 − 3.9

i 6.7 + 5.6   j 9.2 − 3.8   k 4.6 + 5.8   l 9.7 − 6.8

2 Complete each of these addition pyramids.
Each number is the sum of the two numbers below it.

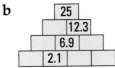

a
```
        [    ]
      [ 10 ]
        [ 6.5 ]
 [ 4.6 ][ 2.9 ][    ]
```

b
```
      [ 25 ]
        [ 12.3 ]
      [ 6.9 ]
 [    ][ 2.1 ][    ]
```

3 Calculate these using a mental method.

a 577 − 189   b 862 − 338   c 5074 − 3678   d 9126 − 4718

e 12.7 + 9.6   f 2.47 − 1.9   g 15.3 − 7.89   h 7.99 − 2.05

4 Use a mental method for each of these questions.

a Duane buys two cakes, each costing £1.85.
He pays with a £5 note. How much change does he get?

b What number do you need to add to 8.73 to make 13.2?

c Harry bought a coat for £37.99 and a scarf for £5.49.
He paid with a £50 note. How much change did he get?

d Indiana can run 100 m in 12.73 seconds. Jerome can run the
same distance in 10.9 seconds. How much quicker (in
seconds) than Indiana does Jerome run the 100 m?

e Three boxes weigh 1.2 kg, 0.98 kg and 1.4 kg.
What is the combined weight of the boxes?

problem solving

Here are seven cards.   ⬚ 1   ⬚ 2   ⬚ 3   ⬚ 4

⬚ 5   ⬚ 6   ⬚ 7

a Place the cards in this sum to make the total equal to 100.

⬚ ⬚ + ⬚ ⬚ + ⬚ ⬚ + ⬚ = 100

b Find another way of placing the cards to make the sum equal to 100.

⬚ ⬚ + ⬚ ⬚ + ⬚ ⬚ + ⬚ = 100

c Place the cards in this sum to make the total equal to 190.

⬚ ⬚ + ⬚ ⬚ + ⬚ ⬚ + ⬚ = 190

• Add and subtract decimals using the standard written method

Keywords
Approximately   Carrying
Borrowing   Estimate

• When you use the standard written method for addition, set the calculation out in columns, making sure you line up the decimal points.

• You should always **estimate** the answer first.

---

example

Calculate $6.06 + 17.8 + 9 + 0.79$.

Estimate first: $6.06 + 17.8 + 9 + 0.79 \approx 6 + 18 + 9 + 1 = 34$
Your answer should be close to 34.

Tens 10	Units 1	•	Tenths $\frac{1}{10}$	Hundredths $\frac{1}{100}$
	¹6	•	¹0	6
²1	7	•	8	0
	9	•	0	0
+	0	•	7	9
3	3	•	6	5

$6.06 + 17.8 + 9 + 0.79 = 33.65$

The $\approx$ sign means 'is approximately equal to'.

You can fill in with **zeros** so that all the numbers have the same number of decimal places.

---

example

A skip is filled with glass bottles for recycling.
When the skip is full it has a mass of 991.4 kg.
When the skip is empty it has a mass of 349.09 kg.
What is the mass of the bottles in the skip when it is full?

Estimate first: $991.4 \text{ kg} - 349.09 \text{ kg} \approx 990 - 350 = 640 \text{ kg}$
Your answer should be about 640 kg.

Hundreds 100	Tens 10	Units 1	•	Tenths $\frac{1}{10}$	Hundredths $\frac{1}{100}$
9	⁸9	¹1	•	³4	¹0
− 3	4	9	•	0	9
6	4	2	•	3	1

$991.4 \text{ kg} - 349.09 \text{ kg} = 642.31 \text{ kg}$

Exercise 1e

1 Calculate these using a written method.

    a 63.4 + 52.3   **b** 18.8 + 17.3   **c** 44.7 + 35.8

    d 16.8 − 11.9   **e** 23.7 − 16.5   **f** 34.6 − 25.8

2 Calculate these using a written method.

    a 4.54 + 8.3   **b** 24.6 + 8.65   **c** 83.4 + 78.69

    d 34.23 − 21.6   **e** 30.2 − 9.07   **f** 41.62 − 5.2

3 Calculate these using a written method.

    a 623.8 − 40.1   **b** 548.65 + 35.8   **c** 45.79 + 751.8

    d 1050.6 − 59.07   **e** 1228.6 − 36.03   **f** 72.4 + 1030.75

4 Calculate these using a written method.

    a 63.2 + 4.15 + 6 + 3.9

    b 43.8 + 31.9 − 56.27

    c 16.87 + 5.8 − 13.74 + 5.04 − 9.6

    d 36.04 + 9.3 − 17.29 + 7.38 − 4.9

5 **a** Liam wants to store some photos on his memory pen.
     The photos are 17.4 MB, 23.6 MB, 9.45 MB and 11.8 MB.
     His pen can hold a maximum of 64 MB.
     Can he fit the photos on his memory pen?
     Explain your answer.

    b The life expectancy of a baby born in Sweden is 79.6 years.
     The life expectancy of a baby born in Niger is 44.8 years.
     How much longer is the life expectancy of a baby born
     in Sweden?

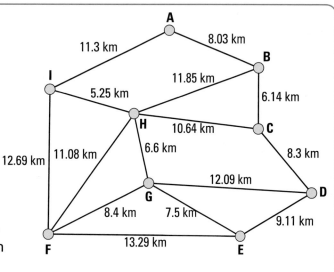

challenge

Adam works for a parcel delivery company. The diagram shows the distances between the towns in his area. The depot is in Town A.

a One day Adam has to deliver some parcels in Town E.
What is the shortest route from Town A to Town E?
Explain your answer.

b On 22 December Adam has to deliver parcels in all nine towns.
What is the shortest route he can take? Explain your answer.

* Use a calculator to work out longer calculations

Keywords
Brackets   Order of operation
Memory   Running total

* When solving problems, make sure you interpret the calculator display correctly.

* You can use the memory keys to keep a running total.

| 23.2 | can mean
* £23.20 (money)
* 23 m and 20 cm (length)
* 23 h and 12 min (time)
  (60 min × 0.2 = 12 min)

example

Nadim wants to buy these items from the shop.
   2 pens at 24p each
   3 writing pads at £1.59 each
   1 calculator at £2.25
What is the total cost of the items?

Always clear the calculator's memory before starting a new calculation.

Key in

Your calculator's memory keys may work differently to these.

The calculator display shows   [7.5]
The total cost of the items is £7.50.

* Scientific calculators follow the accepted **order of operations.** Make sure you know how to use
  * the **bracket** keys
  * the sign change key (for negative numbers).

The sign change key on your calculator might be labelled [+/−] or [(−)].

example

Calculate 4.2 × (3 + -2.1)

Key in [4] [.] [2] [×] [( ] [3] [+] [(−)] [2] [.] [1] [ )] [=]

The calculator should display   [4.2 × (3+−2.1)]

and give the answer   [3.78]

Check: 4.2 × (3 + -2.1)   ≈ 4 × (3 + -2)
                         ≈ 4 × 1 ≈ 4

3.78 is close to 4, so your calculator answer is probably correct.

Exercise 1f

1 Use the memory keys on your calculator to work out these calculations.

   a (2 × 14p) + (3 × £1.79) + £3.19

   b 43p + (2 × 11p) + (2 × 15p) + (4 × £1.79)

   c (5 × 14 cm) + (2 × 11 cm) + (3 × 1.79 m)

   d 1.8 m + (3 × 64 cm) + (2 × 1.1 m)

   e 20 minutes + (3 × 3 hours) + (5 × $2\frac{1}{2}$ hours)

2 Make a mental estimate for each of these calculations and then use a calculator to work out the exact answer.

   a 9.7 − (4.83 + 2.9)

   b 8.46 + -1.3

   c 201.4 − (111.3 − 42.79)

   d 8.5 − -3.07

   e -5.3 + 7.9

   f 3.3 − (5.2 − -6.7)

3 Shabana has £50 to spend on her school uniform.
Her shirt costs £12.99. A tie costs £7.49.
A pair of trousers costs £13.69.
A pair of black shoes costs £17.99.
Can she afford to buy her uniform? Explain your answer.

4 These are the times in hours that Luke takes travelling to and from school each day.

   Monday 1.4 hours

   Tuesday 1 hour 25 minutes

   Wednesday 1.25 hours

   Thursday 1 hour 10 minutes

   Friday 1.1 hours

  a How long does he spend in total travelling to and from school each week? Give your answer in hours and minutes.

  b How long does he spend travelling to and from school each week over the whole school year of 39 weeks?

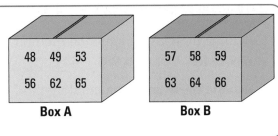

investigation

Sebastian picks three numbers from Box A and adds them together. He then picks three numbers from Box B and adds them together. He multiplies the two answers together. His answer is 29 340. What numbers did he pick from each box?

Box A: 48 49 53 56 62 65

Box B: 57 58 59 63 64 66

1a

1 Place < or > between these pairs of numbers to show which number is the larger.
   a 0.38 ☐ 0.37   **b** 1.72 ☐ 1.8   **c** 10.034 ☐ 10.101   **d** 5.85 ☐ 5.9
   e 4.12 ☐ 4.1   **f** 1.814 ☐ 1.82   **g** 2.085 ☐ 2.0841   **h** 1.03 ☐ 1.3

2 Write each list of numbers in order, starting with the smallest.
   a 2.4   2.39   2.3   2.44   2.05
   b 7.51   7.496   7.501   7.5   7.75
   c 0.091   0.098   0.1   0.09   0.088

1b

3 Calculate
   a 3×10^2 **b** 8×10^3 **c** $240 \div 10^2$ **d** $3940 \div 10^3$
   e 7.3×10^3 **f** 4.8×10^2 **g** $236 \div 10^2$ **h** $469 \div 10^2$
   i 0.43×10^3 **j** 2.96×10^3 **k** $8.4 \div 10^2$ **l** $7.1 \div 10^3$

4 Calculate
   a 590×0.1 **b** 0.4×0.1 **c** $48 \div 0.1$ **d** $8 \div 0.1$
   e 270×0.01 **f** 53×0.01 **g** $6 \div 0.01$ **h** $0.8 \div 0.01$

1c

5 Calculate
   a $13 + \text{-}7$ **b** $14 + \text{-}18$ **c** $\text{-}9 + \text{-}9$
   d $\text{-}12 + \text{-}17$ **e** $14 - \text{-}7$ **f** $13 - \text{-}16$
   g $\text{-}9 - \text{-}15$ **h** $\text{-}18 - \text{-}17$ **i** $\text{-}28 + \text{-}13$

6 Calculate
   a $4 \times \text{-}2$ **b** $\text{-}7 \times 5$ **c** $\text{-}4 \times \text{-}8$ **d** $8 \times \text{-}7$
   e $\text{-}11 \times \text{-}3$ **f** $\text{-}4 \times 8$ **g** $\text{-}30 \div \text{-}3$ **h** $\text{-}42 \div 6$
   i $\text{-}63 \div \text{-}9$ **j** $\text{-}72 \div \text{-}9$ **k** $49 \div \text{-}7$ **l** $\text{-}144 \div \text{-}9$

1d

7 Calculate these using a mental method.
   a $85 + 19$ **b** $96 + 26$ **c** $33 + 95$ **d** $9.7 - 2.9$
   e $2.6 + 5.5$ **f** $8.7 - 4.9$ **g** $12.1 + 3.7$ **h** $10.7 + 3.9$
   i $12.4 - 7.7$ **j** $18.5 + 7.5$ **k** $15.1 - 11.8$ **l** $9.5 - 6.99$

8 Calculate these using a mental method.
   a $689 - 103$ **b** $953 - 449$ **c** $2607 - 986$

9 Calculate these using a mental method.
   a $13.6 + 9.4$ **b** $27.4 - 6.8$ **c** $21.8 + 9.9$
   d $37.4 - 6.1$ **e** $23.5 + 19.8$ **f** $26.4 - 17.9$

10 Calculate these using a written method.

   a 8.8 − 5.3   **b** 17.4 + 13.2   **c** 27.8 − 15.9

   d 32.3 + 21.7   **e** 31.5 + 9.57   **f** 43.82 − 9.6

   g 13.7 − 5.8   **h** 31.2 + 28.4   **i** 71.8 − 34.9

   j 28 − 6.23 + 11.8   **k** 64.24 − 17 + 0.88 − 6.9

11 Belinda has a new pay-as-you-go mobile phone.
These are the costs of her last five calls.

   34.7p   11.7p   23p   5.9p   84.2p

What is the total cost of these calls?

12 These are the prices in the school
stationery shop.
Use the memory or brackets keys on
your calculator to work out which of
these orders are cheaper to buy after
1st January.

   a 4 pens, 2 writing pads, and
      1 calculator

   b 1 ruler, 5 pencils, 4 rubbers and
      2 writing pads

   c 3 pens, 5 pencils, 1 ruler,
      2 writing pads and a calculator

Prices up to 31st December

Pen	Writing pad	Calculator
16p	£1.95	£2.99
Rubber	Pencil	Ruler
25p	18p	49p

Prices after 1st January

Pen	Writing pad	Calculator
11p	£1.89	£3.29
Rubber	Pencil	Ruler
27p	15p	35p

13 a These are the times of each member
of a 4 × 400 m relay team.
What is the total time of the whole
team?

Pete	54.59 secs
Tom	1 min 2.3 secs
Rafael	59.8 secs
Leroy	53.03 secs

   b These are the heights of five pupils.
What is the total height of the five pupils?

Eve	1 m 58 cm
Sarah	1.6 m
Amy	1.45 m
Dawn	151 cm
Bella	1460 mm

1 Summary

Key indicators
- Understand decimal notation **Level 5**
- Multiply and divide numbers by 10, 100 or 1000 **Level 5**
- Add and subtract decimals using mental methods **Level 5**

Level 5

1 Terrie calculates **6.3 + 4.9** in her head.

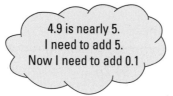

4.9 is nearly 5.
I need to add 5.
Now I need to add 0.1

Terrie's method
6.3 + 5 = 11.3
11.3 + 0.1 = 11.4

Terrie's method is wrong.
a What did Terrie do wrong?
b Give the correct answer.

Alison's answer ✔

| Alison realises 4.9 = 5 − 0.1 | a Terrie should not have added 0.1 She should have subtracted 0.1 <br> b 6.3 + 5 = 11.3
 11.3 − 0.1 = 11.2 | Alison remembers to subtract 0.1 |

Level 5

2 a Calculate the value of each card.

| 45.5 ÷ 100 | | 0.005 × 100 |

4.5 ÷ 10

| 0.055 × 10 | | 45 ÷ 1000 |

b List the numbers in order of size, smallest first.

2 Algebra

Sequences and functions

Fibonacci was an Italian mathematician, born in Pisa (where you will find the famous leaning tower). He studied the mathematics found in nature and architecture and found that some things followed a sequence.

What's the point? The Fibonacci sequence is 1, 1, 2, 3, 5, 8, 13, 21, …
Can you see how it works?

The Fibonacci sequence is very important because it occurs throughout nature, and helps us to understand how some things grow.

Check in

Level 3

1 **a** Start at 8. Count up in 7s until you reach 50.
   b Start at 13. Count up in 9s until you pass 100.
   c Start at 80. Count down in 8s until you reach zero.

Level 4

2 Write the first five numbers in each of these sequences.
   a the odd numbers   **b** the multiples of 3
   c the multiples of 7   **d** the multiples of 9
   Hint: the multiples of 3 are those numbers in the 3 times table.

3 Copy and complete each multiplication without using a calculator.
   a $4 \times 7 = \square$ **b** $6 \times 9 = \square$ **c** $10 \times 11 = \square$ **d** $5 \times \square = 40$
   e $6 \times \square = 42$ **f** $\square \times 7 = 63$ **g** $9 \times \square = 45$ **h** $8 \times \square = 56$

4 Copy and complete these mappings.

   a Input $\longrightarrow$ Output
Input		Output
4		$\square$
$\square$	+12	17
7		$\square$
$\square$		22

   b Input $\longrightarrow$ Output
Input		Output
$\square$		12
4	×6	$\square$
$\square$		30
8		$\square$

- Use a rule to find the next terms in a sequence

Keywords

Difference   Rule

Linear   Sequence

Random   Term

- Some groups of numbers are **random**; others form a pattern, known as a **sequence**.

- Each number in a sequence is called a **term**.
  46, 47, 48, 49, 50 are the first five terms of this sequence.

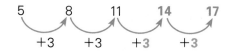

Door numbers often form a sequence.

- If the sequence increases or decreases in equal steps, it is called a **linear** sequence.
  7, 10, 13, 16, 19, …   This sequence increases in steps of 3.
  3, 2, 1, 0, -1, -2, …   This sequence decreases in steps of 1.

example

Write the next two terms of   **a** the linear sequence 5, 8, 11, …

                          b the sequence 3, 4, 7, 12, 19, …

a The sequence is linear so it will always increase in jumps of 3.
14 and 17 are the next two terms of the sequence.

5   8   11   **14**   **17**
   +3   +3   +3   +3

b The sequence increases by odd numbers, so you must now jump by **+9** and **+11**.
28 and 39 are the next two terms of the sequence.

3   4   7   12   19   **28**   **39**
   +1   +3   +5   +7   +9   +11

- A sequence can be described by a **rule**.
  Rule: a sequence starts at 5 and increases by consecutive numbers, starting with 1.

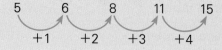

5   6   8   11   15
  +1   +2   +3   +4

Look at the **difference** between one term and the next term to find more terms in a sequence.

example

A sequence is described by the rule 'The first term is 5 and each term is double the previous term'.
Write the first five terms of this sequence.

1st term	2nd term	3rd term	4th term	5th term
5	10	20	40	80

     ×2   ×2   ×2   ×2

Exercise 2a

1 Copy each of these sequences and find the next two terms.
  a 97, 90, 83, 76, 69, …
  b 2, 4, 8, 16, 32, …
  c -17, -14, -11, -8, -5, …
  d 1 000 000, 100 000, 10 000, 1 000, 100, …
  e 3.4, 4.5, 5.6, 6.7, 7.8, …

2 Find the value of the missing terms in each linear sequence.
  a 6, 9, 12, 15, ☐, ☐, …   **b** 2, ☐, 10, 14, ☐, 22, …
  c ☐, ☐, 11, 19, 27, …   **d** ☐, -8, 10, ☐, 46, …

3 Write the first five terms of the sequence described by
  each rule.
  a 'The first term is 10. Each term is 9 more than the previous term.'
  b 'The first term is 40. This is a linear sequence decreasing by 5.'
  c 'The first term is 3. Each term is double the previous term.'
  d 'The first term is 20. Each term is 10 times the previous term.'
  e 'The first two terms are 2 and 3. Each term is the product
    of the two previous terms.'

> 'Product' means you have to multiply.

4 Describe the rule for each sequence in words.
  a 60, 56, 52, 48, 44, …   **b** 1, 5, 25, 125, 625, …
  c 4.6, 5.2, 5.8, 6.4, 7, …   **d** 1, -2, 4, -8, 16, …

5 Ben writes the first three terms of a sequence.
What are three different sequences which Ben
might be thinking of? Describe each rule in words.

> 2, 4, 8,...

6 Chords are played on the piano by playing
certain keys at the same time.
Musical notes show which keys are
to be played.

Can you find the sequence in this chord?
Where will the next note be?

research

Beats, rhythms and melodies are other musical things which
use sequences. Using the Internet, newspapers, magazines
and other books to research other sequences in music.

- Use a rule to find a term when you know its position in a sequence

Keywords
Position-to-term
Sequence
Term-to-term

Sequences can be described using a **term-to-term** rule.

Sequence	Term-to-term rule
3, 7, 11, 15, 19, …	The first term is 3 and add on 4 each time.

To find the 100th term of this sequence you would have to add on 4 many times. For this reason, a **position-to-term** rule is much more convenient.

- A position-to-term rule links the value of the term to its position in the sequence.

The position-to-term rule for this sequence is 'Multiply the position by 4 and take away 1.'

Position	1	2	3	4	5
Multiply by 4 and take away 1	$1 \times 4 - 1$	$2 \times 4 - 1$	$3 \times 4 - 1$	$4 \times 4 - 1$	$5 \times 4 - 1$
Term	3	7	11	15	19

Set your working out in a table to help you get used to starting with the position.

example

Find the first five terms and the 100th term of the sequence described by the rule 'Multiply the position by 3 and add 2.'

Position	1	2	3	4	5	100
Multiply by 3 and add 2	$1 \times 3 + 2$	$2 \times 3 + 2$	$3 \times 3 + 2$	$4 \times 3 + 2$	$5 \times 3 + 2$	$100 \times 3 + 2$
Term	5	8	11	14	17	302

The first five terms are 5, 8, 11, 14, 17 and the 100th term is 302.

example

Peri needs to use the position-to-term rule 'Multiply the position by 7 and subtract 2' to find the 1st, 5th, 10th, 25th and 50th terms of a sequence. What are these terms?

Position	1	5	10	25	50
Multiply by 7 and subtract 2	$1 \times 7 - 2$	$5 \times 7 - 2$	$10 \times 7 - 2$	$25 \times 7 - 2$	$50 \times 7 - 2$
Term	5	33	68	173	348

Exercise 2b

1 Match each sequence with both its term-to-term and its position-to-term rule. An example is given.

Term-to-term rule	Sequence	Position-to-term rule
Add 6	7, 9, 11, 13, 15, ...	Multiply by 3 and add 3
Add 3	4, 5, 6, 7, 8, 9, ...	Add 3
Add 1	2, 8, 14, 20, 26, ...	Multiply by 2 and add 5
Add 2	10, 20, 30, 40, 50, ...	Multiply by 6 and take 4
Subtract 5	20, 15, 10, 5, 0, ...	Multiply by 5 and take from 25
Add 10	6, 9, 12, 15, 18, 21, ...	Multiply by 10

2 Generate the first five terms of the sequences described by these position-to-term rules.

  a 'Add 6 to the position'   **b** 'Subtract 1 from the position'

  c 'Multiply by 4 and add 1'   **d** 'Multiply by 7 and take 4'

  e 'Multiply by itself'   **f** 'Divide by 2 and add 1'

3 A position-to-term rule is given by 'Multiply by ☐ and subtract ☐.' What numbers or words could go in each of the boxes to generate

  a a linear sequence   **b** the multiples of 20

  c a non-linear sequence   **d** the odd numbers

4 Generate the first five terms and the 100th term of the sequences defined by each position-to-term rule.

  a 'Add 5 to the position'

  b 'Multiply the position by 4 and add 1'

  c 'Multiply the position by 6 and subtract 2'

  d 'Multiply the position by itself and add 1'

> The position multiplied by itself is the position squared (n^2).

5 Find a position-to-term rule for each of these linear sequences.

  a 5, 9, 13, 17, 21, ...   **b** 25, 27, 29, 31, 33, ...

6 Describe each of the following sequences using your own position-to-term rule.

  a The multiples of 2

  b The cube numbers 1, 8, 27, 64, 125, ...

  c The sequence 1, 1, 1, 1, 1, ...

discussion

The Fibonacci sequence starts

0 1 1 2 3 5 8 13 21 34 55 ...

Can you describe how each term is generated?
Why is it difficult to find a position-to-term rule to describe the Fibonacci sequence?

- Understand algebraic notation
- Generate a sequence given a position-to-term rule

Keywords

Formula   Position-to-
General   term
  term   Sequence

- You can write a **position-to-term** rule using algebra.
  Make sure you know the rules of algebra.
  - Never write a × sign.
  - Never write a ÷ sign; use a fraction instead.
  - In products, write numbers before letters.

Write $5n$ not $5 \times n$.

Write $\frac{n}{2}$ not $n \div 2$.

Write $6n$ not $n6$.

---

example

Match the algebraic expression with its meaning.

Algebraic expression	Meaning
a $3n - 2$	**A** I think of a number, multiply it by 2 and add 1.
b $2(n + 1)$	**B** I think of a number, multiply it by 3 and subtract 2.
c $\frac{n}{2} + 3$	**C** I think of a number, divide it by 2 and add 3.
d $2n + 1$	**D** I think of a number, add 1, then multiply it by 2.

In a **sequence**, the letter n usually represents the position number, but other letters can be used.

....

a B   **b** D   **c** C   **d** A

- You can use **T**(n) to represent a term of a sequence.
  T(n) $5 = 5n - 1$ generates the linear sequence 4, 9, 14, 19, 24, ...
  1st term = T(1) = $5 \times 1 - 1 = 4$
  2nd term = T(2) = $5 \times 2 - 1 = 9$
  3rd term = T(3) = $5 \times 3 - 1 = 14$
  4th term = T(4) = $5 \times 4 - 1 = 19$
  5th term = T(5) = $5 \times 5 - 1 = 24$

Remember, n represents the position number.
T(n) represents the **n th term** or **general term**.

T(n) = $5n - 1$ is a **formula**.

---

example

Generate the first five terms and the 100th term of the sequence defined by T(n) = $3n + 4$.

....

Position	1	2	3	4	5	100
$3n + 4$	$3 \times 1 + 4$	$3 \times 2 + 4$	$3 \times 3 + 4$	$3 \times 4 + 4$	$3 \times 5 + 4$	$3 \times 100 + 4$
Term	7	10	13	16	19	304

The first five terms of the sequence defined by T(n) = $3n + 4$ are 7, 10, 13, 16, and 19. The 100th term is 304.

Exercise 2b²

1 Emma likes to do magic tricks with numbers.
Write her sentences using algebraic notation.
   a 'I think of a number and divide it by 8.'
   b 'I think of a number, multiply it by 5 and subtract 6.'
   c 'I think of a number, divide it by 3 and add 11.'
   d 'I think of a number, add 5 and then multiply it by 7.'

2 Write a sentence starting with 'I think of a number …' to
   describe what each of these algebraic expressions means.
   a $7n$
   b $\dfrac{n}{4}$
   c $2n - 1$
   d $\dfrac{n}{2} + 4$
   e $5(n - 2)$

3 Generate the first five terms and the 100th term of the
   sequences defined by these rules.
   a $T(n) = 6n - 2$ b $T(n) = \dfrac{n}{2}$

   c $T(n) = 2(n + 1)$ d $T(n) = \dfrac{2n + 2}{4}$

4 The number grid shows the first five terms of each of the
   sequences described below. The sequences lie horizontally,
   vertically or diagonally.
   Copy the grid and ring the first five terms of each sequence.
   $T(n) = 5n - 1$ $T(n) = 3n + 2$
   $T(n) = 10n + 4$ $T(n) = n + 4$
   $T(n) = 4n + 2$ $T(n) = 5n$
   $T(n) = 2n + 6$

4	9	14	19	24	10
17	22	2	5	25	54
14	18	7	20	11	44
11	14	15	3	8	34
8	10	12	14	16	24
5	6	7	8	9	14

---

puzzle

The cards show the position-to-term rule for
four sequences.
   a Which sequence has the largest 5th term?
   b Is this statement true or false?
      'All four sequences have an even 10th term.'
   c As n gets bigger, which sequence gets smaller?
   d Write four rules of your own, each with the same
      second term as one of the given sequences.

$T(n) = 5n - 3$

$T(n) = n(n + 1)$

$T(n) = n^3$

$T(n) = 10 - n$

- Use an algebraic formula to write a linear sequence

Keywords

Difference   Linear

Generate   Sequence

- If the position-to-term rule for a **linear sequence** involves multiplying the position, n, by a number, the **difference** between the terms will equal that number.

    The rule $T(n) = 2n + 3$ generates the sequence 5, 7, 9, 11, 13, …
    The difference between the terms is **2**.

Remember: in a linear sequence the difference between successive terms is the same.

- To find the position-to-term rule for a linear sequence, find the difference between the terms and then compare the sequence to the relevant times table.

example

Find the position-to-term rule for the sequence
   5, 8, 11, 14, 17, …

First find the difference between the terms.

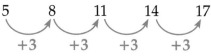

5   8   11   14   17

+3   +3   +3   +3

The difference between the terms is **3**.
Compare the sequence with the **3** times table.

Position	1	2	3	4	5
3 times table	3 +2	6 +2	9 +2	12 +2	15 +2
Term	5	8	11	14	17

The formula for the nth term must involve **3n**.

You **add 2** to the multiples of 3 to get the terms of the sequence.
The rule is
'Multiply the position by 3 and add 2' or $T(n) = 3n + 2$.

example

Generate the position-to-term formula for the sequence
   10, 22, 34, 46, 58, …

The sequence increases in 12s, so the rule involves
'multiply the position by 12'.
The terms of the sequence, 10, 22, 34, 46, 58, …, are each
2 less than the first five multiples of 12: 12, 24, 36, 48, 60, ….
The rule is
'Multiply the position by 12 and subtract 2' or $T(n) = 12n - 2$.

Exercise 2c

1 Find, in words and symbols, the position-to-term rule for each of these linear sequences.

   a 3, 6, 9, 12, 15, …   **b** 4, 6, 8, 10, 12, …

   c 10, 15, 20, 25, 30, …   **d** 5, 13, 21, 29, 37, …

   e 15, 28, 41, 54, 67, …   **f** 8, 6, 4, 2, 0, …

2 For a linear sequence, $T(2) = 9$ and $T(4) = 17$

   a Find $T(1)$

   b Find $T(100)$

> Try finding a formula first.

3 For a linear sequence, $T(5) = 18$ and $T(7) = 12$

   a Find $T(1)$

   b Find $T(100)$

4 A linear sequence is given by the rule $T(n) = an + b$. That is, multiply the position by a and then add b. What could be the values of a and b if

   a the sequence begins with zero

   b the sequence increases

   c the sequence decreases

   d all the terms of the sequence are odd?

5 A linear sequence is given by the rule $T(n) = an + b$. Is this statement true or false?

   'If a is smaller than b, the sequence will always decrease.'

You can generate the terms of any sequence quickly by inserting a position-to-term formula in a spreadsheet. Try inputting this formula into a spreadsheet.

	A	B
1	Position	Term
2	1	= A2*3 + 7
3	= A2 + 1	= A3*3 + 7
4	= A3 + 1	= A4*3 + 7
5	= A4 + 1	= A5*3 + 7
6	= A5 + 1	= A6*3 + 7

	A	B
1	Position	Term
2	1	10
3	2	13
4	3	16
5	4	17
6	5	22

> * means × on a spreadsheet

What formula do you need to input for each of these sequences?

   a 5, 7, 9, 11, 13, …   **b** 2, 8, 14, 20, 26, …

   c 10, 8, 6, 4, 2, …   **d** 1, 4, 9, 16, 25, …

2d Sequences in context

- Find a formula to fit a given sequence

Keywords
Pattern
Sequence

p. 258

- You can often find **sequences** in diagrams. The diagrams that make up a sequence are called **patterns**.

example

How many dots would be in the 10th diagram in this sequence?

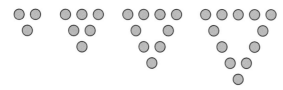

You could draw out the first 10 patterns, but it is quicker to find a position-to-term rule. Use a table to help you.

Position number (n)	1	2	3	4
Number of dots (d)	3	6	9	12

3, 6, 9, 12 is a linear sequence that increases in 3s. It is also the beginning of the 3 times table, so you don't need to add or subtract anything.

To find the number of dots, d, multiply the pattern number, n, by 3.
This can also be written as $T(n) = 3n$ or $d = 3n$

$$T(10) = 3 \times 10 = 30$$

The 10th diagram in the sequence will have 30 dots.

- You can often explain a rule by referring to the sequence diagrams.

example

Explain why the rule $T(n) = 3n$ works for the sequence given above.

The first diagram has 3 lots of 1 dot, the second has 3 lots of 2 dots, the third has 3 lots of 3 dots and so on. Each diagram has 3 lots of the pattern number.

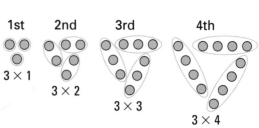

Exercise 2d

1 Here is a sequence of tiles.

    a Find a position-to-term rule which connects
    the pattern number with the number of tiles.

    b How many tiles will be in the 100th pattern?
    Explain why.

> Put your numbers into a table first.

2 Here are some 'up and down' staircases.

   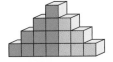

    a Using a table of values to help you, find a rule that
    connects the height of the staircase, H, with the number
    of blocks needed, B.

    b Explain why this rule works.

> You may wish to imagine moving the orange blocks!

3 Strips of cubes are taken and the outside faces painted blue.

Find a formula connecting the number of cubes in a strip, n
with the number of blue faces, b. Explain why this works.

4 In Chemistry, hydrocarbons are made by connecting carbon, C,
and hydrogen, H, atoms together using bonds (–), as shown.

    a The formula connecting the number of hydrogen
    and carbon atoms is $H = 2C + 2$. Explain why this works.

    b Find a formula connecting the number of carbon atoms and
    the number of bonds. Explain why this works.

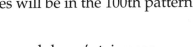

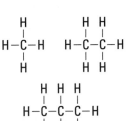

investigation

A child's puzzle involves moving a red counter from the
top left to the bottom right of a square grid.

Start
square

2×2 3×3 4×4 Finish
square

> All counters can move horizontally, vertically, up and down but not diagonally.

Investigate the smallest number of moves needed to
complete the puzzle for different sized grids. Can you
predict the number of moves for a 100×100 grid?

Sequences in context   **25**

2e Functions

- Use a function to find values

Keywords

Function	Output
Input	Rule
Inverse	Symbols

- A **function** is a **rule** that is performed on various **inputs** to produce **outputs**.

- Finding a function is similar to finding the position-to-term rule of a sequence.

> **example**
>
> Find the function that produces these values.
>
> | Input | 1 | 2 | 3 | 4 |
> |---|---|---|---|---|
> | Output | 8 | 11 | 14 | 17 |
>
> ....
>
> The outputs, 8, 11, 14, 17, are each 5 more than the first four multiples of which are 3, 3, 6, 9, 12.
> The function is 'Multiply by 3 and add 5'.

A function machine can help you think about functions

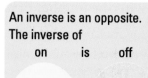

input → output

- Functions can be expressed in **symbols,** as well as in words.
  If we let x represent the input and y the output, the rule 'Multiply by 3 and add 5' could be written as $y = 3x + 5$.

- To find an input, given an output, you first need to find the **inverse** function.

An inverse is an opposite. The inverse of

on   is   off

> **example**
>
> Aisha is using the function $y = 2(x + 1)$.
> Find the missing values in this table.
>
> | Input | 7 | |
> |---|---|---|
> | Output | | 8 |
>
> ....
>
> In the first row, the input is $x = 7$.
> So the output is $2 \times (7 + 1) = 2 \times 8 = 16$.
> In the second row, the output is 8.
> Use the inverse function to find the input.
> So, 'undo' each operation in reverse order.
> The reverse of 'Add 1 and multiply by 2' is 'Divide by 2 and subtract 1'. $8 \div 2 - 1 = 3$

Exercise 2e

1 Copy the tables and fill in the missing function values.

a

Multiply by 3 and subtract 4	
Input	Output
3	
6	
12	
50	

b

Add 4 and divide by 2	
Input	Output
1	
6	
11	
	4.5

c

Multiply by itself and subtract 1	
Input	Output
4	
7	
10	
	80

2 What function maps these inputs to these outputs?

a

Input	Output
1	11
2	12
3	13
4	14

b

Input	Output
1	4
2	9
3	14
4	19

c

Input	Output
3	7
8	17
10	21
50	101

3 An input of 4 is used in five different functions.
Match the outputs to their correct functions.

Function	$y = 3x - 1$	$y = 5(x - 2)$	$y = 7x + 1$	$y = x^2$	$y = 10 - x$
Output	10	16	11	6	29

4 For each function, copy and complete the table of values.
a $y = 2x + 2$
b $y = 3(x - 1)$
c $y = 10 - 3x$

x	1	2	3	4	5	6	
y							24

5 Are these statements true or false? Give some examples of inputs and outputs to support your decision.
a Multiplying positive inputs by 3 will always give a larger output.
b Multiplying inputs by 2 and adding 1 will always give even inputs.
c Multiplying an input by 6 and dividing by 2 is the same as multiplying by 3.

A function has two operations. For example, the first operation could be 'Multiply by 2' and the second operation could be 'Add 6'.
Investigate this statement:
'Swapping the order of operations in a function always produces different outputs.'

investigation

- Find the output of a function which is given in words or algebra

Keywords

Mapping

Mapping diagram

- A function is also known as a **mapping** and can be represented by a **mapping diagram.**

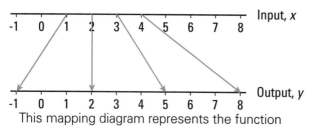

Input, x

Output, y

This mapping diagram represents the function 'Multiply by 3 and subtract 4'.

Sometimes a mapping is written as:

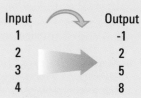

Input	Output
1	-1
2	2
3	5
4	8

- **Mappings are often expressed in symbols, using an arrow.**

The function 'Multiply by 3 and subtract 4' can be written as $x \to 3x - 4$.

This is also written

$y = 3x - 4$

---

example

Draw a mapping diagram to represent the function $x \to 2(x - 1)$. Use inputs from 0 to 5.

. . . .

Work out the inputs and put them in a table.

Then draw the mapping diagram.

0 maps to $2 \times (0 - 1) = -2$

1 maps to $2 \times (1 - 1) = 0$

Input	0	1	2	3	4	5
Output	-2	0	2	4	6	8

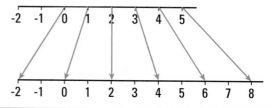

---

example

Draw a mapping diagram to represent the function $x \to x^2 - 1$. Use inputs from 0 to 4.

x^2 means 'x squared' multiply x by itself.

. . . .

Work out the inputs and put them in a table.

Then draw the mapping diagram.

0 maps to $(0 \times 0) - 1 = -1$

1 maps to $(1 \times 1) - 1 = 0$

Input	0	1	2	3	4
Output	-1	0	3	8	15

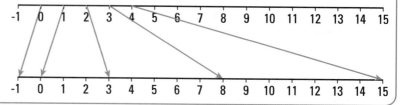

Exercise 2f

1 Draw a mapping diagram for each of these functions.
Use inputs from 0 to 5.

a $x \rightarrow x + 4$ **b** $x \rightarrow 3x - 2$ **c** $x \rightarrow 4(x + 7)$

d $x \rightarrow x^2 + 6$ **e** $x \rightarrow 2x + 1$ **f** $x \rightarrow 3(x - 1)$

g $x \rightarrow \dfrac{x}{2}$ **h** $x \rightarrow 6 - x$ **i** $x \rightarrow \dfrac{4(x + 1)}{2}$

2 Use algebra to write each mapping as a function.

a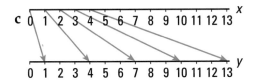

b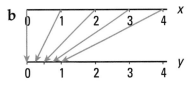

c

d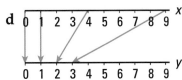

3 Draw a mapping diagram for each of these functions.
Use inputs from -5 to 5.

a $x \rightarrow x + 3$ **b** $y = 2x - 2$
c $x \rightarrow 4(x + 2)$ **d** $y = x^2 - 1$

> If you find the negative inputs difficult, start with the positive values and follow any patterns in the mapping diagrams that you can see.

4 Inputs from 1 to 5 are put into a function, f.
The outputs are then put into another function, g.
The mapping diagram shows the result.

a Find the functions f and g.
b Suggest other pairs of functions
that would produce the same effect
when applied one after another.

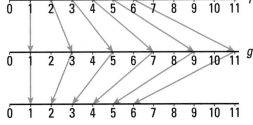

What functions could lead to the following arrangement of
arrows on a mapping diagram?

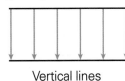

Parallel lines

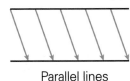

Vertical lines

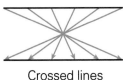

Crossed lines

2a

1 Copy each of these sequences and find the next two terms.
  a 3, 9, 15, 21, 27, …   b 1, 4, 9, 16, 25, …
  c 100, 94, 88, 82, 76, …   d 4, 8, 16, 32, 64, …
  e 50 000, 5000, 500, 50, 5, …

2 Copy each of these sequences and find the next two terms.
  a The linear sequence 4, 7, …
  b The linear sequence 10, 6, …

3 Generate the first five terms of the sequence described by each rule.
  a 'The first term is 7. Add on 8 each time.'
  b 'The first term is 4. Multiply by 3 each time.'
  c 'The first term is 100. Divide by 10 each time.'
  d 'The first term is 1. Multiply by 1 each time.'
  e 'The first two terms are 3 and 5. Add the two previous
    terms each time.'
  f 'The first term is 6. Halve the term each time.'

2b

4 Generate the first five terms of the sequences described by each rule.
  a 'Add 4 to the position'
  b 'Multiply the position by 5 then subtract 1'
  c 'Multiply the position by itself'
  d 'Divide the position by two'
  e 'Multiply the position by 3 and subtract the result *from* 20'

2b²

5 Generate the first five terms and the 100th term of the
  sequences with these position-to-term rules.

  a $T(n) = 3n + 1$ b $T(n) = 5n - 4$ c $T(n) = n^2 + 1$
  d $T(n) = 10 - n$ e $T(n) = 4(n + 3)$ f $T(n) = \dfrac{4n}{2}$

2c

6 Find a formula for the nth term, $T(n)$, of each of these
  linear sequences.
  a 5, 8, 11, 14, 17, …   b 2, 8, 14, 20, 26, 32, …
  c 11, 21, 31, 41, 51, …   d 30, 39, 48, 57, 66, …
  e 20, 18, 16, 14, 12, …

7 The diagram shows a pattern made from tiles.

Use a table to help you.

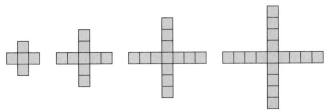

a Find a formula to connect the pattern number with the number of tiles used.

b Use your formula to work out the number of tiles in the 100th pattern.

c Explain why your formula works.

8 For each function described below, copy and complete this table of values.

Input	1	5	12	20
Output				14

a 'Multiply the input by 6 and subtract 4'

b 'Multiply the input by itself and add 5'

c $x \rightarrow x + 2$

d $x \rightarrow 2(x - 1)$

9 Draw a mapping diagram for each of these functions. Use inputs from 1 to 5.

a $x \rightarrow x - 2$ **b** $x \rightarrow 4(x + 2)$ **c** $x \rightarrow x^2 - 1$

d $x \rightarrow \dfrac{2x + 8}{4}$ **e** $x \rightarrow 20 - 2x$

10 Find the function represented by each of these mapping diagrams. Express your answer in symbols.

a

b
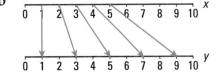

c
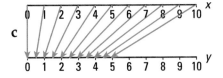

d
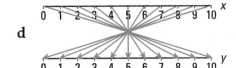

2 Summary

Key indicators
- Generate terms of a sequence using term-to-term definitions **Level 6**
- Generate terms of a sequence using position-to-term definitions **Level 6**

1 The rule to find the next term in a sequence is 'add the two previous terms.'

The first five terms in the sequence are 1, 1, 2, 3, 5.

a Write down the next 10 terms in the sequence.

b Copy and complete these sentences;

'Every 5th term is divisible by _____'

'Every _____th term is divisible by 3'

Graham's answer ✔

Graham adds 3 and 5 to give 8

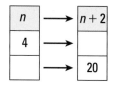

a 1, 1, 2, ⟨3, 5,⟩ 8, 13, 21, 34, 55,

89, 144, 233, 377, 610

b 'Every 5th term is divisible by 5'

'Every 4th term is divisible by 3'

Graham knows 5, 55 and 610 are divisible by 5 and 3. 21, 144 are divisible by 3 as the digits add to a multiple of 3

2 a A function maps the number n to the number $n + 2$.
Complete the missing values.

n	→	$n + 2$
4	→	
	→	20

Mappings can be written horizontally or vertically.

b A different function maps the number n to the number $2n$.
Complete the missing values.

n	→	$2n$
4	→	
	→	20

c Many different functions can map the number 25 to the number 5.
Complete the tables by writing two different functions.

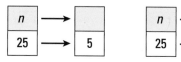

n	→	
25	→	5

n	→	
25	→	5

Key Stage 3 2004 4–6 Paper 1

3 Shape

Measures

The Great Pyramid of Giza is one of the oldest and largest buildings in the world. It was built over 4500 years ago with measurements so precise that you still cannot fit a sheet of paper between the stones.

What's the point? Ancient Egyptian builders didn't have laser levels and computers to help with their measurements. They built the pyramids largely with human hands and brain power.

 **Check in**

Level 3

1 What units of measurement would you use to measure
   a the height of a building   b the length of a drawing pin
   c the width of your textbook   d the distance between two towns?

Level 4

2 Work these out.

   a $\dfrac{5 \times 6}{2}$ b $\dfrac{4 \times 8}{2}$ c $\dfrac{1}{2} \times 6 \times 9$ d $\dfrac{1}{2} \times 3 \times 7$

3 Count the number of cubes in each of these cuboids.

   a
   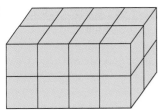
   b
   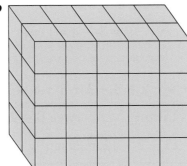

3a Perimeter and area of a rectangle

• Calculate the perimeter and area of a rectangle

Keywords
Area   Rectangle
Perimeter   Square
            centimetre

Harry is papering this room.
The border goes around the perimeter of the room.
The wallpaper covers the area of the wall.

• The **perimeter** is the distance around a 2-D shape.

• The **area** of a 2-D shape is the amount of surface it covers.
You measure area in squares.
One metric unit of area is the
square centimetre (cm^2).

1 cm

1 cm

You can use a formula to find the area of a rectangle.

• Area of a rectangle = length × width

Calculate **a**   the perimeter.
         b   the area of this rectangle.

3 cm

2 cm

a Add up the side lengths
   3 cm + 2 cm + 3 cm + 2 cm = 10 cm
   Perimeter = 10 cm

b Area = length × width
   = 3 × 2   There are 2 rows of 3 squares.
   = 6 cm^2

You can find the perimeter and area of shapes made from rectangles.

Calculate
a the perimeter.
b the area of this shape.

3 cm

3 cm

5 cm

4 cm

z

x

4 cm

A   B y C

8 cm

a First calculate the missing lengths

   $x = 8 - 3 - 3 = 2$ cm $y = 5 - 4 = 1$ cm

   $z = 4 - 1 = 3$ cm

Perimeter = 5 + 3 + 4 + 2 + 3 + 3 + 4 + 8 = 32 cm

b Area A = 3 × 5 = 15 cm^2 Area B = 2 × 1 = 2 cm^2 Area C = 3 × 4 = 12 cm^2

Area of the shape = 15 + 2 + 12 = 29 cm^2

Exercise 3a

1 Calculate the perimeter of each rectangle.
  State the units of your answers.

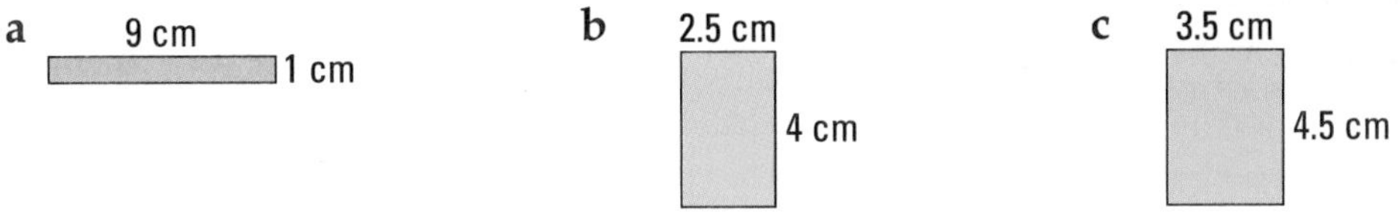

a   9 cm
    ▭ 1 cm

b   2.5 cm
    4 cm

c   3.5 cm
    4.5 cm

2 Calculate the area of each rectangle.

a   6 cm
    2 cm

b   6.5 cm
    4 cm

c   5 cm
    3.5 cm

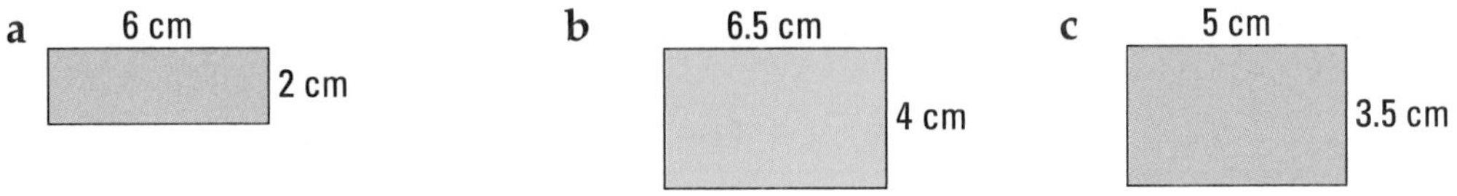

3 Calculate the perimeter and area of each rectangle.

a   8 cm
    4 cm

b   2 cm
    3.5 cm

c   10 cm
    8.5 cm

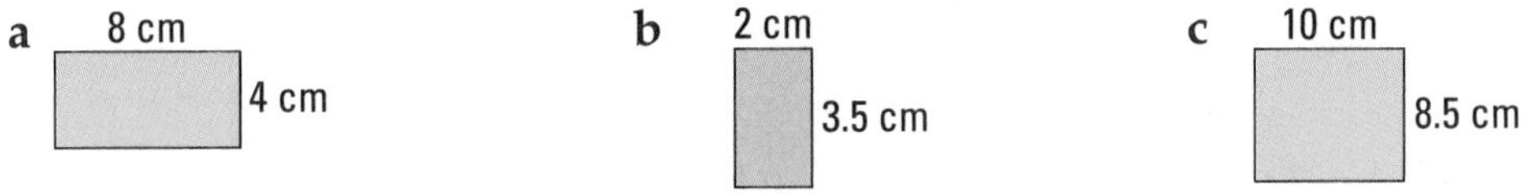

4 Calculate the perimeter and area of each rectangle.

a   3 mm
    8 mm

b   5.5 m
    6 m

c   30 mm
    1.4 cm

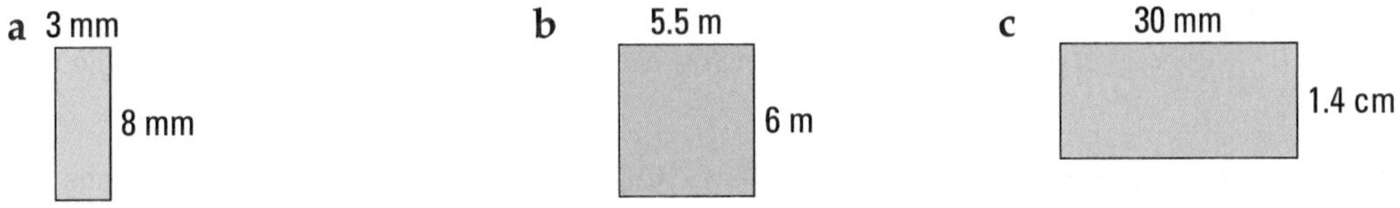

5 Calculate the area of each shape.
  Find the area of each rectangle first.

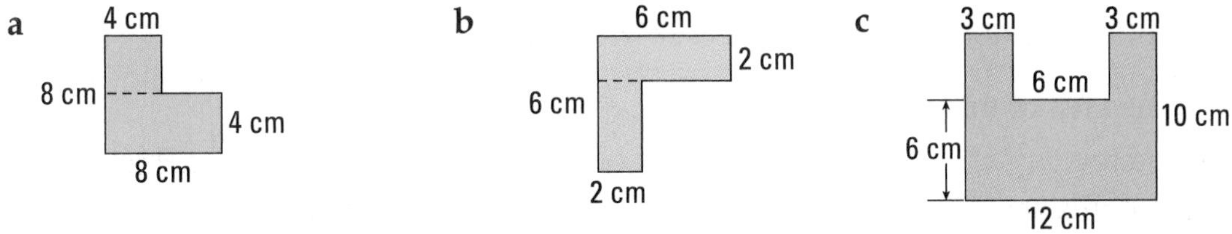

a   4 cm
    8 cm
    4 cm
    8 cm

b   6 cm
    2 cm
    6 cm
    2 cm

c   3 cm   3 cm
    6 cm
    6 cm   10 cm
    12 cm

investigation

A Year 7 gardening club planted these two vegetable plots. Each plot is surrounded by a path. Find the area of each vegetable plot and the area of each path.

a   5 m
    15 m
    10 m
    20 m

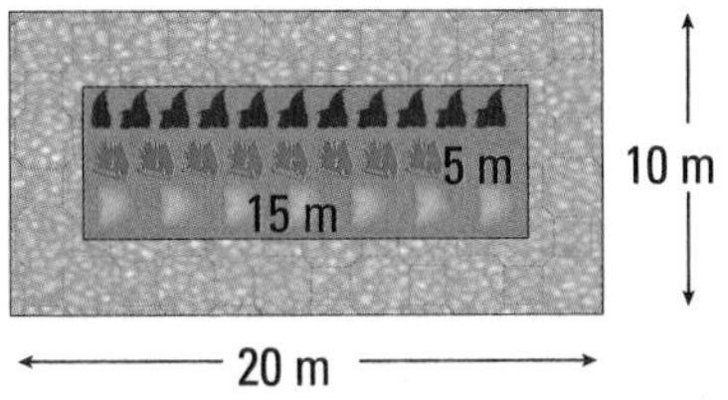

b   18 m
    8.5 m
    2 m

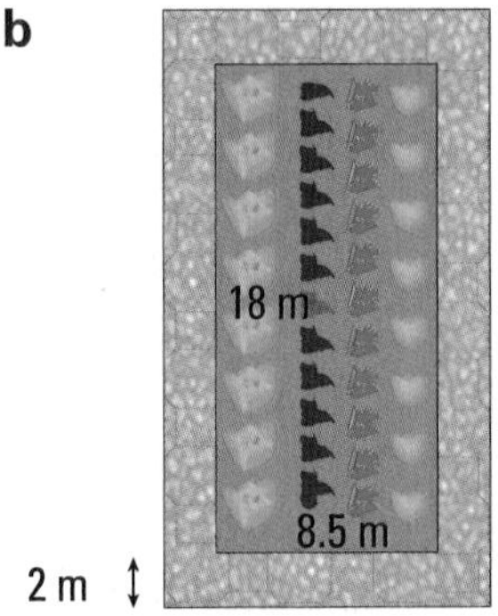

- Calculate the perimeter and area of a triangle

Keywords
Area   Perpendicular
Perimeter   Triangle

- To find the **perimeter** of a **triangle,**
  you add the lengths of all three sides.

example

Calculate the perimeter of this triangle.

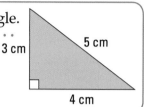

Perimeter = 3 + 4 + 5

= 12 cm

- You can find the formula for the **area** of a triangle

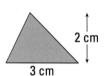 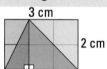

Split the triangle into two right-angled triangles.

The **perpendicular** height is the height of the rectangle.

The area of the triangle is half the area of the rectangle.

- Area of a triangle = $\frac{1}{2}$ (base × perpendicular height)

  $= \frac{1}{2} \times b \times h$

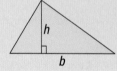

Perpendicular means 'at right angles to'.

example

Calculate the area of this triangle.

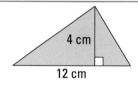

Area $= \frac{1}{2} \times b \times h$ base = 12 cm, height = 4 cm

$= \frac{1}{2} \times 12 \times 4$

$= 24 \text{ cm}^2$

Exercise 3a²

1 Calculate the perimeter of each triangle.
State the units of your answers.

a
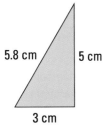
5.8 cm   5 cm

3 cm

b
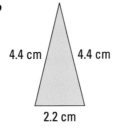
4.4 cm   4.4 cm

2.2 cm

c
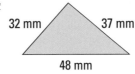
32 mm   37 mm

48 mm

2 Calculate the area of each triangle.

a

9 cm

8 cm

b
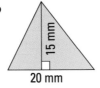
15 mm

20 mm

c
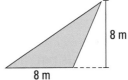
8 m

8 m

3 Calculate the area of each triangle.

a

8 cm   10 cm

6 cm

b
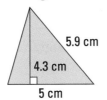
5.9 cm

4.3 cm

5 cm

c

3 cm

5 cm   4 cm

4 Calculate the perimeter and area of the shapes.

a

12 cm   13 cm

5 cm

b
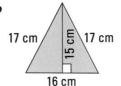
17 cm   15 cm   17 cm

16 cm

c

5 cm   4   5 cm

5 cm   3   3   5 cm
   4

5 Calculate the missing values of b and h.

a
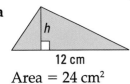
h

12 cm

Area = 24 cm²

b
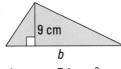
9 cm

b

Area = 54 cm²

c

h

b

Area = 50 cm²

Two identical right-angled triangles can be
combined to make different shapes.
Sketch the shape that has a perimeter of

a 28 cm   **b** 32 cm
c 36 cm   **d** 36 cm (a different arrangement)

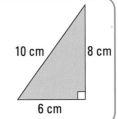
10 cm   8 cm   10 cm   8 cm

6 cm   6 cm

challenge

- Calculate the area of a parallelogram and a trapezium

Keywords

Area   Perpendicular
Base   height
Parallel   Trapezium
Parallelogram

The **area** of this **parallelogram** is the same as the area of this rectangle.

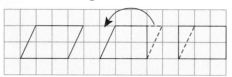

> A parallelogram has two pairs of **parallel** sides.

- Area of a parallelogram = **base × perpendicular height**
  = $b \times h$

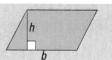

example

Calculate the area of this parallelogram.

Area = $b \times h$ base = 8 cm, height = 4.5 cm
     = 8×4.5
     = 36 cm^2

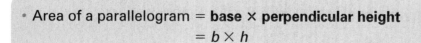

The area of this **trapezium** is half the area of this parallelogram.

- Area of a trapezium = $\frac{1}{2}(a + b) \times h$
  a and b are the lengths of the parallel sides.
  h is the perpendicular height.

example

Calculate the area of the trapezium.

Area = $\frac{1}{2} \times (9 + 15) \times 6$ $a = 9, b = 15, h = 6$

     = $\frac{1}{2} \times 24 \times 6 = 72 \text{ cm}^2$

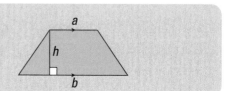

example

The area of the parallelogram is 180 cm².
Calculate the value of h.

Area = $b \times h$
180 = $20 \times h$
   h = 9 cm $180 \div 20 = 9$

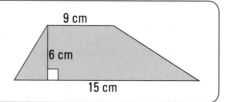
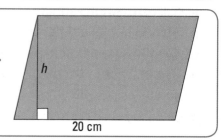

Exercise 3b

Always state the units of your answers.

1 Calculate the area of each parallelogram.

a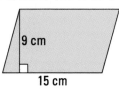
9 cm
15 cm

b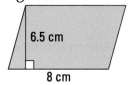
6.5 cm
8 cm

c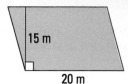
15 m
20 m

2 Calculate the area of each trapezium.

a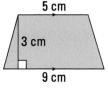
5 cm
3 cm
9 cm

b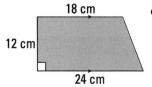
18 cm
12 cm
24 cm

c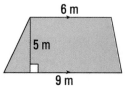
6 m
5 m
9 m

3 Calculate the values of h and b.

a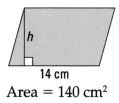
h
14 cm
Area = 140 cm²

b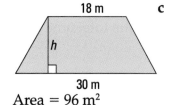
18 m
h
30 m
Area = 96 m²

c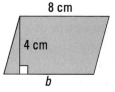
8 cm
4 cm
b
Area = 40 cm²

4 Calculate the area of each shape.

a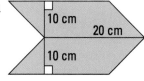
10 cm
20 cm
10 cm

b
10 cm
5 cm
5 cm
15 cm
10 cm

5 Use centimetre square grid paper to
   a draw a rectangle with an area of 10 cm²
   b draw an isosceles triangle with an area of 10 cm²
   c draw a scalene triangle with an area of 10 cm²
   d draw a parallelogram with an area of 10 cm²
   e draw a trapezium with an area of 10 cm².

An isosceles triangle has two equal sides.

A scalene triangle has no equal sides.

activity

a Calculate the area of the trapezium using the trapezium area formula.
b Calculate the area of parallelogram A.
c Calculate the areas of triangles B and C.
d Add the areas of A, B and C.
Copy the trapezium on square grid paper and cut out the three shapes A, B and C.
Rearrange the shapes to form a rectangle.
e Calculate the area of this rectangle.

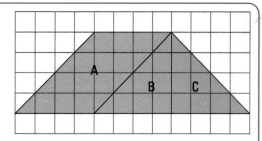

• Find the surface area of a cuboid

Keywords

3-D   Face
Cube   Net
Cuboid   Surface area

3-D means '3-Dimensional'

• A **cuboid** is a **3-D** shape with six rectangular **faces**.

When you unfold a cuboid, the six rectangles form a **net**.

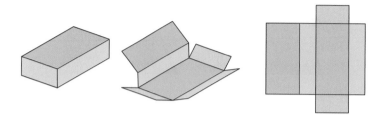

• The **surface area** of a cuboid is the total area of its faces, or the area of the net.

example

A cuboid measures 10 cm by 5 cm by 2 cm.

Calculate the surface area of the cuboid.

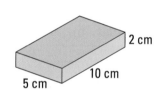

Area of the pink rectangle $= 10 \times 5 = 50$ cm²

Area of the green rectangle $= 2 \times 10 = 20$ cm²

Area of the blue rectangle $= 5 \times 2 = 10$ cm²

Surface area $= 80 \times 2$ $\overline{80\ cm^2}$

         $= 160$ cm²

The cuboid has two rectangles of each colour.

The units of area are cm².

• A **cube** has six square faces.

example

The surface area of a cube is 73.5 cm².
Calculate
a the area of one face
b the length of one side of the cube.

a Area of one face $= 73.5 \div 6 = 12.25$ cm²

b Length of one side $= \sqrt{12.25} = 3.5$ cm

Use your calculator to find the square root.

Exercise 3c

1 Calculate the surface area of these cuboids.
Which two cuboids have the same surface area?

Always state the units of
your answers.

a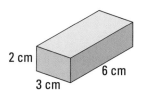

2 cm
6 cm
3 cm

b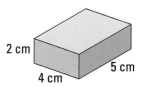

2 cm
5 cm
4 cm

c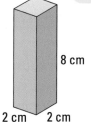

8 cm
2 cm 2 cm

2 Calculate the surface area of these cuboids.

a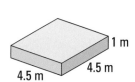

1 m
4.5 m
4.5 m

b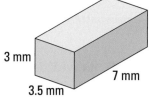

3 mm
7 mm
3.5 mm

c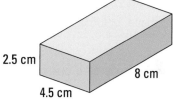

2.5 cm
8 cm
4.5 cm

3 Calculate the length of one side of a cube, if the surface area
of the cube is

a 96 cm² **b** 512 cm² **c** 1350 cm²

4 Twelve containers are stacked on the ground as shown.
Each container measures 6 m by 2.5 m by 2.5 m.

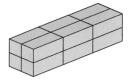

2.5 m
2.5 m 6 m

Calculate the surface area of the stacked containers
that is not in contact with the ground.

5 A cuboid has length l, width w and height h.
Calculate the surface area of the cuboid in terms of l, w and h.

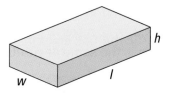

h
w
l

challenge

Neela wants to gift-wrap a small box of chocolates that
measures 5 cm by 7.5 cm by 10 cm. She finds a gift box
on the Internet. The box is a cuboid, and the areas of
three of the faces are 48 cm², 72 cm² and 96 cm².
Will the chocolates fit in the gift box?

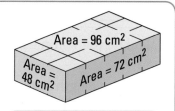

Area = 96 cm²
Area = 48 cm²
Area = 72 cm²

Find the length, width and
height of the cuboid.

• Find the volume of a cuboid

Keywords

Cubic
  centimetre
Cuboid
Dimensions

Height
Length
Volume
Width

• **Volume** is the amount of space inside a 3-D shape.

• You measure volume in cubes.
  • A metric unit of volume is a **cubic centimetre**. A cubic centimetre (cm³) measures 1 cm by 1 cm by 1 cm.
  • For larger volumes, you can use cubic metres (m³).
  • For smaller volumes, you can use cubic millimetres (mm³).

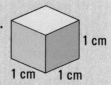

1 cm
1 cm   1 cm

The volume of a room could be 50 m³.

The volume of a small bead could be 1 mm³.

• The **dimensions** of a **cuboid** are its **length**, its **width** and its **height**.

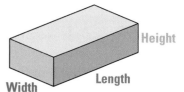

Height
Width   Length

You can find the volume of a cuboid by counting layers of cubes.

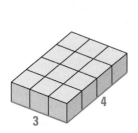

4
3

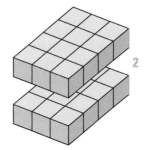

2
4
3

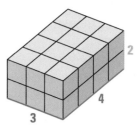

2
4
3

In one layer there are
4 × 3 = 12 cubes.

In two layers there are
2 × **12** = 24 cubes.

The volume of this cuboid is 24 cubes.

This is the same as multiplying the **length**, **width** and height.

• **Volume of a cuboid = length × width × height**

example

Calculate the volume of this cuboid.
....

Volume = length × width × height
       = 6 × 4 × 2
       = 48 cm³

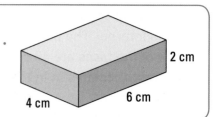

2 cm
4 cm   6 cm

Exercise 3d

1 Choose the most appropriate unit to measure the volume of

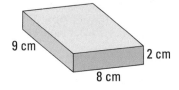

| Cubic millimetres | Cubic centimetres | Cubic metres |

  a a rubbish bin   **b** a bread bin
  c a pyramid in Egypt   **d** a pin head
  e a small iceberg.

2 Calculate the volume of each cuboid.
Which cuboids have the same volume?

> Always state the units of your answers.

a

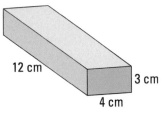

12 cm   3 cm   4 cm

b

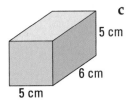

5 cm   6 cm   5 cm

c

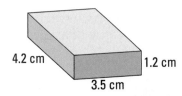

9 cm   2 cm   8 cm

3 Calculate the volume of each cuboid.

a

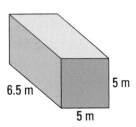

6.5 m   5 m   5 m

b

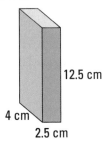

12.5 cm   4 cm   2.5 cm

c

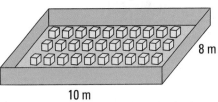

4.2 cm   1.2 cm   3.5 cm

4 A classroom is in the shape of a cuboid.
It measures 10 m by 8 m by 2.4 m.
  a Calculate the volume of the classroom.
There are 30 students in the classroom.
  b Calculate the volume each student is entitled to.

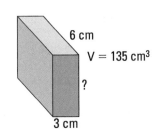

8 m   2.4 m   10 m

5 Calculate the missing lengths.

a

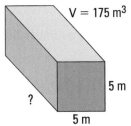

$V = 175 \text{ m}^3$ 5 m   ?   5 m

b

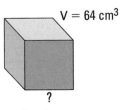

$V = 64 \text{ cm}^3$?   A cube

c

6 cm $V = 135 \text{ cm}^3$?   3 cm

challenge

12 cubes are arranged to form a cuboid.
Write down the four possible cuboids that can be made.
Calculate the surface area of each cuboid.
Which cuboid has the smallest surface area?

• Know facts about angles at a point and in triangles

• An **angle** is a measure of turn.
  You can measure the turn in degrees.
  ° is the symbol for degrees
  You can describe this angle in different ways.
  angle *ABC*   angle *CBA*   angle *B*

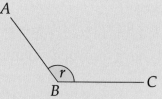

There are 90° in
a **right angle.**
This is a $\frac{1}{4}$ turn at
a point.

There are 180° on
a **straight line.**
This is half a full
turn at a point.

There are 360°
in a full turn at
a **point.**

---

example

Calculate the value of angles *a* and *b*.

a

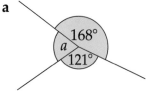

b

. . . .

a $121° + 168° = 289°$ Angles at a point
     $360° - 289° = 71°$ add to 360°.
           $a = 71°$

b $180° - 102° = 78°$ Angles on a straight
          $2b = 78°$ line add to 180°.
           $b = 39°$

A **triangle** is a 2-D shape with 3 sides and 3 angles.
   You can draw any triangle   ...   tear off the corners   ...   put them together to make a straight line.

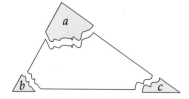

• The angles in a triangle add to 180°.
    $a + b + c = 180°$

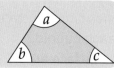

Exercise 3e

1 Use the small letters to describe

   a angle *C*   **b** angle *ABC*   **c** angle *BDC*

   d angle *CDE*   **e** angle *DBC*

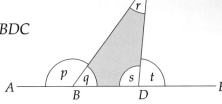

2 Calculate the unknown angles.

  a   **b**   **c**

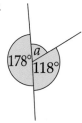
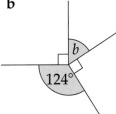

  d   **e**   **f**

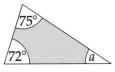

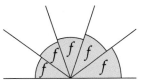

3 Calculate the unknown angles.

  a   **b**   **c**

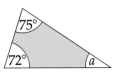

  d   **e**   **f**

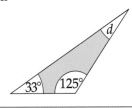
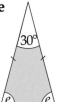

> The dash means sides of equal length.

The shape consists of five identical isosceles triangles and a pentagon.
One angle in the triangle is 72°.

  a Calculate the value of the 19 unknown angles.

  b Draw the diagram accurately.

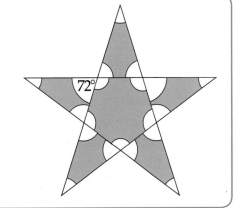

- Know facts about angles on parallel and intersecting lines

Keywords

Alternate   Parallel
Corresponding   Perpendicular
Intersect   Vertically opposite

When two lines **intersect**, four angles are formed.

- **Vertically opposite** angles are equal.
  The two pink obtuse angles are equal.
  The two green acute angles are equal

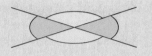

- **Perpendicular** lines meet at a right angle.
  A horizontal line and a vertical line are perpendicular.

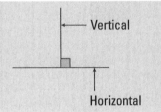

- **Parallel** lines are always the same distance apart.
  Parallel lines are shown using arrows.

When a line intersects two parallel lines, alternate and corresponding angles are formed.

- **Alternate** angles are equal.
  They are in a Z shape.

- **Corresponding** angles are equal.
  They are in an F shape.

example

Find the unknown angles. Give reasons for your answers.

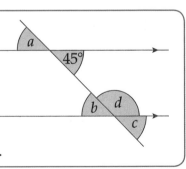

$a = 45°$ Vertically opposite angles are equal (a and the 45° angle).

$b = 45°$ Alternate angles are equal (b and the 45° angle).

$c = 45°$ Corresponding angles are equal (c and 45°).

$d = 135°$ Angles on a straight line add to 180° (d and c (45°)).

Exercise 3f

1 Copy the diagram.
Colour the acute angles one colour and
the obtuse angles another colour.

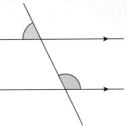

2 Copy the diagrams and label the alternate angles to those shown.

a 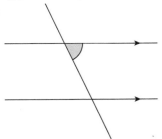   b 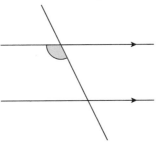   c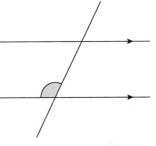

3 Copy the diagrams and label the corresponding angles to those shown.

a 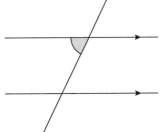   b 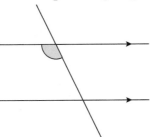   c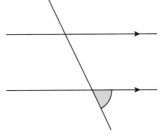

4 Calculate the unknown angles.

a 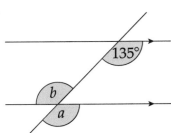   b 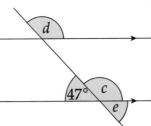   c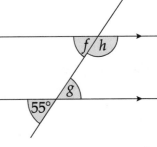

5 Calculate the unknown angles.

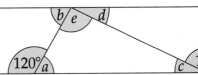

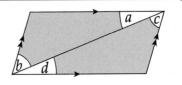

Prove that the opposite angles of a parallelogram
are equal. You need to prove $a + c = b + d$.

3g Angles in triangles and quadrilaterals

- Know more facts about angles in triangles and quadrilaterals

Keywords

Exterior   Quadrilateral

Interior   Triangle

- **Interior** angles are the angles inside a shape.

You know that the interior angles in a **triangle** add to 180°.

A **quadrilateral** is a 2-D shape with 4 sides and 4 angles.
It can be divided into two triangles.

$$a + b + c = 180°$$
$$d + e + f = 180°$$
So $a + b + c + d + e + f = 360°$

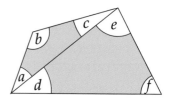

- The interior angles of a quadrilateral add to **360°**.

$$p + q + r + s = 360°$$

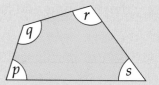

example

Calculate the value of angle a.

. . . .

$75° + 127° + 90° = 292°$

$\quad 360° - 292° = 68°$ Angles in a quadrilateral add to 360°.

$\qquad\qquad a = 68°$

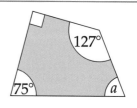

- You find the **exterior** angles of a shape by extending one side of the shape at each corner.

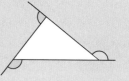

$a + b + c = 180°$ Angles in a triangle add to 180°.

$a + d = 180°$ Angles on a straight line add to 180°.

So $b + c = d$ Comparing the two equations.

- The exterior angle of a triangle is equal to the sum of the two interior opposite angles.

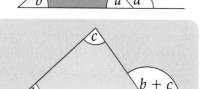

Exercise 3g

1 Calculate the unknown angles.

a

b
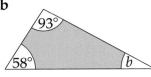

c
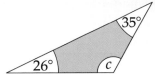

d
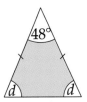

e
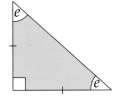

f

2 Explain why this diagram is incorrect.

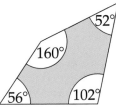

3 Calculate the unknown angles.

a
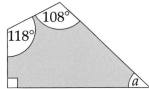

b
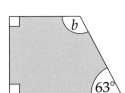

c
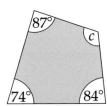

d
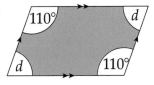

e

f

4 Calculate the unknown angles.

a
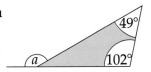

b
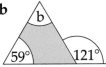

c
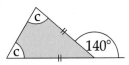

Use the diagram to find another proof that the exterior angle of a triangle is equal to the sum of the two interior opposite angles.

You need to prove $c + b = p + q$.

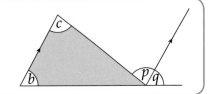

3a

1 Calculate the area of each shape.

a

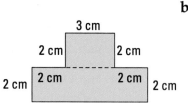

b

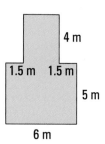

c

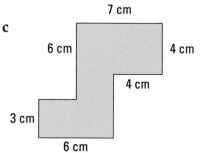

3a²

2 Copy and complete the table for these triangles.

	Base	Perpendicular height	Area
a	15 cm	8 cm	
b	2.5 cm	2 cm	
c	5 cm		40 cm²
d	6 cm		12 cm²
e	9 cm		31.5 cm²
f	25 cm		40 cm²

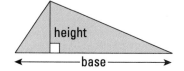

3b

3 Calculate the area of each quadrilateral.

a

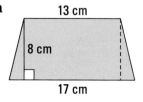

b

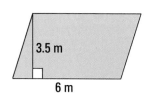

c

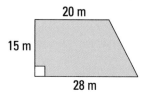

3c

4 Calculate the surface area of these cuboids. Which two cuboids have the same surface area?

a

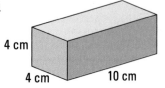

b

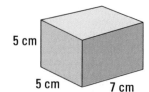

c

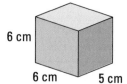

5 Calculate the length of one side of the cube, if the volume
of the cube is

a 216 cm³   b 512 cm³   c 91.125 cm³

length

6 Cereal boxes measure 20 cm by 5 cm by 25 cm.
Large boxes measure 1 m by 1 m by 0.5 m.
How many cereal boxes will fit in the large box?
Does it matter how the cereal boxes are packed?

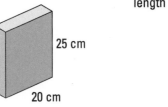

25 cm

5 cm   20 cm

7 Find the unknown angles.

a

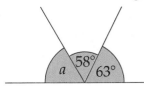

b

c

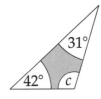

8 Find the unknown angles in these parallelograms.

a

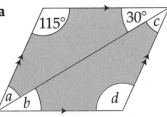

b

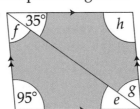

c

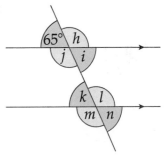

9 Calculate the unknown angles.

a

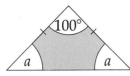

b

c

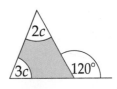

d

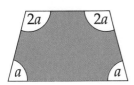

e

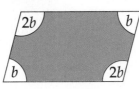

f

Free-Range

Free-range eggs are laid by free-range hens. Strict rules must be obeyed for hens to be called 'Free-range.'

Free-range rules

Outside: Shade, grass, dirt, about 1 hen to every 4 m²

Inside: Fresh straw, lots of perches, 7 hens to every 1m²

Fill in the blanks

			Free-Range?
FARM A	18 hens	60 m²	
FARM B	250 hens	1000 m²	
FARM C	___ hens	440 m²	✔
FARM D	24 hens	___ m²	✔

ORGANIC FEED

THIS FARM IS 4 M BY 8 M

COULD THESE HENS BE CONSIDERED FREE RANGE?

FREE-RANGE EGGS £1.92 PER DOZEN

CAGED EGGS £1.20 PER DOZEN

How much would you pay for

a 2 dozen free-range eggs
b 2 dozen caged eggs
c 4 dozen free-range eggs
d 4 dozen caged eggs
e 1 free-range egg
f 1 caged egg?

BAKED CUSTARD (Serves 8)

8 egg yolks
75 g castor sugar
500 ml whipping cream
freshly grated nutmeg

Why do you think that free-range eggs are more expensive than caged eggs? Would you pay more?

Cost of eggs by serving		
	Free-range eggs	Caged eggs
Serves 8	£ 1.28	
Serves 4		£ 0.80
Serves 16		
Serves 12		
Per serving		

3 Summary

Key indicators

- Calculate the perimeter and area of shapes made from rectangles **Level 5**
- Know the sum of the angles at a point, on a straight line and in a triangle **Level 5**
- Calculate the area of a triangle and a parallelogram **Level 5**

1 Calculate the value of the angles g and h.

a

b

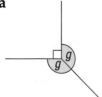

Simeon's answer ✔

Simeon knows there are 360° at a point.

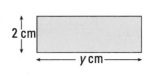

a $360° - 90° = 270°$
  $270° \div 2 = 135°$
    $g = 135°$
b $180° - 90° = 90°$
  $90° \div 2 = 45°$

Simeon divides 270° into two equal parts

Simeon knows the angle sum of a triangle is 180°.

2 a The square and the rectangle have the same area.
Work out the value of y.

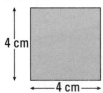

4 cm   4 cm   2 cm y cm

b The triangle and the rectangle have the same area.
Work out the value of w.
Show your working.

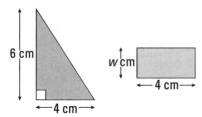

6 cm   4 cm w cm   4 cm

Key Stage 3 2004 4–6 Paper 2

4 Number

Fractions, decimals and percentages

Before 1971, the UK system of money counted pounds, shillings and pence instead of just pounds and pence like we use now. It took 12 pence to make a shilling and 20 shillings to make a pound. How many pence were in a pound?

What's the point? Our modern system of money is based on 100 pence in a pound. Ask an older family member or friend if they remember the old system of money. Do they find the modern system easier to use than the old system?

✓ Check in

Level 3

1 Write down the fraction of each shape that is shaded.

a   b   c

Level 4

2 Use each diagram to write a pair of equivalent fractions.

a 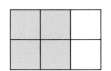   b 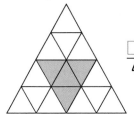 $\dfrac{\square}{4} = \dfrac{\square}{\square}$ c $\dfrac{\square}{\square} = \dfrac{\square}{\square}$

with $\dfrac{\square}{3} = \dfrac{\square}{6}$

3 Copy and complete this table of common equivalents.

Fraction	Decimal	Percentage
$\dfrac{1}{10}$		
		25%
	0.5	
$\dfrac{3}{4}$		

4a Fraction notation

- Express a proportion as a fraction

Keywords
Cancel
Denominator
Fraction
HCF

Numerator
Proportion
Simplest fo

- You use a **fraction** to describe a part of a whole. The **denominator** tells you how many equal parts the whole is divided into. The **numerator** tells you how many of these parts there are.

example

A pizza is cut into slices. Anna, Kamal and Steven each take a slice. What fraction of the pizza is left?

The whole pizza is cut into 8 equal sized pieces.
There are 5 pieces left.
$\frac{5}{8}$ of the pizza is left.

p. 242

- You can express a **proportion** of a whole as a fraction.
  There are 20 students in class 7C. Seven of them support Manchester United. The proportion of students who support Manchester United is $\frac{7}{20}$.

The numerator is the top number in the fraction.

The denominator is the bottom number.

example

What fraction of 1 day is 11 hours?

11 hours is $\frac{11}{24}$ of a day.   There are 24 hours in 1 day.

You must compare like with like – make sure both numbers have the same units.

- You can express a fraction in its **simplest form** by **cancelling**. To cancel a fraction you divide the numerator and denominator by the **highest common factor (HCF).**

The highest common factor is the largest number that will divide into both numbers.

example

Express these fractions in their simplest form.
a $\frac{6}{24}$ **b** $\frac{60}{90}$

a $\frac{6}{24} \overset{\div 6}{\underset{\div 6}{=}} \frac{1}{4}$ The highest common factor of 6 and 24 is 6.

b $\frac{60}{90} \overset{\div 30}{\underset{\div 30}{=}} \frac{2}{3}$ The highest common factor of 60 and 90 is 30.

Exercise 4a

1 Write the fraction of each shape that is shaded.

a 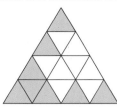 b 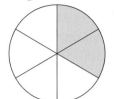 c 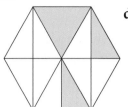 d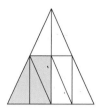

2 Copy these shapes and shade the fraction stated.

  a a rectangle   **b** a regular pentagon   **c** an arrowhead

 $\frac{1}{2}$ $\frac{7}{10}$ $\frac{3}{4}$

3 Write each of these fractions in its simplest form.

  a $\frac{6}{8}$ **b** $\frac{6}{9}$ **c** $\frac{2}{6}$ **d** $\frac{6}{10}$ **e** $\frac{8}{12}$

  f $\frac{10}{15}$ **g** $\frac{16}{24}$ **h** $\frac{21}{28}$ **i** $\frac{60}{75}$ **j** $\frac{48}{84}$

4 Give your answers as fractions in their simplest form.

  a What fraction of 180 is 150?

  b What fraction of £2.40 is 30p?

  c What fraction of 2 hours is 42 minutes?

  d What fraction of 1 hour is 45 seconds?

5 **a** There are 35 pupils in a class. 21 are boys and 14 are girls. What fraction of the class are boys?

  b Gary has a memory stick which can hold 512 MB. He has 384 MB of music stored on his stick. What fraction of the memory stick has music stored on it?

> Always give your answer to this sort of question in its simplest form.

investigation

Sharli is making gift tags for the school fête.
She needs lots of different sizes.
She has a 6 × 3 rectangle of card.

  a Divide the rectangle into four smaller rectangles, which are all different unit fractions of the whole: $\frac{1}{2}$, $\frac{1}{3}$, $\frac{1}{9}$ and $\frac{1}{18}$. Shade each fraction of the rectangle a different colour.

  b Investigate other sizes of rectangles. Which ones can be divided into unit fractions?

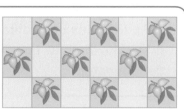

> A unit fraction has a numerator of 1.

- Add and subtract fractions

Keywords
Common
   denominator
Denominator
Equivalent
Fraction
Improper
   fraction
Mixed
   number
Numerator

- **Equivalent fractions** have the same value. You can find an equivalent fraction by multiplying or dividing the **numerator** and **denominator** by the same number.

$\frac{6}{18}$ and $\frac{1}{3}$ are equivalent fractions.

$$\frac{6}{18} \quad = \quad \frac{1}{3}$$

example

Copy and complete these equivalent fractions.

a $\frac{2}{5} = \frac{\boxed{?}}{15}$ **b** $\frac{4}{5} = \frac{56}{\boxed{?}}$

a Multiply both numerator and denominator by 3.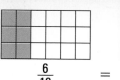

b Multiply both numerator and denominator by 14.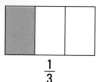

- You can add and subtract fractions which have a **common denominator**.

example

Calculate $\frac{3}{8} + \frac{2}{8}$

The fractions have a common denominator, so you just add the numerators.

$$\frac{3}{8} \quad + \quad \frac{2}{8} \quad = \quad \frac{5}{8}$$

- If the fractions have different denominators, you must first write them as equivalent fractions with a common denominator.

Common denominator means 'the same denominator'.

example

Calculate $\frac{2}{5} + \frac{1}{3}$

Make the fractions equivalent.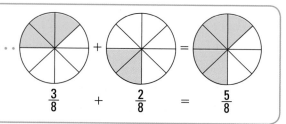

Then add the numerators

$$\frac{6}{15} + \frac{5}{15} = \frac{11}{15}$$

$$\frac{2}{5} \overset{\times 3}{\underset{\times 3}{=}} \frac{6}{15} \qquad \frac{1}{3} \overset{\times 5}{\underset{\times 5}{=}} \frac{5}{15}$$

Exercise 4b

1 Find the missing number in each of these pairs of equivalent fractions.

a $\dfrac{2}{3} = \dfrac{?}{15}$ **b** $\dfrac{3}{5} = \dfrac{?}{40}$ **c** $\dfrac{7}{8} = \dfrac{?}{48}$ **d** $\dfrac{7}{10} = \dfrac{?}{120}$

e $\dfrac{10}{35} = \dfrac{?}{7}$ **f** $\dfrac{18}{?} = \dfrac{3}{7}$ **g** $\dfrac{?}{5} = \dfrac{154}{110}$ **h** $\dfrac{5}{13} = \dfrac{?}{78}$

2 Calculate each of these, giving your answer as a fraction in its simplest form.

a $\dfrac{2}{5} + \dfrac{2}{5}$ **b** $\dfrac{3}{8} + \dfrac{7}{8}$ **c** $\dfrac{7}{20} - \dfrac{2}{20}$ **d** $\dfrac{17}{18} - \dfrac{7}{18}$

e $\dfrac{3}{28} + \dfrac{4}{28}$ **f** $\dfrac{11}{5} - \dfrac{6}{5}$ **g** $\dfrac{15}{16} - \dfrac{7}{16}$ **h** $\dfrac{11}{12} + \dfrac{4}{12}$

i $\dfrac{11}{6} + \dfrac{7}{6}$ **j** $1\dfrac{5}{8} - \dfrac{3}{8}$ **k** $2\dfrac{3}{4} - 1\dfrac{1}{4}$ **l** $3\dfrac{1}{5} - \dfrac{4}{5}$

3 Calculate each of these, giving your answer as a fraction in its simplest form.

a $\dfrac{1}{2} + \dfrac{1}{5}$ **b** $\dfrac{1}{3} + \dfrac{2}{5}$ **c** $\dfrac{1}{6} + \dfrac{3}{5}$ **d** $\dfrac{2}{3} - \dfrac{1}{4}$

e $\dfrac{2}{5} - \dfrac{1}{3}$ **f** $\dfrac{4}{7} + \dfrac{1}{5}$ **g** $\dfrac{3}{5} - \dfrac{2}{7}$ **h** $\dfrac{3}{4} - \dfrac{2}{3}$

i $\dfrac{5}{9} - \dfrac{3}{11}$ **j** $\dfrac{9}{13} + \dfrac{1}{3}$ **k** $\dfrac{11}{15} + \dfrac{4}{7}$ **l** $\dfrac{13}{17} - \dfrac{5}{9}$

4 Calculate each of these, giving your answer as a fraction in its simplest form.

a $\dfrac{3}{5} - \dfrac{4}{15}$ **b** $\dfrac{4}{5} + \dfrac{4}{15}$ **c** $\dfrac{1}{2} - \dfrac{1}{3}$ **d** $\dfrac{7}{10} + \dfrac{1}{5}$

e $\dfrac{1}{5} + \dfrac{3}{20}$ **f** $\dfrac{1}{3} - \dfrac{1}{12}$ **g** $\dfrac{1}{2} + \dfrac{5}{6}$ **h** $\dfrac{1}{4} + \dfrac{7}{12}$

5 Calculate each of these, giving your answer as a fraction in its simplest form.

a $1\dfrac{1}{2} + \dfrac{2}{5}$ **b** $1\dfrac{1}{3} - \dfrac{1}{4}$ **c** $1\dfrac{2}{3} + 1\dfrac{1}{4}$ **d** $2\dfrac{1}{5} - \dfrac{3}{8}$

e $1\dfrac{4}{7} + \dfrac{3}{5}$ **f** $1\dfrac{2}{5} + \dfrac{1}{3}$ **g** $2\dfrac{2}{5} - 1\dfrac{1}{3}$ **h** $2\dfrac{3}{7} + 1\dfrac{2}{3}$

i $3\dfrac{3}{8} - 2\dfrac{2}{5}$ **j** $2\dfrac{2}{3} + 1\dfrac{1}{5}$ **k** $4\dfrac{2}{3} - 2\dfrac{3}{4}$ **l** $4\dfrac{2}{7} + 2\dfrac{5}{9}$

> Remember to turn mixed numbers into 'top-heavy' improper fractions.

6 a Sarah wins some money on the lottery.

    She gives $\dfrac{1}{2}$ the money to her family and spends $\dfrac{2}{7}$ on a car.

    What fraction of her money does she have left?

b Tony spends $\dfrac{2}{7}$ of his pocket money on a computer game.

    He also spends $\dfrac{1}{5}$ of his pocket money on a ticket for the cinema.

    What fraction of his pocket money is left?

The ancient Egyptians used to write all fractions as unit fractions. For example, they would write

$\dfrac{5}{8}$ as $\dfrac{1}{2} + \dfrac{1}{8}$ $\dfrac{11}{12}$ as $\dfrac{1}{2} + \dfrac{1}{4} + \dfrac{1}{6}$

a Write these fractions in the Egyptian way.

    $\dfrac{5}{6}$ $\dfrac{17}{24}$ $\dfrac{9}{20}$ $\dfrac{7}{10}$

b What other fractions can be written in this way?

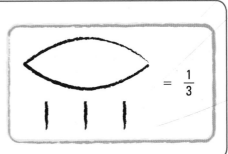

$= \dfrac{1}{3}$

- Change a fraction to a decimal and vice versa

- A **decimal** is another way of writing a **fraction**.

Keywords
Decimal   Simplest
Equivalent   form
  fraction   Terminating
Fraction   decimal

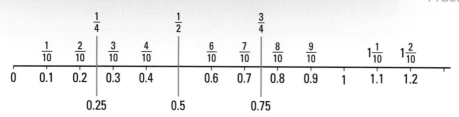

- You can use place value to convert a **terminating decimal** to a fraction, or to convert a fraction to a decimal.

A terminating decimal comes to an end.

---

example

a Convert 0.84 to a fraction in its **simplest form**.   **b** Convert $\frac{13}{20}$ to a decimal.

· ·

a The number 0.84 stands for 8 tenths + 4 hundredths.

$$0.84 = \frac{8}{10} + \frac{4}{100}$$

$$0.84 = \frac{80}{100} + \frac{4}{100} = \frac{84}{100} \overset{\div 4}{\underset{\div 4}{=}} \frac{21}{25}$$

Using **equivalent fractions**
$$\frac{8}{10} = \frac{80}{100}$$

b First write $\frac{13}{20}$ as a fraction with a denominator of 100.

$$\frac{13}{20} \overset{\times 5}{\underset{\times 5}{=}} \frac{65}{100} = 0.65$$

- You can order fractions by converting them to decimals, and ordering the decimals.

---

example

Put these fractions in order, from lowest to highest.

$$\frac{2}{3} \qquad \frac{5}{6} \qquad \frac{3}{4}$$

· ·

$\frac{2}{3} = 2 \div 3 = 0.666...$ $\frac{5}{6} = 5 \div 6 = 0.833...$ $\frac{3}{4} = 3 \div 4 = 0.75$

The order of the decimals is 0.666..., 0.75, 0.833...

The order of the fractions is $\frac{2}{3}, \frac{3}{4}, \frac{5}{6}$

You can also convert a fraction to a decimal by dividing the numerator by the denominator.

Exercise 4c

1 Write each of these decimals as a fraction in its simplest form.

a 0.8   **b** 0.44   **c** 0.25   **d** 0.24   **e** 0.96

f 0.6   **g** 0.75   **h** 0.64   **i** 0.375   **j** 0.288

2 Write each of these fractions as a decimal without using a calculator.

a $\dfrac{7}{10}$ **b** $\dfrac{17}{20}$ **c** $\dfrac{9}{25}$ **d** $\dfrac{1}{4}$ **e** $\dfrac{17}{50}$

f $\dfrac{2}{5}$ **g** $\dfrac{37}{125}$ **h** $\dfrac{7}{8}$ **i** $\dfrac{26}{80}$ **j** $\dfrac{15}{24}$

k $\dfrac{13}{10}$ **l** $\dfrac{11}{40}$ **m** $\dfrac{17}{40}$ **n** $\dfrac{17}{8}$ **o** $\dfrac{19}{25}$

p $\dfrac{61}{200}$ **q** $\dfrac{22}{8}$ **r** $\dfrac{159}{150}$ **s** $\dfrac{57}{40}$ **t** $\dfrac{195}{120}$

3 Write each of these fractions as a decimal.

a $\dfrac{29}{50}$ **b** $\dfrac{11}{12}$ **c** $\dfrac{2}{3}$ **d** $\dfrac{7}{8}$ **e** $\dfrac{17}{20}$

f $\dfrac{52}{32}$ **g** $\dfrac{15}{13}$ **h** $\dfrac{54}{60}$ **i** $\dfrac{13}{7}$ **j** $\dfrac{9}{22}$

4 For each pair of fractions, write down which is the larger fraction, giving an explanation for your choice.

a $\dfrac{3}{8}$ and $\dfrac{2}{5}$ **b** $\dfrac{4}{7}$ and $\dfrac{5}{9}$

c $\dfrac{4}{7}$ and $\dfrac{2}{5}$ **d** $\dfrac{7}{12}$ and $\dfrac{8}{11}$

5 Put these fractions in order, from lowest to highest.

a $\dfrac{3}{7}$ $\dfrac{11}{15}$ $\dfrac{16}{19}$ $\dfrac{11}{25}$ **b** $\dfrac{2}{3}$ $\dfrac{3}{8}$ $\dfrac{5}{13}$ $\dfrac{13}{19}$

6 These are Fiona's exam marks.
In which subject did she do best?
Explain your answer.

French	Maths	English	History
$\dfrac{33}{40}$	$\dfrac{41}{50}$	$\dfrac{49}{60}$	$\dfrac{62}{75}$

investigation

Every unit fraction can be turned into a decimal by dividing the numerator by the denominator.

$$\dfrac{1}{2} = 1 \div 2 = 0.5$$

$$\dfrac{1}{3} = 1 \div 3 = 0.333\,333...$$

a Use your calculator to convert each of the unit fractions from $\dfrac{1}{4}$ to $\dfrac{1}{25}$ into a decimal.
Write all the decimal places on your calculator display.

b Which of your fractions give decimals which terminate (e.g. $\dfrac{1}{2} = 0.5$) and which give recurring decimals (e.g. $\dfrac{1}{3} = 0.333...$)?
Write anything you notice.

4d Fraction of a quantity

- Find a fraction of a quantity

Keywords
Denominator
Fraction
Numerator

- You can find a **fraction** of a number or quantity using a mental method.

example

Calculate $\frac{5}{8}$ of 240 cm².

. . . .

$\frac{1}{8}$ of 240 cm² = 240 ÷ 8 = 30 cm²

$\frac{5}{8}$ of 240 cm² = 5 × 30 = 150 cm²

A quick way to find a fraction of an amount is to divide by the **denominator** and then multiply by the **numerator**

e.g. 240 ÷ 8 × 5 = 150

- You can multiply a fraction by a whole number.

example

Calculate $\frac{5}{8} \times 6$.

. . . .

$\frac{5}{8} \times 6 = \frac{1}{8} \times 5 \times 6 = \frac{1 \times 30}{8} = \frac{30}{8} = 3\frac{3}{4}$

Think of $\frac{5}{8}$ as $\frac{1}{8} \times 5$.

Multiplying by $\frac{1}{8}$ is the same as dividing by 8.

- You can find a fraction of an amount by multiplying the fraction by the amount.

example

Find   **a** $\frac{4}{7}$ of 56 kg   **b** $\frac{5}{9}$ of 8 km.

. . . .

a $\frac{4}{7}$ of 56 = $\frac{1}{7} \times 4 \times 56 = \frac{1 \times 224}{7} = \frac{224}{7} = 32$ kg

b $\frac{5}{9}$ of 8 = $\frac{1}{9} \times 5 \times 8 = \frac{1 \times 40}{9} = \frac{40}{9} = 4\frac{4}{9}$

- You can find a fraction of an amount by changing the fraction into a decimal and then multiplying the amount by the decimal.

example

Find $\frac{5}{9}$ of 8 km.

. . . .

$\frac{5}{9}$ of 8 = $\frac{5}{9} \times 8$

        = 5 ÷ 9 × 8 = 0.555... × 8 = 4.444... km

Change $\frac{5}{9}$ into a decimal by dividing the numerator by the denominator.

Exercise 4d

1 Calculate each of these, giving your answer in its simplest form.

a $3 \times \frac{1}{7}$ b $6 \times \frac{1}{9}$ c $7 \times \frac{1}{14}$ d $12 \times \frac{1}{3}$

e $7 \times \frac{1}{5}$ f $20 \times \frac{1}{8}$ g $11 \times \frac{1}{4}$ h $\frac{1}{4} \times 8$

i $\frac{1}{3} \times 12$ j $\frac{1}{5} \times 10$ k $\frac{1}{3} \times 7$ l $\frac{1}{8} \times 28$

2 Calculate each of these, giving your answer in its simplest form.

a $3 \times \frac{2}{7}$ b $6 \times \frac{4}{9}$ c $7 \times \frac{3}{14}$ d $12 \times \frac{2}{3}$

e $7 \times \frac{2}{5}$ f $20 \times \frac{7}{8}$ g $9 \times \frac{7}{6}$ h $4 \times \frac{7}{8}$

i $15 \times \frac{9}{20}$ j $\frac{3}{8} \times 12$ k $\frac{4}{5} \times 28$ l $\frac{6}{7} \times 28$

3 Use a written method to calculate these. Where appropriate, give your answer in its simplest form.

a $\frac{3}{5} \times 10$ MB   b $\frac{7}{8} \times £640$ c $\frac{2}{5} \times \$40$ d $\frac{3}{4} \times 24$ mins

e $\frac{5}{9} \times 504$ m   f $\frac{2}{5} \times 4100$ kg   g $\frac{4}{7} \times 161$ m   h $\frac{6}{5} \times 145$ mm

i $\frac{3}{5} \times 11$ apples   j $\frac{2}{3} \times 34$ kg   k $\frac{5}{7} \times 40$ mm   l $\frac{3}{4} \times 25$ inches

m $\frac{2}{9} \times 15$ hours   n $\frac{5}{8} \times 60$ GB   o $\frac{5}{6} \times 63$ g   p $\frac{5}{11} \times 528$ calories

4 Use an appropriate method to calculate these amounts. Where appropriate, give your answer to 2 decimal places.

a $\frac{3}{7} \times 308$ kg   b $\frac{8}{13} \times £793$ c $\frac{7}{9} \times 12.4$ km   d $\frac{5}{12} \times \$3600$

e $\frac{7}{19} \times 28.6$ km   f $\frac{6}{17} \times 180$ ml   g $\frac{7}{20} \times 24\,850$ MB   h $\frac{15}{11} \times 64$ tonnes

5 a A file takes $\frac{1}{4}$ hour to download.
How long will it take to download 8 files?

b Imran wins £500. He spends $\frac{4}{13}$ of his winnings on a new mobile phone. How much does the phone cost?

c A file is 48.6 MB. Mushraf has downloaded $\frac{3}{7}$ of the file from the Internet. How much of the file has been downloaded?

challenge

A baby gorilla weighs 1.25 kg at birth.
It grows by the same fraction each month.
After 3 months it weighs 7.29 kg.
By what fraction does the gorilla grow each month?

- Change a fraction to a percentage and vice versa

Keywords
Decimal   Fraction
Denominator   Numerator
Equivalent   Percentage
  fraction

- A **percentage** is a fraction written as the number of parts per 100.

$$23\% = \frac{23}{100} \qquad 5\% = \frac{5}{100} \xrightleftharpoons[\div 5]{\div 5} \frac{1}{20}$$

example

Convert these percentages to decimals.
  a 67%   **b** 117%   **c** 37.5%

. . . .

  a $67\% = \frac{67}{100}$ **b** $117\% = \frac{117}{100}$ **c** $37.5\% = \frac{37.5}{100}$

Write the percentage as a fraction.

       $= 0.67$ $= 1.17$ $= 0.375$

Divide by 100.

- You can convert a fraction or a decimal to a percentage by writing it as an **equivalent fraction** with a denominator of 100 or by multiplying it by 100.

example

Convert these to percentages.   **a** $\frac{16}{25}$ **b** 0.125

. . . .

  a $\frac{16}{25} \xrightleftharpoons[\times 4]{\times 4} \frac{64}{100} = 64\%$ **b** $\frac{125}{1000} \xrightleftharpoons[\div 10]{\div 10} \frac{12.5}{100} = 12.5\%$

   or $\frac{16}{25} \times 100 = 64\%$ or $0.125 \times 100 = 12.5\%$

- You can use a known percentage to calculate other percentages of amounts.

example

Calculate 5% of £280

. . . .

Find 10% 10% of £280 $= \frac{1}{10}$ of £280   5% is half 10% 5% of £280 $= \frac{1}{2}$ of £28

                    $= £280 \div 10$ $= £14$

                    $= £28$

Exercise 4e

1 Write these percentages as fractions in their simplest form.
   a 80%   **b** 95%   **c** 84%   **d** 1%   **e** 120%
   f 7.5%   **g** 62.5%   **h** 6.4%   **i** 3.25%   **j** 66.6...%

2 Write these percentages as decimals.
   a 64%   **b** 8%   **c** 127%   **d** 36%   **e** 3.6%
   f 87.5%   **g** 8.75%   **h** 240%   **i** 12.86%   **j** 128.6%

3 This number line is split into twentieths.

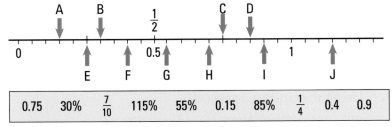

| 0.75 | 30% | $\frac{7}{10}$ | 115% | 55% | 0.15 | 85% | $\frac{1}{4}$ | 0.4 | 0.9 |

   a Match each of the fractions, decimals and
      percentages to the letters on the number line.
   b Give a percentage, fraction and decimal
      equivalent for each letter.

4 Write these fractions as percentages without using a calculator.
   a $\frac{7}{10}$ **b** $\frac{23}{50}$ **c** $\frac{11}{25}$ **d** $\frac{5}{4}$ **e** $\frac{17}{40}$
   f $\frac{12}{5}$ **g** $\frac{14}{25}$ **h** $\frac{39}{20}$ **i** $\frac{57}{40}$ **j** $\frac{23}{8}$

5 Write these fractions as percentages. Where appropriate,
   give your answer to 1 decimal place.
   a $\frac{7}{16}$ **b** $\frac{23}{40}$ **c** $\frac{11}{23}$ **d** $\frac{5}{9}$ **e** $\frac{6}{7}$
   f $\frac{12}{3}$ **g** $\frac{14}{11}$ **h** $\frac{19}{13}$ **i** $\frac{17}{15}$ **j** $\frac{15}{8}$

6 Write these decimals as percentages.
   a 0.78   **b** 0.38   **c** 0.4   **d** 0.09   **e** 1.45
   f 0.03   **g** 0.345   **h** 1.01   **i** 0.333...   **j** 0.9925

7 Use a mental method to calculate these percentages.
   a 10% of 60 dogs   **b** 50% of 27 m   **c** 25% of 1440 men   **d** 5% of 80 cm
   e 15% of £650   **f** 60% of 70 goals   **g** 30% of 44 m   **h** 2.5% of 28 m
   i 35% of 720p   **j** 11% of £155

challenge

Stelios has converted a fraction into a percentage using a calculator.
He writes the answer as 73.9% (to 1 decimal place).
What fraction could he have started with?

- Find a percentage of a quantity

Keywords
Decrease
Equivalent
Increase
Percentage change
Unitary method

- You can calculate a percentage of an amount by
  - using an **equivalent** fraction
  - using an equivalent decimal
  - using the **unitary method**.

example

Calculate 17% of 58 litres.

Using an equivalent decimal
17% of 58 = 0.17 × 58 = 9.86 litres

Using an equivalent fraction
17% of 58 = $\frac{17}{100}$ of 58

$= \frac{17 \times 58}{100} = \frac{986}{100}$

$= 9.86$ litres

Using the unitary method
1% of 58 = 58 ÷ 100
$= 0.58$
So 17% of 58 = 0.58 × 17
$= 9.86$ litres

- You can calculate a **percentage change** by working out the **increase** or **decrease** and adding it to the original amount.

example

a A packet of biscuits weighs 350 g. The packet is increased in weight by 16%. What is the new weight of the biscuits?
b Another 350 g packet is reduced in weight by 16%. What is the new weight of the biscuits?

a First find the size of the increase.
16% of 350 g = 0.16 × 350
$= 56$ g
Add the increase to the original weight.
New weight = 350 + 56 = 406 g

b The decrease is 56 g, as before.
Subtract the decrease from the original weight.
New weight = 350 − 56 = 294 g

Exercise 4f

1 Calculate using mental methods.

    a 20% of £30   **b** 40% of 320 g   **c** 60% of 170 cm   **d** 11% of $5300

    e 70% of 98 kg   **f** 15% of 140 MB   **g** 35% of £16 000   **h** 21% of 48 litres

    i 95% of 140 mm   **j** 99% of $5000   **k** 30% of 90 cars   **l** 9% of 620 tonnes

2 Calculate using an appropriate method.

    a 11% of 30 cm   **b** 22% of 78 ml   **c** 60% of $580   **d** 15% of 90 apples

    e 16% of 40 km   **f** 14% of 85 g   **g** 65% of 32 sec   **h** 3% of 15 MB

    i 7.5% of £360   **j** 35% of 48 cm   **k** 95% of 66 days   **l** 11% of €64

3 Calculate these. Show all the steps of your working out.

    a 17% of £148   **b** 29% of 9400 cm

    c 113% of 64 MB   **d** 7.5% of 88 m

    e 6.4% of 260 cm   **f** 1.5% of £180 000

    g 53% of 94 ml   **h** 81% of €58

4 **a** Increase £48 by 15%   **b** Decrease 360 g by 10%

    c Increase 35 kg by 8%   **d** Decrease £19 000 by 17%

    e Increase £240 000 by 5.5%   **f** Decrease 3400 ml by 7.6%

5 **a** There are 72 034 seats at a football ground. On Saturday the ground is 93% full. How many people are at the ground?

    b A 30 g packet of crisps contains 6.4% fat. How much fat is that?

6 **a** A dress normally costs £55. It is reduced in a sale by 35%. What is the sale price of the dress?

    b Amjay orders a computer online. The bill comes to £499 + VAT. What is the price of the computer including VAT?

> VAT is a tax. The current rate is 17.5%.

In a sale, Bonhommes reduce all their prices by 15%.

a Calculate the sale price of each item. The sales assistant works out the sale price of each item using a single multiplication.

b Investigate how this can be done.

15% OFF EVERYTHING

JEANS £30   T-SHIRTS £20   HOODIES £28   SOCKS £10

4a

1 Write each of these fractions in its simplest form.

    a $\frac{24}{28}$ **b** $\frac{16}{40}$ **c** $\frac{36}{42}$ **d** $\frac{24}{39}$ **e** $\frac{48}{72}$

    f $\frac{56}{84}$ **g** $\frac{81}{108}$ **h** $\frac{84}{154}$ **i** $\frac{104}{160}$ **j** $\frac{99}{171}$

2 Give your answers to these questions as fractions in their simplest form

    a What fraction of 270 is 81?

    b What fraction of £3.20 is 85p?

    c What fraction of 3 hours is 48 minutes?

    d What fraction of 1 litre is 375 ml?

4b

3 Find the missing number in each of these pairs of equivalent fractions.

    a $\frac{12}{19} = \frac{?}{38}$ **b** $\frac{8}{?} = \frac{32}{20}$ **c** $\frac{4}{11} = \frac{?}{121}$ **d** $\frac{?}{5} = \frac{75}{125}$

    e $\frac{?}{9} = \frac{117}{81}$ **f** $\frac{11}{18} = \frac{?}{216}$ **g** $\frac{13}{17} = \frac{?}{272}$ **h** $\frac{8}{13} = \frac{?}{195}$

4 Calculate each of these, giving your answer as a fraction in its simplest form.

    a $\frac{1}{3} + \frac{1}{4}$ **b** $\frac{2}{7} + \frac{3}{5}$ **c** $\frac{5}{6} - \frac{4}{15}$ **d** $\frac{5}{11} - \frac{2}{9}$

    e $\frac{3}{8} - \frac{1}{16}$ **f** $\frac{3}{7} + \frac{4}{21}$ **g** $\frac{9}{16} - \frac{7}{24}$ **h** $\frac{11}{15} + \frac{7}{10}$

    i $1\frac{1}{5} - 1\frac{1}{7}$ **j** $1\frac{1}{3} + 2\frac{7}{15}$ **k** $2\frac{2}{5} - 1\frac{1}{3}$ **l** $2\frac{4}{9} + 1\frac{1}{3}$

4c

5 Write each of these decimals as a fraction in its simplest form.

    a 0.3   **b** 0.64   **c** 0.05   **d** 0.375   **e** 0.915

    f 1.05   **g** 1.75   **h** 1.84   **i** 1.175   **j** 1.333…

6 Write each of these fractions as decimals.

    a $\frac{19}{40}$ **b** $\frac{13}{15}$ **c** $\frac{5}{6}$ **d** $\frac{7}{11}$ **e** $\frac{17}{23}$

    f $\frac{3}{7}$ **g** $\frac{13}{40}$ **h** $\frac{5}{9}$ **i** $\frac{23}{16}$ **j** $1\frac{4}{15}$

7 For each pair of fractions, write down which is the larger fraction, giving an explanation for your choice.

    a $\frac{3}{7}$ and $\frac{7}{15}$ **b** $\frac{5}{9}$ and $\frac{12}{23}$ **c** $\frac{3}{13}$ and $\frac{4}{17}$ **d** $\frac{5}{19}$ and $\frac{11}{42}$

8 Put these fractions in order, from lowest to highest.

    a $\frac{3}{8}$ $\frac{5}{13}$ $\frac{1}{4}$ $\frac{9}{25}$ **b** $\frac{2}{5}$ $\frac{17}{40}$ $\frac{10}{26}$ $\frac{5}{12}$

9 Use a mental method to calculate these.

a $\frac{3}{8}$ of 40 dogs **b** $\frac{7}{12}$ of 96 MB **c** $\frac{5}{11}$ of $121 **d** $\frac{5}{7}$ of 91 hours

10 Calculate each of these, giving your answer in its simplest form.

a $\frac{4}{9}$ of 18 kg **b** $\frac{2}{5}$ of 45 cm **c** $\frac{5}{8}$ of 54 litres **d** $\frac{3}{7}$ of 21 cars

11 Calculate each of these, giving your answer in its simplest form.

a $4 \times \frac{3}{13}$ **b** $8 \times \frac{5}{12}$ **c** $14 \times \frac{9}{21}$

d $15 \times \frac{7}{10}$ **e** $22 \times \frac{4}{7}$ **f** $27 \times \frac{7}{18}$

12 Write each of these percentages as a fraction in its simplest form.

a 8% **b** 22% **c** 105% **d** 11.5% **e** 8.4%

13 Write each of these percentages as a decimal.

a 14% **b** 4% **c** 148% **d** 2.7% **e** 17.4%

14 Write each of these fractions as a percentage, without using a calculator.

a $\frac{3}{25}$ **b** $1\frac{3}{5}$ **c** $\frac{13}{40}$ **d** $\frac{5}{8}$ **e** $1\frac{24}{80}$

15 Write each of these fractions as a percentage.
Where appropriate, give your answer to 1 decimal place.

a $\frac{9}{15}$ **b** $1\frac{3}{7}$ **c** $\frac{19}{13}$ **d** $\frac{15}{9}$ **e** $\frac{14}{8}$

16 Write each of these decimals as a percentage.

a 0.24 **b** 0.08 **c** 0.1 **d** 0.095 **e** 1.111…

17 Calculate

a 10% of 40 kg **b** 1% of 785 cm **c** 5% of 48 ml **d** 11% of £260
e 35% of 240 mm **f** 15% of 65 MB **g** 60% of 35 m **h** 95% of $440

18 **a** Increase £78 by 35%
   b Decrease £28 by 5%
   c Increase 635 m by 12%
   d Decrease $47 by 3%

4 Summary

Key indicators

- Recognise equivalent fractions, decimals and percentages **Level 5**
- Find a percentage of an amount **Level 5**

Level 5

1 There are 20 pupils in class 7W.

Each pupil chooses a colour from red, blue, green or yellow.

8 pupils choose red, 2 pupils choose blue and 9 pupils choose green.

a How many pupils choose yellow?

b Complete the table.

The first line has been done for you.

	Cancelled fraction	Decimal number	Percentage
Red	$\frac{2}{5}$	0.4	40%
Blue			
Green			
Yellow			

Philip's answer ✔

Philip cancels $\frac{8}{20}$ to give $\frac{2}{5}$

$\frac{9}{20} = \frac{45}{100} = 45\%$

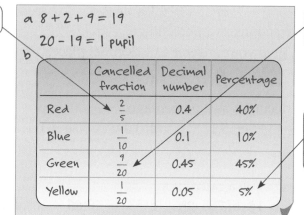

a 8 + 2 + 9 = 19

20 − 19 = 1 pupil

b

	Cancelled fraction	Decimal number	Percentage
Red	$\frac{2}{5}$	0.4	40%
Blue	$\frac{1}{10}$	0.1	10%
Green	$\frac{9}{20}$	0.45	45%
Yellow	$\frac{1}{20}$	0.05	5%

Philip checks by adding
40% + 10% + 45% + 5%
= 100%

Level 5

2 a Work out the missing values

10% of 84 =

5% of 84 =

$2\frac{1}{2}$% of 84 =

b The cost of a CD player is £84 plus $17\frac{1}{2}$% tax.

What is the total cost of the CD player?

You can use part **a** to help you.

Key Stage 3 2006 3–5 Paper 1

5 Data

Representing and interpreting data

Carl Linnaeus was a Swedish scientist who classified all living things into categories. His system organises human beings as:

Kingdom	Animalia
Phylum	Chordata
Class	Mammalia
Order	Primates
Family	Hominidae
Genus	Homo
Species	sapiens

What's the point? Classifying data into groups with similarities makes it easier to use and present the data.

✔ Check in

Level 3

1 Order these sets of numbers from smallest to largest.
  a 10, 12, 15, 10, 9, 11, 12, 10
  b 104, 110, 101, 99, 94, 100, 98, 101, 103, 98
  c 234, 423, 342, 324, 243, 432

Level 4

2 Work these out without using a calculator.
  a $\dfrac{12 + 14 + 16}{3}$ **b** $\dfrac{18 + 23 + 25 + 30}{4}$ **c** $\dfrac{105 + 108 + 110 + 112 + 115}{5}$

3 In a survey children chose their favourite storybook villain.
  a What fraction of the children chose the Wicked Stepmother?
  b What fraction of the children chose Cruella de Ville?
  c 32 children took part in this survey. How many chose the White Witch?

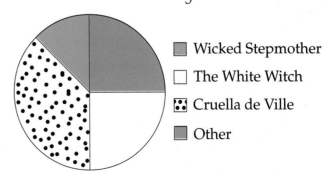

■ Wicked Stepmother
□ The White Witch
▦ Cruella de Ville
■ Other

- Tell the difference between different kinds of data
- Find the mode, median and range of numerical data

Keywords
Continuous   Midpoint
Data   Mode
Discrete   Range
Median

Non-numerical data does not use numbers.

- Numerical **data** can be either **discrete**, when data is counted (whole numbers), or **continuous**, when data is measured (whole numbers or decimals).

example

Are the following discrete, continuous or non-numerical data?
a The number of children in a family
b The fabrics used to make clothing
c The time an athlete takes to run 100 metres
d Shoe sizes

a Discrete   There will be 0, 1, 2, 3, …. children.
b Non-numerical   Data may be cotton, nylon or wool.
c Continuous   The time will be recorded to the nearest 0.1 or 0.01 second, but the exact time can be any value.
d Discrete   Shoe sizes could be 4, or $4\frac{1}{2}$ or 5 . You can't have a size $4\frac{1}{4}$ shoe.

You can use certain values to represent the information in a set of data instead of looking at the whole set.

- The **median** is the middle value when the data are arranged in order.

Where there are two middle numbers which are different, the median is the **midpoint** of the two values.

- The **mode** is the value which occurs most often.

For non-numerical data there can still be a mode.

- The **range** is the difference between the highest and lowest values.   Range = highest value − lowest value

example

Where possible, give the median, mode and range of these sets of data.
a Number of emails Jim received each day last week   1, 2, 1, 0, 0, 1
b Number of letters in Josie's text messages   22, 7, 82, 35, 4, 15, 28

p. 224

a Put the values in order 0, 0, 1, 1, 1, 2
   The median is 1.   There are 6 values, so the 3rd and 4th values are in the middle.
                            The midpoint between 1 and 1 is also 1.
   The mode is 1.   1 occurs the greatest amount of times.
   The range is 2.   Highest value = 2 and lowest value = 0.   2 − 0 = 2
b Put the values in order 4, 7, 15, 22, 28, 35, 82
   The median is 22.   There are 7 values so the 4th value is in the middle. The 4th value is 22.
   There is no mode.   No value occurs more often than the others.
   The range is 78.   Highest value = 82 and lowest value = 4.   82 − 4 = 78

Exercise 5a

1 Are the following discrete, continuous or non-numerical data?
   a The length of steps you take when walking
   b The number of stairs in the staircases in a building
   c The colours of the cars in a car park
   d The length of time that students in a class can hold their breath

2 Find the mode of these data sets.
   a Rolls of a dice: 2, 5, 5, 6, 3, 2, 5, 1, 6, 4, 5
   b Costs of CDs Frank bought: £8.99, £12.99, £8.99, £4, £5, £8.99
   c Colour of book covers on this bookcase ——————→

3 Find the median and the range of these data sets.
   a Resting pulse rates of a group of Year 7 students:
      61, 71, 80, 66, 68
   b Resting pulse rates of a group of Year 2 students:
      93, 78, 81, 81, 71, 95, 82
   c Pulse rates of a group of Year 7 students after running for 5 minutes:
      113, 147, 127, 139, 122, 135, 119

4 Find the median and range of these data sets.
   a Daily temperature highs in one week in Bristol in
      February (in °C): 7, 9, 8, 3, -1, 5, 5
   b Daily temperature highs in one week in Sydney in
      February (in °C): 27, 29, 26, 29, 31, 28, 29
   c Cost of Jamie's Christmas presents:
      £3.99, £7, £5.60, £29.99, £6

Bondi Beach, Sydney

5 Find the median and the range of the length of time each
   business is open.
   a The local library   b A local supermarket

LIBRARY	
Mon	1.00 p.m. - 8.00 p.m.
Tues	10.00 a.m. - 5.00 p.m.
Weds	1.00 p.m. - 8.00 p.m.
Thurs	9.00 a.m. - 6.00 p.m.
Fri	10.00 a.m. - 5.00 p.m.
Sat	9.00 a.m. - 1.00 p.m.

SUPERMARKET	
Mon	7.00 a.m. - 8.00 p.m.
Tues	7.00 a.m. - 8.00 p.m.
Weds	7.00 a.m. - 8.00 p.m.
Thurs	7.00 a.m. - 8.00 p.m.
Fri	7.00 a.m. - 8.00 p.m.
Sat	8.00 a.m. - 6.00 p.m.
Sun	8.00 a.m. - 3.00 p.m.

puzzle

a Find five numbers which have a mode of 7 and
   a median of 6.
b Explain why it is not possible to find three numbers
   with a mode of 7 and a median of 6.

* Calculate the mean for discrete data

Keywords
Average
Mean

When people talk about the '**average**' and don't say which one, they are usually referring to the **mean**.

> * Mean = $\dfrac{\text{The total of the values}}{\text{The number of values}}$
>
> Test scores: 3, 4, 4, 8, 8, 9
>
> Mean = $\dfrac{3 + 4 + 4 + 8 + 8 + 9}{6} = \dfrac{36}{6} = 6$

The mean does not have to be one of the data values, or even a possible value in the context.

For example, in the 2006–2007 season, Manchester United scored a mean of 2.18 goals per match. You can score 2 goals, but how do you score 0.18 goal?

The mean was $\dfrac{83 \text{ goals scored in}}{38 \text{ games played}} = 2.18$ goals per game

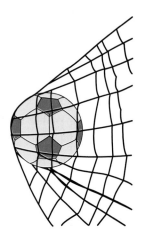

example

Find the mean of each set of data.
a Resting pulse rates of a group of Year 7 pupils:
    67, 71, 70, 66, 63, 71 beats per minute
b Cost of Christmas presents Jamie bought:
    £3.99, £7, £5.60, £29.99, £6

. . . .

a Total = 67 + 71 + 70 + 66 + 63 + 71 = 408
  Mean pulse rate = $\dfrac{408}{6} = 68$

b Total = £3.99 + £7 + £5.60 + £29.99 + £6 = £52.58.
  Mean cost = $\dfrac{£52.58}{5} = £10.52$ (to the nearest penny)

example

Martina recorded her test scores for five maths tests during the term. She calculated a mean score of 7.8. Unfortunately, she put a cup of tea on her record book and smudged one of her scores. What was the smudged score?

Maths tests this term
19 Jan   6
26 Jan   9
2 Feb
9 Feb   7
16 Feb   9

. . . .

For a mean of 7.8, the total must be 7.8 × 5 = 39.
The four known scores total 31 so the last one must be 8.   39 − 31 = 8

Exercise 5b

1 Find the mean of each of these data sets.

   a Resting pulse rates of a group of Year 7 students:
      61, 71, 80, 66, 68

   b Resting pulse rates of a group of Year 2 students:
      93, 78, 81, 81, 71, 95, 82

   c Pulse rates of a group of Year 7 students after running for 5 minutes:
      113, 147, 127, 139, 122, 135, 119

2 The length of time between eruptions of Old Faithful geyser
in Yellowstone National Park is recorded on one day during
the park's opening hours.
The times are (in minutes) 65, 89, 65, 95, 55, 89, 56, 92.
Calculate the mean length of time between eruptions that day.

3 A golf instructor asked each of his students to stand
100 metres from the flag. Using a rangefinder, he
measured their actual distances, in metres.
    107, 95, 102, 110, 96, 98, 107, 93, 101, 91
Calculate

   a the range

   b the mean.

4 The number of Year 7 students present each day for two weeks is
    159, 159, 153, 149, 152, 158, 161, 160, 161, 154.

   a Calculate the mean number of Year 7 students present.

   b There are 163 Year 7 students on the roll in the school.
      Calculate the mean number of Year 7 students absent.

5 A psychologist measures the reaction times (in hundredths
of a second) of different groups of people under different
conditions.
Calculate the mean reaction time for each of the groups.

   a Normal conditions: 16, 19, 15, 19, 22, 17, 16, 17, 21, 18, 17

   b Using their non-writing hand to react: 19, 22, 23, 19, 17, 24, 27, 21, 18

   c Blindfolded: 20, 21, 18, 19, 23, 21, 24, 18, 17, 22, 19, 23, 20

   d After two alcoholic drinks: 22, 19, 14, 21, 15, 26, 23, 19, 24

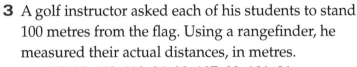

puzzle

   a Find a set of five numbers which have a mode of 3, a median
     of 5 and a range of 4.

   b How many different sets of five numbers can you find
     which have a mode of 5, a median of 5 and a range of 4?

- Construct a frequency table for discrete data
- Use a frequency table to find any average (mode, median or mean) and the range

Keywords
Frequency table Median
Mean Mode
Range

- A large set of data can be summarised in a **frequency table**.

- You can find the **median** from a frequency table by counting a running total.

- You can find the **mean** from a frequency table by multiplying each value by its frequency and adding the results together, then dividing by the total frequency.

example

Class 7C were asked how many pets they had. The frequency table shows their answers.
Calculate
a the range
b the mode
c the median
d the mean of these data.

Number of pets	Frequency
0	8
1	7
2	4
3	1

a The highest value is 3 pets, the lowest is 0 pets. $3 - 0 = 3$
The range is 3 pets.
b 8 students have 0 pets.
8 is the highest number in the frequency column.
The mode is 0 pets.
c There are $8 + 7 + 4 + 1 = 20$ students, so the median is between the 10th and 11th values. The 10th and 11th values are both 1.   The median is 1 pet.

The first row on the table tells you that 8 students have 0 pets.

Values 1–8 are 0 pets.
Values 9–15 are 1 pet.

d The mean $= \dfrac{\text{Total number of pets}}{\text{Total number of students}}$

$$= \frac{(0 \times 8) + (7 \times 1) + (2 \times 4) + (3 \times 1)}{20}$$

$$= \frac{0 + 7 + 8 + 3}{20} = \frac{18}{20} = 0.9$$

The mean is 0.9 pets.

The third row of the table tells you that 4 students have 2 pets. Between them, they have 8 pets.

Exercise 5c

1 Sally writes down her scores as she throws a dice.

   3, 6, 3, 2, 5, 1, 3, 6, 1, 4, 3, 2, 4, 2, 5, 2, 2

   a Show this information in a frequency table.

   b Write down the modal score.

   c Calculate the median score.

   d Calculate the range of the scores.

2 These are the ages of children in a day care centre.

   2, 3, 4, 1, 4, 2, 5, 2, 3, 3, 4, 5, 1, 5, 3

   a Show this information in a frequency table.

   b Calculate the modal age of the children.

   c Calculate the median age of the children.

   d Calculate the range of the ages.

   e Calculate the mean age of the children.

3 The number of letters in the words of a child's
   first reading book are

   3, 3, 2, 4, 3, 1, 3, 3, 4, 2, 3, 3, 3, 2

   a Show this information as a frequency table.

   b Calculate the modal number of letters in a word.

   c Calculate the median number of letters in a word.

   d Calculate the range of the number of letters in the words.

   e Calculate the mean number of letters in a word.

4 For a Science project, Simon shells some peas and
   records the number of peas in each pod.

   3, 4, 3, 8, 2, 3, 6, 7, 2, 7, 5, 5, 3, 3, 7, 8, 3, 4, 5, 6, 2, 8, 3

   a Show this information in a frequency table.

   b Calculate the modal number of peas in each pod.

   c Calculate the median number of peas.

   d Calculate the range of the number of peas.

   e Calculate the mean number of peas.

puzzle

In a rugby team the mean weight of the 8 forwards is 95 kg
and the mean weight of the 7 backs is 83 kg.

a Bill says the mean weight of the team is 89 kg.
   Is he correct? Explain your answer.

b If the median weight of the forwards is 95 kg and the
   median weight of the backs is 83 kg, what can you say
   about the median weight of the team?

- Understand and use information given on different kinds of bar charts

Keywords
Bar chart   Frequency
Comparative   Stacked
    bar chart   bar chart

- You can represent **frequency** using a **bar chart**.

- You can use a **comparative bar chart** to compare different sets of data.

Sometimes a comparative bar chart is called a multiple bar chart.

example

The bar chart below shows how many students achieved grades A–E in their maths A level in 2006. The table shows how many students achieved grades A–E in their English A level in the same year.

a Add the English data to the bar chart.

b Comment on what the chart tells you about the results for A level maths and English in 2006.

Grade	Number of candidates
A	20 000
B	20 000
C	25 000
D	15 000
E	5 000

a

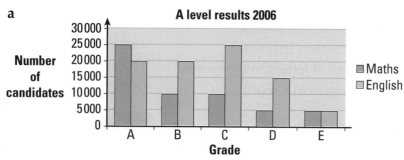

Always include a key.

The height of bar A for English is 20 000 because 20 000 candidates achieved grade A.

b The modal grade in maths was A. The modal grade in English was C.

The modal grade has the highest bar.

- A **stacked bar chart** can be used to show how much each group contributes to the total.

Sometimes a stacked bar chart is called a component or composite bar chart.

From this graph, it is easy to tell that there were more candidates for English than for maths. You can also see that more candidates got at least a grade B in English than in maths, but more got A grades in maths.

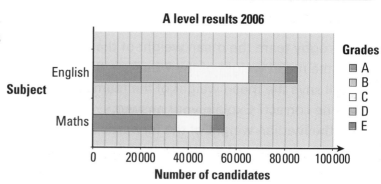

Exercise 5d

1 The table shows the average daily temperatures in °C in London and Sydney.

	Jan	Feb	Mar	Apr	May	Jun	Jul	Aug	Sep	Oct	Nov	Dec
London	3.9	4.2	5.7	8.5	11.9	15.2	17	16.6	14.2	10.3	6.6	4.8
Sydney	25.7	25.6	24.6	22.2	19.2	16.7	16	17.5	19.7	21.9	23.5	25.1

a Draw a comparative bar chart to represent this information.
b Compare the average temperatures in London and Sydney over the year.

2 The table shows the percentages of UK households with access to at least one car, in 1990 and in 2000.

% of households		Year
1990	2000	
60	63	London boroughs
58	62	Metropolitan built-up areas
65	68	Large urban (population over 250 000)
67	73	Medium urban (population 25 000 to 250 000)
72	78	Small urban (population 3000 to 10 000)
81	85	Rural

a Draw a comparative bar chart to represent this information.
b Describe the change from 1990 to 2000.

3 The chart shows the ages of MPs in 1997 and 2005.
  a i How many MPs were under 30 in 1997?
   ii How many MPs were aged 30–39 in 1997?
  iii How many MPs were aged 40–49 in 1997?
   iv How many MPs were under 50 in 1997?
  b How many MPs were under 50 in 2005?
  c How many more MPs were under 60 in 1997 than in 2005?

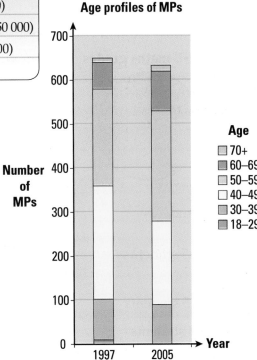

Age profiles of MPs

Number of MPs

Age
- ☐ 70+
- ▨ 60–69
- ☐ 50–59
- ☐ 40–49
- ▨ 30–39
- ▨ 18–29

Using the graph in question **3**, do you think the average age of MPs was higher in 1997 or in 2005?
Give a reason for your answer.
Can you be sure from the information provided?

• Understand and use information given on pie charts

Keywords
Frequency
Pie chart
Proportion

• A **pie chart** is a circular chart divided into 'slices'.

• If you know the total **frequency**, or the frequency of any one group, you can calculate the frequency of each group.

> Pie charts are useful when you want to know the **proportion** of each category, compared to the whole.

• You can use two pie charts to compare the relative size of the groups within each chart.

example

p. 218

The pie charts show the GCSE maths and French grades of the Year 11 students at a small school.

Thirty students achieved an A grade in maths.

a How many Year 11 students are there at the school?

b How many students achieved grades A*, B, C and D in maths?

c Did more students achieve grade A in French than in maths? Explain your answer.

GCSE maths grades   **GCSE French grades**

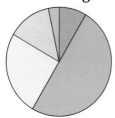 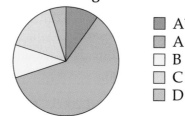

■ A*
■ A
□ B
□ C
■ D

a 60 students

You can see that half of the students achieved an A grade. $30 \times 2 = 60$

> There are 360° in a circle.

b A* : 5 students

Measure the A* sector with a protractor. The angle is 30°. $\frac{30}{360} \times 60 = 5$

B : 15 students

The angle is 90°. $\frac{90}{360} \times 60 = 15$

C : 8 students

The angle is 48°. $\frac{48}{360} \times 60 = 8$

D : 2 students

The angle is 12°. $\frac{12}{360} \times 60 = 2$

c The **proportion** of students achieving an A grade is greater in French than in maths, but you cannot say whether the number of students is greater because you don't know how many students took French GCSE.

Exercise 5e

1 An airport classifies flight arrivals as **early** if they land more than 5 minutes before the scheduled time, and as **late** if they land more than 5 minutes after it. The pie chart shows information about the arrival times of a sample of 100 flights. 10 planes landed early.
  a How many planes were late?
  b How many planes landed on time?

Arrivals of flights

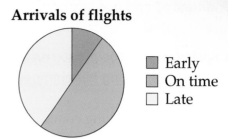

- ■ Early
- ■ On time
- □ Late

2 The pie chart shows the number of different types of pets owned by the pupils in an infants' school. There are 30 cats.
  a How many pets are there altogether?
  b How many dogs are there?

Pet ownership

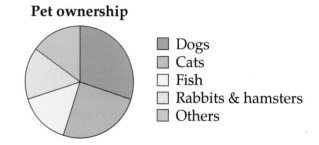

- ■ Dogs
- ■ Cats
- □ Fish
- □ Rabbits & hamsters
- ■ Others

3 The pie charts show the type of film preferred by the 15 girls and 20 boys in class 7C.
  a How many **i** girls **ii** boys like science fiction/fantasy best?
  b Comment on what else the pie charts tell you about the types of film the girls and boys in class 7C like best.

Favourite film type (girls)

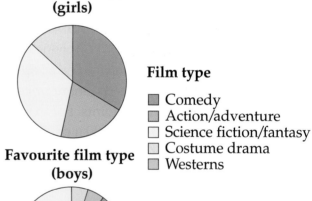

Film type

- ■ Comedy
- ■ Action/adventure
- □ Science fiction/fantasy
- □ Costume drama
- ■ Westerns

Favourite film type (boys)

Computer spreadsheets make it easy to produce very fancy '3-D' charts. What are the advantages and disadvantages of this kind of chart?

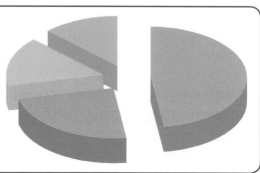

discussion

5f Line graphs for time series

- Understand and use information given on line graphs

Keywords
Estimate
Line graph
Time series

- A **time series** can be plotted as a **line graph** to show you how something has changed over time.

example

A new company making computer games sells shares on the stock market. The table shows the share price at hourly intervals between 10:00 and 15:00 on the first day of trading.

Time of day	10:00	11:00	12:00	13:00	14:00	15:00
Share price	£2.10	£2.70	£2.90	£3.50	£3.60	£3.20

a Plot these data on a line graph.
b **Estimate** the share price at 12:30.
c Can you tell from the graph what the highest share price was? Explain your answer.

a Plot a point showing the value at each recorded time. Join them with a broken line.

b £3.20   Read up from 12:30 on the Time axis, then across to the Share price axis.

c No. We don't know the share price at the times between the points. For example, between 14:00 and 15:00 it could have risen beyond £3.60 (the highest recorded price) before falling to £3.20.

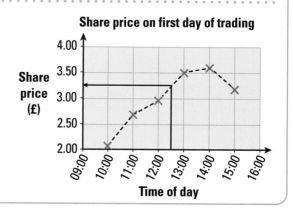

Share price on first day of trading

- Two time series can be plotted on the same graph.
  This helps you to compare the two sets of data.

example

The graph shows the number of traffic accidents at different times of day in Sefton in 1980 and 2006. Comment on the similarities and differences between the two series.

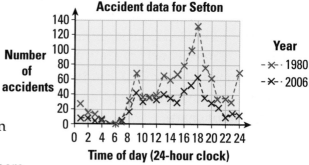

Accident data for Sefton

In both series there are more accidents in the morning and evening rush hours.
In 2006 there were fewer accidents and there is no rise in the number of accidents around midnight.

Exercise 5f

1 The graph shows the average house prices in London and in Northern Ireland between 1975 and 2005.

   a Describe what has happened to the average house price in London over this period.

   b Describe what has happened to the average house price in Northern Ireland over this period.

Average house prices

2 The table shows the life expectancy at birth for males and females in the UK between 1981 and 2004.

Year	1981	1986	1991	1996	1997	1998	1999	2000	2001	2002	2003	2004
Males	70.8	71.9	73.2	74.3	74.5	74.8	75.0	75.4	75.7	75.9	76.3	76.6
Females	76.8	77.7	78.7	79.4	79.6	79.7	79.9	80.2	80.4	80.5	80.7	81.0

   a Plot two time series graphs on one set of axes to show this information.

   b Describe any similarities and differences you see in the two time series.

challenge

The graph shows the percentage of different age groups who said that they visit the cinema at least once a month.

   a Which age group goes to the cinema most often?

   Sanjit says that when he goes to the cinema, there are more people over 35 than in any other age group. He says that the graphs must be wrong.

   b Assuming Sanjit is right in saying there are more people over 35 when he goes to the cinema, is he correct that the graphs must be wrong? Explain your answer.

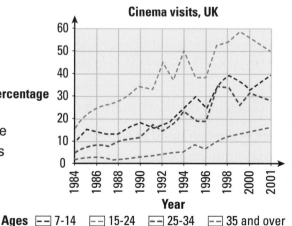

Cinema visits, UK

Ages ⊟ 7-14   ⊟ 15-24   ⊟ 25-34   ⊟ 35 and over

1 Are the following discrete, continuous or non-numerical data?
   a The heights of the buildings on Trafalgar Square
   b The number of people in Trafalgar Square at different times
   c The cost of entry to exhibitions in the National Gallery
   d The colours of the vehicles in Trafalgar Square at a particular time

2 Find the median and range of each of these sets of data.
   a The resting pulse rates of a group of professional athletes:
      53, 62, 71, 58, 61, 65, 59, 67, 64, 64
   b The resting pulse rates of a group of accountants:
      65, 72, 68, 79, 83, 63, 59, 80, 69
   c The heights (in cm) of a group of professional athletes:
      175, 182, 184, 170, 186, 179, 180, 178, 179, 182
   d The heights (in cm) of a group of accountants:
      183, 171, 178, 179, 183, 177, 179, 181, 174

3 Find the means of the sets of data in question **2** using a calculator.

4 The number of text messages sent in an hour by a group of
   Year 7 students on a school trip is summarised in the table.

Number of text messages	0	1	2	3	4	5
Frequency (Boys)	7	5	2	1	2	0
Frequency (Girls)	3	4	4	2	3	4

Answer these questions for **i** the boys **ii** the girls.
   a Write the modal number of text messages.
   b Write the range of the number of text messages.
   c Calculate the mean number of text messages.

5 Jamie goes on holiday to Milan in October. He records the
   maximum temperature (in °C) each day.
      17, 17, 20, 21, 20, 18, 18, 19, 21, 21, 22, 19, 18, 17, 17
   a Show this information in a frequency table.
   b Write the modal maximum temperature.
   c Calculate the median maximum temperature.
   d Calculate the range of the maximum temperatures.
   e Calculate the mean maximum temperature.

6 Show the data in question **5** on a bar chart.

7 The pie charts show the bmi (body mass index) of males and females.

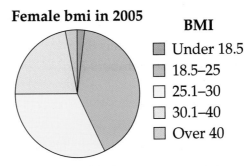

Male bmi in 2005   Female bmi in 2005

BMI
- ▨ Under 18.5
- ▨ 18.5–25
- ☐ 25.1–30
- ☐ 30.1–40
- ▨ Over 40

a What percentage of male adults have a bmi which is over 18.5 but 25 or under?

b A bmi of over 30 is classed as obese.
What percentage of adult males were obese in 2005?

c A bmi of between 25.1 and 30 is classed as overweight.
What percentage of adult females were overweight in 2005?

8 The graph shows the average annual temperature in central England at 50 year intervals from 900 AD to 2000 AD.

a In which year was the lowest average annual temperature recorded?

b By how much did the average annual temperature drop between 1200 AD and 1400 AD?

c If the same drop in average annual temperature takes place between 2000 AD and 2200 AD, what will the average annual temperature be in 2200 AD?

d Estimate the average annual temperature in 1925.

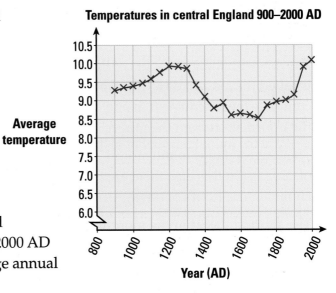

Temperatures in central England 900–2000 AD

Average temperature

Year (AD)

5 Summary

Key indicators

- Interpret diagrams and graphs (including pie charts) **Level 5**

Level 5

1 a Six students in Zeenat's class calculate the distance from their home to school.
   The distances, in kilometres, are 7, 2, 6, 4, 1, 7.
   Calculate the median distance.

b The mode of three numbers is 8.
   The mean of the three numbers 7.
   Find the three numbers.

Mandy's answer ✔

Mandy finds the total of the three numbers

Mandy puts the numbers in numerical order

a 1, 2, 4, 6, 7, 7
   Median is (4 + 6) ÷ 2 = 5
b 7 × 3 = 21
   21 − (8 + 8) = 5
   The three numbers are 5, 8, 8

Mandy knows two of the numbers are 8

Level 5

2 The graph shows at what time the sun rises and sets in the American town of Anchorage, Alaska.

The day with the most hours of light is called the longest day. Copy and complete these sentences, using the information from the graph.

The longest day is in the month of _____ On this day, there are about _____ hours of daylight.

The shortest day is in the month of _____ On this day, there are about _____ hours of daylight.

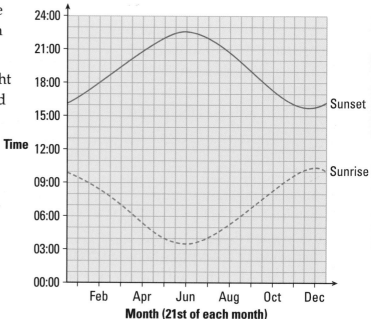

Key Stage 3 2004 3–5 Paper 1

6 Algebra

Expressions and formulas

The word algebra derives from the Arabic phrase *al-jabr*, meaning 'the reunion of broken parts.' The Arabic mathematician al-Khwarazmi first used this term in a book he wrote which described finding missing numbers and collecting like terms.

What's the point? Algebra isn't a modern or 'western' idea. It has been used for over 1000 years to discover missing information.

Check in

1 a Rashid wanted to make a list of square numbers.
Which of these numbers could go in his list?

49   27   16   24   90   1   10   9   25

b Give another number, smaller than 100, that could be in the list.

c Give another number, between 150 and 200, that could be in the list.

2 Evaluate

a $-3 + 8$ **b** $-2 - 9$ **c** $5 - -3$ **d** $-4 + -9$

e -2×6 **f** $-10 \div -2$ **g** 3×-7 **h** $-18 \div -2$

3 Given that $n = 3$, put these expressions in ascending order.

$4n$ $n + 10$ $2n - 1$ n^2 $\dfrac{n}{3}$ $2(n - 2)$

• Substitute numbers into a formula

Keywords
Algebra   Substitute
BIDMAS   Variable
Expression

Algebra is the language of mathematics. It can be used to communicate mathematically with other people.

p. 180

• In algebraic **expressions**, unknown numbers or **variables** are represented by letters, using these rules.
  • Never write a × sign.
  • Never write a ÷ sign; use a fraction instead.
  • In products, write numbers before letters.

Write $5a$ not $5 \times a$.
Write bc not $b \times c$.

Write $\frac{x}{2}$ not $x \div 2$.

Write $6p$ not $p6$.
Write $2xy$ not $x2y$.

---

example

Write these sentences using the rules of algebra.
a I think of a number, multiply it by 4 and subtract 6.
b I think of a number, subtract it from 10 and multiply by 2.
c I think of a number, divide by 8 and add 11.

a $4x - 6$
b $2(10 - x)$
c $\frac{x}{8} + 11$

• You can **substitute** a number for a variable in an expression and work out its value.

Substitute means 'put in the place of'.

• Algebraic operations are performed in the same order as arithmetic operations They follow **BIDMAS**.

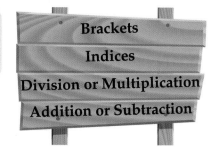

Brackets

Indices

Division or Multiplication

Addition or Subtraction

---

example

When $x = 4$, which is larger, $3x^2$ or $(3x)^2$?

$3x^2 = 48$ I think of a number, multiply it by itself and then multiply it by 3. $3 \times 4^2 = 3 \times 16 = 48$

Indices come before multiplication.

$(3x)^2 = 144$ I think of a number, multiply it by 3 and then multiply the result by itself. $(3 \times 4)^2 = 12^2 = 144$

Brackets come before indices.

$(3x)^2$ is larger when $x = 4$.

Exercise 6a

1 Write these sentences using algebraic notation.
   a 'I think of a number, multiply it by 7 and add 1.'
   b 'I think of a number, divide it by 4 and subtract 2.'
   c 'I think of a number, add 6 and then multiply by 5.'
   d 'I think of a number and multiply it by itself.'
   e 'I think of a number and multiply it by another number.'

2 Given that $x = 3$ and $y = 5$, find the value of each of these expressions.
   a $4x$
   b $y + 4$
   c $2x - 3$
   d $3(y - 1)$
   e $\dfrac{y + 1}{3}$
   f $x^2 + y^2$
   g xy
   h $x(y + 2)$

3 Given that $m = 4$ and $n = -3$, find the value of each of these expressions.
   a $2m - 9$
   b $mn + 1$
   c n^2
   d $\dfrac{m + 5}{n}$
   e $m(n - 2)$
   f $3n^2$

4 Here are some expressions.
   a Roll a dice and let the number you roll be y.
     Which expression gives the smallest value
     and which gives the largest value?
   b Which expression gives the maximum value?
     For what value of y?

$$2(y - 4) \qquad 3y^2$$

$$\dfrac{y + 4}{2}$$

$$12 - 2y \qquad 5y + 2$$

5 Three friends each write an expression.
   They each substitute a number into their
   expression. They all get 25. What number(s)
   did each friend use?

Clare   Ally   Nick

Try this sequence of operations on different numbers of your
choice. What do you notice? Use algebraic expressions to show
why this happens.

Now make up a 'Think of a number' problem of your own.

Think of a number
Multiply it by four
Add 6
Divide by 2
Subtract 3
Halve it

- Simplify expressions by collecting 'like terms'

Keywords
Collect   Simplify
Expression   Term
Like terms

- Each part of an algebraic **expression** is called a **term**.

  $3p - 2t + 3w - 9$ consists of four terms, $3p$, $-2t$, $3w$ and -9.

- Terms which involve the same unknown are called **like terms**.

  $3x + 9y - 2x$ consists of three terms. $3x$ and $-2x$ are like terms because the unknown in both is x.

  $4x^2 + 8x$ consists of two terms. They are not like terms because $4x^2$ involves x^2 and $8x$ only involves x.

  $4ab + 9ba$ consists of two terms. They are like terms because $ab = ba$ (just as $2 \times 3 = 3 \times 2$).

- If an expression is the sum or difference of terms, then the like terms can be **collected** together.

example

Simplify these expressions.
a $4a + 9b + 7a + 6b$
b $9y^2 + 7y - 5y^2 + y$
c $5p + 6pq + 4q - 3qp$

. . . .

a $4a + 9b + 7a + 6b = 11a + 15b$

b $9y^2 + 7y - 5y^2 + y = 4y^2 + 8y$

c $5p + 6pq + 4q - 3pq = 5p + 4q + 3pq$

Simplify means 'collect like terms'.

Rewrite the expression with like terms together. Remember to move the positive or negative sign with the term.

In the terms involving both p and q, write the variables in alphabetical order.

- Expressions that do not contain like terms cannot be simplified.   The expression $3m - 8mn + 4$ cannot be simplified.

example

Simplify each of these expressions, if possible.
a $4mn + 9nm$ **b** $5y - 3$ **c** $5q - q^2$ **d** $8y + 9y - y$

. . . .

a $4mn + 9nm = 4mn + 9mn = 13mn$ **b** Cannot be simplified.
c Cannot be simplified.   **d** $8y + 9y - y = 16y$

$y = 1y$
We do not write the '1'.

Exercise 6b

1 Copy the grid. Colour cells containing like terms in the same colour.

4x	5p	3t	$9t^3$	2yx
-5	15t	7xy	$4p^2$	x
2p	p^2	-8x	11t	8

2 Simplify these expressions, if possible.

a $a + a + a$ **b** $10x + 9x$

c $3t + t + 9t$ **d** $6w - 6$

e $7f + 9f - 6f$ **f** $4x + 8y + 11x - 2y$

g $4m + 2n - m + n$ **h** $11q + 5 - 5q - 9$

i $6p + 9p^2 + 2p$ **j** $11st + 5ts + 6st$

k $3m + 3n - m^2 + 5$ **l** $5x + 7y - 6x - 4$

3 An expression simplifies to $4x + 7y$.
What could the expression have been?

4 Here are some algebraic expressions.

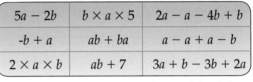

$5a - 2b$	$b \times a \times 5$	$2a - a - 4b + b$
$-b + a$	$ab + ba$	$a - a + a - b$
$2 \times a \times b$	$ab + 7$	$3a + b - 3b + 2a$

a Which two expressions are equivalent to $4a + a - 3b + b$?

b Which expressions are equivalent to $a - b$?

c Which expressions are equivalent to $\frac{1}{2}(3ab + ba)$?

5 The diagram shows a grid of streets.
The police are trying to catch the burglar.
The police car can travel north or east.

a Write expressions for the different routes that the police may take.

b Simplify your expressions.

c What do you notice?

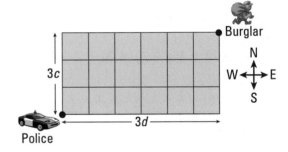

6 Find the missing expressions, giving your answers as simply as possible.

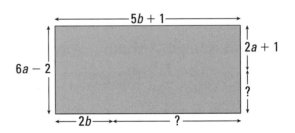

• Expand brackets and then simplify expressions

Keywords
Bracket
Expand
Simplify

These bags of terms can be thought of in two ways.

> The total value of all the terms is
> $2p + 3 + 2p + 3 + 2p + 3 = 6p + 9$

or

> There are three bags, each containing $2p + 3$.
> The value of all three bags is $3(2p + 3)$.
> So $3(2p + 3) = 6p + 9$

• To **expand brackets**, you multiply all the terms inside
  the brackets by the term outside the brackets.
  $$3(2p + 3) = 3 \times 2p + 3 \times 3 = 6p + 9$$

Expand means
'multiply out'.

example

Expand and simplify each expression.
a $2(q + 1) + 4(q + 3)$ **b** $k(k + m)$

. . . .

a $2(q + 1) + 4(q + 3) = 2q + 2 + 4q + 12 = 6q + 14$

b $k(k + m) = k \times k + k \times m = k^2 + km$

Use the rules of algebra
to tidy each term. $4 \times q$ is
written as $4q$.

Multiplying a number by
itself is called squaring.
$k \times k = k^2$

example

Write a fully simplified expression for
the area of this compound shape.

. . . .

Area A = length × width   Area B = length × width
$= (g - 2) \times 3$ $= (5 - g) \times 9$
$= 3(g - 2)$ $= 9(5 - g)$
$= 3g - 6$ $= 45 - 9g$

Total area $= 3g - 6 + 45 - 9g$
$= 39 - 6g$

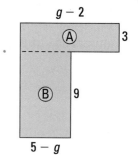

Exercise 6c

1 Expand these brackets.

a $4(x + 3)$ **b** $7(y + 6)$

c $5(p + 14)$ **d** $3(2m + 4)$

e $4(b - 4)$ **f** $12(k - 8)$

g $x(x + 5)$ **h** $w(w - 2)$

i $m(m - n)$ **j** $2x(3x + y)$

2 Use brackets to write an expression for the area of each of these rectangles. Then expand each expression.

a

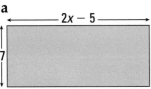

b

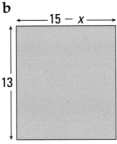

c

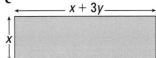

3 Expand and simplify each of these expressions.

a $3(x + 9) + 4(x + 2)$ **b** $4(y - 3) + 5(y + 4)$

c $7(2x - 1) + 3(3x - 5)$ **d** $x(x + 7) + x(x - 1)$

e $m(m + n) + n(n + m)$

4 A farmer buys 100 m of fencing for a new animal enclosure against the side of an existing barn.

a If the width of the enclosure is w, write an expression for its length.

b Write an expression for the area of the enclosure, expanding and simplifying your answer.

c Investigate the value of w which will give the farmer the maximum area in which to keep her animals.

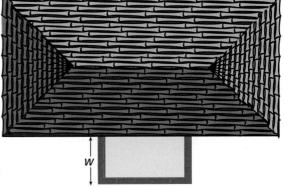

6d Using a formula

- Use formulas in real-life situations

p. 25

Keywords   *Variable*
Formula
Substitute

- A **formula** describes the relationship between **variables**. They appear in many areas of life.

  $$\text{Speed} = \frac{\text{distance}}{\text{time}}$$

  $F = \frac{9}{5}C + 32$, where F and C = Fahrenheit and Celsius temperatures.

- Many formulas have two unknown variables. If you know the value of one, you can find the value of the other by **substituting** the known value into the formula.

---

example

Alex is going on holiday. He needs to convert his £80 spending money into euros. At the airport, he sees this sign. How much spending money will Alex have in euros?

Change currency here
We pay €1.5
for every £1

....

Number of euros = 1.5 × number of pounds

$E = 1.5P$ This is the formula

$E = 1.5 \times 80$ Substitute 80 (Alex's spending money in pounds) for *P*.

To convert pounds to euros, Alex must multiply by 1.5.

$E = 120$

Alex will have € 120 spending money.

---

example

Holly is going on the school ski trip to France. She needs to write her weight, to the nearest kilogram, so that her skis can be adjusted correctly. Holly knows that she weighs 8 stone. Use the formula $W = \frac{14s}{2.2}$ to work out Holly's weight in kilograms. W = weight in kilograms and s = weight in stones.

....

$W = \frac{14s}{2.2}$

$W = \frac{14 \times 8}{2.2}$ Substitute 8 (Holly's weight in stones) for *s*.

$W = \frac{112}{2.2} = 50.909\,090\ldots$

Holly weighs 51 kg to the nearest kilogram.

Exercise 6d

1 The perimeter of a rectangle can be found using the formula
$P = 2l + 2w$, where l is the length of the rectangle and w is the width.
  a Use the formula to find the perimeter of a rectangle with
    length 12 mm and width 5 mm.
  b Explain why the formula works.

2 Thomas's monthly mobile phone bills are calculated using
the formula $C = 20 + 0.4n$, where C = cost in pounds and
n = number of minutes spent on calls.
  a Work out how much Thomas' monthly bill will be if he
    spends 40 minutes on the phone.
  b Thomas is on holiday for the whole of July and leaves his
    phone at home. Does this mean that he will not be charged
    for that month? Explain your answer.

3 The area of a shape is found using the formula $A = 4(l + 2)$,
where l is the length of the shape.
  a Find the area of a shape with length 12 cm.
  b What is the length of a shape with area of 28 m²?

4 If you liked hot weather, would you rather go to
Majorca in August, where the average temperature
is 80 °F, or to Rome where the average temperature is 27 °C?

  Use the formula $C = \dfrac{5(F - 32)}{9}$ to convert °F to °C.

5 Any object that is moving has kinetic energy. Kinetic
energy, KE, is found using the formula $KE = \frac{1}{2}mv^2$,

where m = the object's mass and v = the object's speed.

> Kinetic energy is energy
> which a moving object
> has.

  a Find the kinetic energy of a 2000 kg car travelling at 10 m/s
    and the kinetic energy of the same car travelling at 20 m/s.
  b Will faster objects always have more kinetic energy than
    slower ones? Use the formula to help you decide.

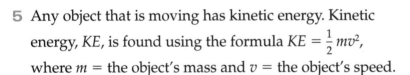

investigation

Questions **4** and **5** use scientific formulas.
What other formulas have you met in science lessons?
Use the internet to find some more scientific formulas.
What can you use each formula to find?

6e Deriving a formula

- Make a formula to describe a real-life situation

Keywords

Derive   *Generalise*
Expression   *Subject*
Formula   *Variable*

- The **subject** of a **formula** is the **variable** on the left-hand side.
  In the formula for the volume of a cuboid, $V = lwh$, V is the subject.

  lwh on its own is an **expression**. A formula needs a subject and an equals sign.

- You can **derive** a formula for a specific situation by considering the information given.

  Derive means 'find using logic'.

---

example

Find a formula for the area, A, of the vegetable patch.

You know that the formula for the area of a rectangle is
Area = length × width
The length of the vegetable patch is $10 - x$ and its width $10 - y$.
So $A = (10 - x)(10 - y)$

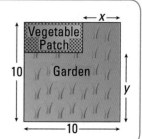

If a formula is difficult to see, generating some examples may help you to see a pattern so that you can **generalise**.

Generalise means making a statement that is always true.

---

example

Isla is paid to babysit her nephew, Matthew. She is paid £5 plus an extra £2 per hour. Write a formula for the payment, P, that Isla receives.

Make a table to show some possible payments.

Hours worked (h)	Basic pay (£)	Extra payment (£)	Total payment (£P)
1	5	$1 \times 2 = 2$	$5 + 2 = 7$
2	5	$2 \times 2 = 4$	$5 + 4 = 9$
3	5	$3 \times 2 = 6$	$5 + 6 = 11$
4	5	$4 \times 2 = 8$	$5 + 8 = 13$
h	5	$h \times 2 = 2h$	$5 + 2h = P$

Use the first four rows to help you generalise and fill in a row for *h* hours.

The formula for her payment is $P = 5 + 2h$

Exercise 6e

1 Ikram spends his £50 birthday money on computer games.
   The games cost £6 each.
   a If he buys two games, how much money will he have left over?
   b If he buys five games, how much money will he have left over?
   c Write a formula to find M, the amount of money he has left over
      if he buys n games.

2 Explain why each formula is correct.
   a The shaded area of this square is found using $A = x^2 - y^2$.
   b The entrance fee for a funfair is £3 and each ride costs £2.
      The total cost of attending the funfair is found using
      $C = 2r + 3$, where C is the cost in pounds and r is the
      number of rides you go on.

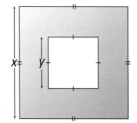

3 Annika draws some circles and some squares then joins
   every circle to every square.
   a If Annika draws three circles and five squares, how many
      lines will she draw to connect them?
   b Write a formula to show the total number of lines that are
      needed for different numbers of circles and squares.
      Explain what each unknown in your formula represents.

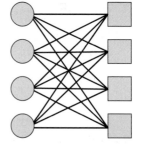

4 A gardener is laying a path around a garden using
   slabs of length one metre.
   Write a formula to show the total number of slabs
   that he will need for any size rectangular garden.

Use the Internet to find the current exchange rate
between pounds and another currency (e.g. euros,
American dollars). Then build a spreadsheet that will
allow you to convert any amount.

	A	B
1	Pounds	Euros
2	10	= A2*1.5

	A	B
1	Pounds	Euros
2	10	15

This spreadsheet
converts pounds to
euros, with an exchange
rate of £1 = €1.5.

If you enter any number
of pounds in cell A2, cell
B2 will show you the
value in euros.

1 Write these sentences using algebraic notation.
 a 'I think of a number and I multiply it by 5.'
 b 'I think of a number, add 8 and then multiply by 4.'
 c 'I think of a number, divide it by 7 and subtract 2.'
 d 'I think of a number and multiply it by itself.'
 e 'I think of a number and subtract it from 15.'

2 Given that $m = 4$, $n = 5$ and $p = -2$, find the value of each of these expressions.
 a $3m - 2$ b $mn + 1$ c $(2n)^2$ d $2n^2$
 e mp f $10 + p$ g $mnp + 5$

3 Simplify these expressions, if possible, by collecting like terms.
 a $3x + 10x - 4x$ b $2h + 8m + 9h - m$
 c $12t + 12$ d $3x + 8x^2 + 9x$
 e $4mn + 9nm + mn$ f $x + x^2 + x^2 + x^4$

4 Jo got all of her homework wrong.
 Explain her mistakes and correct them.

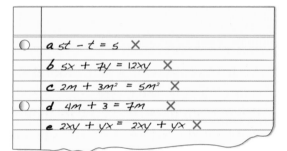

a $5t - t = 5$ ✗
b $5x + 7y = 12xy$ ✗
c $2m + 3m^2 = 5m^2$ ✗
d $4m + 3 = 7m$ ✗
e $2xy + yx = 2xy + yx$ ✗

5 Expand and simplify
 a $3(x + 7) + 2(x + 3)$ b $4(2x - 3) + 3(3x + 2)$
 c $2(3m + 1) + 7(m + 2)$ d $4(2p - 3) + 9(3p - 1)$
 e $q(q + 8) + q(q - 3)$

6 a Use brackets to write an expression
    for the area of this shape.

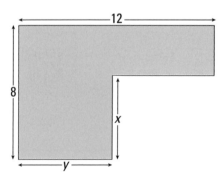

 b Expand and simplify your answer.

7 The poster shows the charging formula for a campsite in the Lake District.

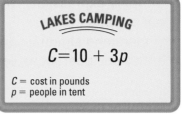

LAKES CAMPING

$C = 10 + 3p$

C = cost in pounds
p = people in tent

   a How much would it cost for a family of four to camp at the site?

   b Harry wants to take some friends camping for the night. If he has £30 to spend, how many friends can he take?

   c A new campsite opens up down the road. It charges £5 per tent then £5 per person staying in the tent. How large would a family have to be to find this new campsite cheaper?

8 The formula $V = IR$ is used to find the potential difference, in volts, between two points on an electric circuit. I represents the current in amps and R the resistance in ohms.

   a Find the potential difference when the current is 5 amps and the resistance is 10 ohms.

   b Give possible values for current and resistance that would make the potential difference 24 volts.

9 **a** A website charges members 90p to download a music track. Membership costs £3. Write a formula for the total cost, C, of joining and downloading t tunes.

   b Use your formula to find the total cost of joining and downloading 40 tracks.

   c You have £10 to spend on downloading tracks from the site, but you are not yet a member. How many tracks can you download?

10 Karen takes a square piece of paper measuring 10 cm by 10 cm and cuts a square of side x cm from the bottom right hand corner.

   a Write a formula for the perimeter of the piece of paper left when the little square has been removed. Simplify your answer.

   b Compare your answer with the perimeter of the original piece of paper. What do you notice? Why is this?

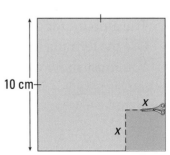

10 cm

6 Summary

Key indicators

- Substitute integers (whole numbers) into simple formulas **Level 5**
- Simplify expressions by collecting like terms and multiplying out a bracket **Level 5**
- Understand algebraic operations follow the same order as arithmetic operations **Level 5**

1 Simplify these expressions.

   a $2a + 3 + 4a$

   b $b + 5 + b - 1$

   c $3(c + 2)$

Monik's answer ✔

Monik expands the expression.

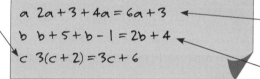

$$a \quad 2a + 3 + 4a = 6a + 3$$
$$b \quad b + 5 + b - 1 = 2b + 4$$
$$c \quad 3(c + 2) = 3c + 6$$

Monik adds $2a$ and $4a$ to give $6a$.

Monik knows b means $1b$.

2 Doctors sometimes use this formula to calculate how much medicine to give a child.

$$c = \frac{ay}{12 + y}$$

c is the correct amount to give a child, in ml

a is the amount for an adult, in ml

y is the age of the child, in years.

A child who is 4 years old needs some medicine.
The amount for an adult is 20 ml.
Use the formula to work out the correct amount for this child.
You must show your working.

Key Stage 3 2004 4–6 Paper 2

7 Number

Calculation and measure

In 1991 Australia stopped using 1 cent and 2 cent coins. Some people say that the UK should take up this idea and get rid of the 1p and 2p coins. If this did happen, all prices would need to be rounded to the nearest 5p. Do you think shops would round up or down?

What's the point? Rounding the prices up to the nearest 5p would mean that the shops would take more money from you!

✔ Check in

1 a Copy and complete this table by placing these units of measurement under the correct headings.

Measure of length	Measure of mass	Measure of capacity

millimetre gallon ounce
litre   centimetre   foot
kilometre gram centilitre
tonne millilitre pound
kilogram metre inch

b Draw a table with two columns and classify these units of measurement as metric or imperial.

2 Work out these calculations mentally.

a 32 + 33 + 34   **b** 64 − 32 − 16   **c** 3 × 4 × 5   **d** 150 ÷ 5 ÷ 3

3 Use multiplication facts to copy and complete these sums.

a 3 × 5 = ☐   **b** 4 × 8 = ☐   **c** 7 × ☐ = 21   **d** 6 × ☐ = 30
e ☐ × 8 = 56   **f** 7 × ☐ = 63   **g** 8 × 6 = ☐   **h** ☐ × 6 = 54

4 Copy and complete this grid in order to calculate 57 × 38.

×	50	7
30		210
8		

57 × 38 = ☐

- Round whole numbers and decimals

Keywords
Decimal place   Round
Power of 10   Whole
Recurring   number

- You can **round** a number to the nearest **whole number**, or to a given number of **decimal places**. In each case, look at the next digit. If it is 5 or more, round up. If it is less than 5, round down.

example

Round 132.185 to the nearest
a 100   **b** 10
c whole number   **d** tenth (1dp)
e hundredth (2dp).

1 dp means 1 decimal place.

2 dp means 2 decimal places.

a 100   Look at the tens digit.
It is 3, so round down to 100.
You can see on the number line that
132.185 is closer to 100 than to 200.

132.185
100   200

b 130   Look at the units digit.
It is 2, so round down to 130.
132.185 is closer to 130 than to 140.

132.185
130   140

c 132   Look at the first digit after the decimal point. It is 1, so round down to 132.
132.185 is closer to 132 than to 133.

132.185
132   133

d 132.2   Look at the second decimal place.
It is 8, so round up to 132.2.
132.185 is closer to 132.1 than to 132.2.

132.185
132.1   132.2

e 132.19   Look at the third decimal place.
It is 5, so round up to 132.19.
132.185 is halfway between 132.18
and 132.19. The convention is to
round up.

132.185
132.18   132.19

- **Recurring** decimals contain an infinitely repeating set of one or more digits.
  The digits that recur are written with a dot over them.
  0.833 333... is written as $0.8\dot{3}$
  0.454 545... is written as $0.\dot{4}\dot{5}$

A recurring decimal can be written as a fraction.

Exercise 7a

1 Round each number to the nearest

   i 1000   **ii** 100   **iii** 10

  a 3281   **b** 8079   **c** 2765   **d** 6417

  e 26 282   **f** 30 592   **g** 64 949   **h** 73 928

2 Round each number to the nearest

   i 1000   **ii** 100   **iii** 10

  a 3973.8   **b** 5492.03   **c** 959.84   **d** 2003.5

3 Luke wins the jackpot of £1 263 493.29 in the Lottery.
In the local newspapers there are different headlines.
  a Explain why there are different numbers in the headlines.
  b Which newspaper is the more accurate?

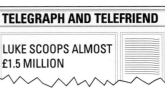

4 Round each number to the nearest

   i whole number   **ii** tenth   **iii** hundredth.

  a 4.847   **b** 5.329   **c** 12.747

  d 19.047   **e** 5.4072   **f** 6.9475

  g 1.0485   **h** 2.693 34

5 Round each number to the nearest

   i whole number   **ii** tenth   **iii** hundredth.

  a 15.8847   **b** 104.7493   **c** 2.199   **d** 9.999

6 Convert each fraction into a decimal, using a calculator.
Give your answer to 2 decimal places or write as a recurring decimal
where appropriate.

  a $\dfrac{1}{3}$ **b** $\dfrac{3}{16}$ **c** $\dfrac{13}{9}$

  d $\dfrac{29}{7}$ **e** $\dfrac{18}{11}$ **f** $\dfrac{12}{13}$

puzzle

Each of these measurements and amounts has been rounded to
the given degree of accuracy.

> 74 cm (nearest cm)
> 180 g (nearest 10 g)
> 2.6 m (1dp)
> 9.79 sec (nearest hundredth of a second)
> 5 million people (nearest million)

  a Write down **i** the minimum value **ii** the maximum value
    each measurement could be.
  b Explain how you worked out the maximum and minimum values.

7b Order of operations

- Know the order in which to do a calculation
- Know how to use brackets in a calculation

Keywords
BIDMAS   Operation
Calculation

- When a **calculation** contains more than one **operation**, you must do the operations in the correct order.

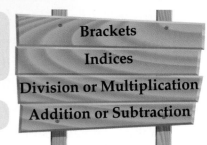

Brackets

Indices

Division or Multiplication

Addition or Subtraction

- Use the word **BIDMAS** to help you remember.

---

example

Calculate   **a** $3 + 4^2 \times 2$ **b** $(3 + 4^2) \times 2$

. . . .

a $3 + 4^2 \times 2 = 3 + 16 \times 2$ No brackets, so indicies first.

$ = 3 + 32$ Next, multiplication

$ = 35$ Finally, addition

b $(3 + 4^2) \times 2 = (3 + 16) \times 2$ Brackets first, then indicies

$ = 19 \times 2$ Next, addition within the brackets

$ = 38$ Finally, multiplication

It is always a good idea to show your working out a line at a time. On each line, work out one set of operations.

- You work out a string of divisions from left to right.

---

example

Calculate $120 \div 6 \div 2$

. . . .

$120 \div 6 \div 2 = 20 \div 2$ Work out **120 ÷ 6** first.

$ = 10$ Now work out $20 \div 2$.

- You work out nested brackets from the inside out.

---

example

Calculate $120 \div [40 - (13 + 12)]$

. . . .

$120 \div [40 - (13 + 12)] = 120 \div [40 - 25]$ Work out the inner brackets first.

$ = 120 \div 15$ Work out the outer brackets next.

$ = 8$ Finally, division

---

p. 86

Exercise 7b

1 Calculate

a $7 + 8 \times 3$ **b** $20 - 4 \times 2$ **c** $17 + 3 \times 6$

d $23 - 18 \div 3$ **e** $7 \times 3 - 2 \times 4$ **f** $3 \times 6 + 8 \times 2$

g $8 + 3 \times 2 - 4$ **h** $14 \div 2 - 10 \div 5$

2 Yvette is trying to match each question with the correct answer.

	Question	Answer X	Answer Y
a	$2 + 3^2 \times 4$	38	100
b	$(12 - 3^2) \times 4$	12	324
c	$4 \times (2 + 3)^2$	400	100
d	$22 - 2 \times (3^2 + 2)$	0	220
e	$5 \times 6 - 3^2 \times 2$	1458	12

i Write the correct answer to each question, explaining why you chose it.

ii Yvette got all of her answers wrong. Write the error she made in each of her answers.

3 Calculate

a $\dfrac{4^2 - 1}{3^2 + 1}$ **b** $\dfrac{105 - 5^2}{(7 - 3)^2}$ **c** $\dfrac{(5 + 3)^2}{3^2 - 1}$

4 Calculate

a $6 \times 2 \times 5$ **b** $40 \div 8 \div 5$

c $5 \times [13 - (4 - 1)]$ **d** $36 \div [15 - (2^2 - 1)]$

e $7 \times [19 - (13 - 5)]$ **f** $64 \div [23 - (4^2 - 1)]$

g $30 \div 2 \div 5$ **h** $30 \div (2 \times 5)$

5 Use a calculator to work out these calculations. Where appropriate, give your answer to 2dp.

a $(4 + 3.7) \div 6$ **b** $54 - 3.8^2 \times 3$

c $8 \times (2.5 - 1.9)^2$ **d** $(5 + 2.3) \times 37$

e $\dfrac{9 + 4}{15 - 4}$ **f** $\sqrt{23^2 - 11^2}$

g $\dfrac{46}{19 \times 8}$ **h** $\dfrac{(2 + 3)^2}{(14 - 9)^2}$

---

puzzle

Use the numbers 2, 3, 7 and 8, brackets () and the signs $+, -, \times, \div$ to make all the numbers from 20 to 50. You can use each number only once in each calculation.

e.g. $27 = (2 + 3) \times 7 - 8$

- Use mental methods to multiply and divide whole numbers and decimals

Keywords
Compensate   Multiplication
Division   Partition
Factor   Round
Multiple

There are many mental strategies you can use to help you work out **multiplications** and **divisions** in your head.

- You can re-write **multiples** of 10 and 100 as a pair of **factors** and then do two simpler multiplications.

A factor is a number that divides into another.

example

Calculate   **a** 17×200 **b** 4.3×30
....

a $17 \times 200 = 17 \times 100 \times 2$ **b** $4.3 \times 30 = 4.3 \times 10 \times 3$
$\qquad\qquad = 1700 \times 2$ $\qquad\qquad = 43 \times 3$
$\qquad\qquad = 3400$ $\qquad\qquad = 129$

- You can **partition** (split) numbers into parts to make them easier to multiply or divide.

example

Calculate   **a** 15×8.2 **b** $430 \div 13$
....

a $15 \times 8.2 = (10 \times 8.2) + (5 \times 8.2)$ **b** $430 \div 13 = (390 \div 13) + (40 \div 13)$
$\qquad\qquad = 82 + 41$ $\qquad\qquad = 30 + 3 \text{ r } 1$
$\qquad\qquad = 123$ $\qquad\qquad = 33 \text{ r } 1$ r means 'remainder'.

- You can **round** the number you need to multiply or divide to make the calculation easier. You must then **compensate** for the rounding by adding or subtracting as necessary.

example

Calculate   **a** 34×21 **b** 19×3.8
....

a $34 \times 21 = (34 \times 20) + (34 \times 1)$ 21 is close to 20, so multiply by 20.
$\qquad\qquad = 680 + 34$ Then add one more to compensate
$\qquad\qquad = 714$
b $19 \times 3.8 = (20 \times 3.8) - (1 \times 3.8)$ 19 is close to 20, so multiply by 20.
$\qquad\qquad = 76 - 3.8$ Then subtract 3.8 to compensate
$\qquad\qquad = 72.2$

Exercise 7c

1 Calculate these using a mental method.

    a 4×16 **b** 8×17 **c** 6×13 **d** 5×29

    e 3×36 **f** 37×5 **g** 6×28 **h** 9×41

2 Calculate these using a mental method.

    a 40×6 **b** 300×7 **c** 60×8 **d** 7×900

    e 8×70 **f** $490 \div 7$ **g** 9×800 **h** $4500 \div 5$

3 Calculate these using a mental method.

    a 40×17 **b** 200×19 **c** 30×28 **d** 800×12

    e 4.8×20 **f** 5.2×40 **g** 700×6.1 **h** 80×3.5

    i 0.8×70 **j** 400×8.2 **k** 70×5.4 **l** 300×9.3

4 Calculate these using the method of partitioning.

    a 6.2×12 **b** 7.3×15 **c** 13×4.1 **d** 16×8.5

    e 9.8×11 **f** $308 \div 7$ **g** 1.9×12 **h** $288 \div 5$

    i $286 \div 4$ **j** 13×1.4 **k** $264 \div 8$ **l** 2.8×15

5 Calculate these using the method of compensation.

    a 26×9 **b** 19×44 **c** 37×21 **d** 16×41

    e 2.8×19 **f** 3.2×29 **g** 19×1.6 **h** 21×3.5

    i 1.8×29 **j** 6.9×19 **k** 21×0.7 **l** 49×2.7

6 Earl decides to sell all his old PC games, DVDs and CDs.
This is his price list.
Work out how much money he will get for each of
these orders. Can you use mental methods?

    a 11 PC games

    b 19 DVD films

    c 15 CDs, 5 DVDs and 12 PC games

    d 19 PC games, 14 DVDs and 31 CDs

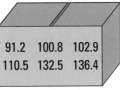

PC Games	£4.90
DVD Films	£7.20
CD Music	£1.90

a Find a number from box A and a number from box B which
multiply to give a number in box C.

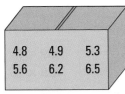

Box A			Box B			Box C		
4.8	4.9	5.3	17	18	19	91.2	100.8	102.9
5.6	6.2	6.5	21	22	25	110.5	132.5	136.4

b Find all the other pairs of numbers from boxes A and B
which when multiplied make an answer in box C.

7d Written methods of multiplication

- Use written methods to multiply whole numbers and decimals

Keywords
Equivalent
Estimate
Multiplication

- If a **multiplication** involves decimals, you can change the calculation into an **equivalent** whole number calculation by multiplying by a power of 10.

- You should always **estimate** the answer first.

example

Use the grid method to calculate 31×2.9.

First estimate the answer.
$31 \times 2.9 \approx 30 \times 3 = 90$
Next, change the calculation to an equivalent whole number calculation.
$31 \times 2.9 = 31 \times 29 \div 10$
Now do the multiplication using the grid method.

$\times$	20	9
30	$30 \times 20 = 600$	$30 \times 9 = 270$
1	$1 \times 20 = 20$	$1 \times 9 = 9$

$31 \times 29 = 600 + 270 \times 20 \times 9 = 899$
So $31 \times 2.9 = 899 \div 10 = 89.9$

- You can use the standard method for multiplying whole numbers and decimals.

example

Larissa buys 17 DVDs for £4.39 each.
What is the total cost of the DVDs?

First estimate the answer.
$17 \times £4.39 \approx 17 \times £4 = £68$
Next, change the calculation to an equivalent whole number calculation.
$17 \times 4.39 = 17 \times 439 \div 100$
Now do the multiplication.
$17 \times 439 = 7463$
So the total cost of the DVDs $= 7463 \div 100 = £74.63$

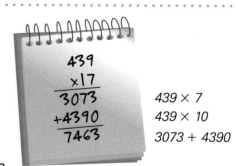

```
  439
  x17
 3073      439 × 7
+4390      439 × 10
 7463      3073 + 4390
```

Exercise 7d

Remember to do a mental approximation first.

1 Calculate these using the grid method.

  a 7 × 23   **b** 9 × 33

  c 48 × 27   **d** 53 × 38

  e 64 × 46   **f** 6 × 125

  g 138 × 9   **h** 9 × 287

  i 147 × 78   **j** 279 × 38

  k 195 × 61   **l** 391 × 46

2 **a** Kylie is running in a 10 000 m race. She runs every 400 m in 68 seconds. How long will it take her to complete the 25 laps of the race?

  b Luca has downloaded 28 music tracks from the Internet. The average length of each track is 135 seconds. What is the total playing time of the music tracks?

  c Maia can read at a speed of 235 words per minute. How many words can she read in 15 minutes?

3 Calculate these with an equivalent whole number calculation.

  a 14 × 3.6   **b** 24 × 4.3

  c 2.8 × 39   **d** 5.7 × 42

  e 8 × 39.7   **f** 9 × 54.2

  g 8 × 77.3   **h** 9 × 96.9

4 Calculate these using a written method.

  a 13 × 1.73   **b** 14 × 48.8

  c 38 × 3.69   **d** 57 × 28.4

  e 47 × 3.43   **f** 69 × 5.79

  g 88 × 48.3   **h** 74 × 9.99

5 **a** Carina buys four jars of coffee for £4.59 each. What is the total cost?

  b Kenia has a paper round each evening, for six days of the week. It takes her two hours each evening. She is paid £4.65 an hour. How much will she earn in two weeks?

---

investigation

Here are some expensive bad habits.

Smoking – 1 packet of cigarettes each day costing £4.65.

Eating – 1 packet of crisps a day costing £0.43.

Drinking – 1 bottle of fizzy pop costing £1.15.

Calculate the cost of each of these bad habits for

  a a week   **b** a month

  c a year   **d** a lifetime (75 years)

- Use written methods to divide whole numbers and decimals

- When you **divide** a number there is sometimes a **remainder** left over. You can write a remainder as a whole number or you can use a decimal.

- You can think of division as repeated subtraction.

The method of repeated subtraction is also known as 'chunking'. You subtract multiples of the divisor until you cannot subtract any more.

- You should always **estimate** the answer first.

example

Calculate

a $87 \div 5$

b $110.4 \div 8$

a $87 \div 5 \approx 90 \div 5 = 18$

```
87
-50     5 × 10 = 50
37
-35     5 × 7 = 35
 2      Remainder 2
87 ÷ 5 = 10 + 7 r 2
       = 17 r 2
```

b $110.4 \div 8 \approx 120 \div 8 = 15$

```
110.4
 -80     8 × 10 = 80
 30.4
 -24     8 × 3 = 24
  6.4
 -6.4    8 × 0.8 = 6.4
   0
110.4 ÷ 8 = 10 + 3 + 0.8 = 13.8
```

- You can also use the method of short division.

example

Calculate $238.92 \div 6$

$238.92 \div 6 \approx 240 \div 6 = 40$

$$6 \overline{)2 3^{5}8 .^{4}9^{1}2}$$
$$3 9 . 8 2$$

$23 \div 6 = 3$ remainder 5
$58 \div 6 = 9$ remainder 4
$49 \div 6 = 8$ remainder 1
$12 \div 6 = 2$

$238.92 \div 6 = 39.82$

Short division involves subtracting multiples of the divisor and carrying the remainder.

Write the answer at the top and carry the remainder.

Exercise 7e

1 Calculate these using repeated subtraction.

  a $144 \div 6$ **b** $189 \div 7$ **c** $176 \div 8$
  d $234 \div 9$ **e** $272 \div 16$ **f** $414 \div 18$
  g $289 \div 17$ **h** $624 \div 26$

2 Calculate these using repeated subtraction.
  Where appropriate, give your answer as a decimal to 1dp.

  a $27.3 \div 7$ **b** $37.6 \div 8$ **c** $31.8 \div 6$
  d $65.7 \div 9$ **e** $69.6 \div 8$ **f** $67.2 \div 7$
  g $76.8 \div 6$ **h** $98.4 \div 8$ **i** $102.9 \div 7$
  j $103.2 \div 6$ **k** $185.6 \div 8$ **l** $250.2 \div 9$

3 Calculate these using a written method.
  Where appropriate, give your answer with a remainder.

  a $136 \div 15$ **b** $264 \div 18$ **c** $293 \div 21$
  d $309 \div 28$ **e** $378 \div 25$ **f** $493 \div 29$
  g $604 \div 33$ **h** $746 \div 36$

4 Calculate these using short division.
  Where appropriate, give your answer as a decimal to 2dp.

  a $48.92 \div 4$ **b** $73.4 \div 5$ **c** $103.74 \div 6$
  d $128.59 \div 7$ **e** $153.52 \div 8$ **f** $208.98 \div 9$
  g $172.76 \div 7$ **h** $227.12 \div 8$ **i** $198.24 \div 6$
  j $346.32 \div 8$ **k** $528.03 \div 9$ **l** $442.33 \div 7$

5 **a** Vikram shares £306 equally amongst his 8 grandchildren.
       How much money will they each receive?
   b Duncan buys 5 computer games for his new game console.
       The total cost of the games is £149.25.
       What is the price of each game?
   c Darlene takes 837.6 seconds to run 12 laps of the track.
       How long does she take to run each lap?

puzzle

a Identify this number from the clues given.

  ❋ I am between 1 and 500.
  ❋ When I am divided by 63 the remainder is 7.
  ❋ When I am divided by 16 there is no remainder.
  ❋ When I am divided by 15 the remainder is 13.

b Write any strategies you used to solve this problem.

7f Calculator methods

- Use a calculator for more complicated calculations

Keywords
Divisor   Square
Remainder   Square root

- You need to be able to use the **square** and **square root** keys on a scientific calculator.

  The square key is usually labelled x^2.
  The square root key is usually labelled $\sqrt{x}$.

---

example

Use a calculator to work out $5 \times \sqrt{1.3 + 2.87}$.

. . . .

Press

The calculator should display $\boxed{5 \times \sqrt{(1.3 + 2.87)}}$

and give the answer $\boxed{10.21028893}$

$5 \times \sqrt{1.3 + 2.87} = 10.21$ (to 2 dp)

> The brackets contain the numbers under the long square root sign.

- When solving problems, make sure you interpret the calculator display correctly.

---

example

Use your calculator to work out
a $60\text{ m} \div 8$ **b** $60\text{ hours} \div 8$

. . . .

a $60 \div 8 = 7.5\text{ m}$ **b** $60 \div 8 = 7.5\text{ hours}$
         $= 7\text{ m and }50\text{ cm}$ $= 7\text{ hours and }30\text{ minutes}$

> In both cases the calculator displays 7.5. You need to interpret each answer carefully.

- When you use a calculator for a division, you get a decimal instead of a remainder. To convert a decimal answer to a whole number remainder, multiply it by the **divisor**.

> The divisor is the number you are dividing by.

---

example

A box holds 75 nails. A machine packs 2000 nails into boxes. How many nails will be left over at the end?

. . . .

$2000 \div 75 = 26.666\,666\ldots$ boxes
$0.66666\ldots$ boxes $= 0.666\,666\ldots \times 75$ nails
                           $= 50$ nails
$2000 \div 75 = 26$ boxes r 50 nails. 50 nails will be left over.

> Multiply the decimal part of your answer by 75.

Exercise 7f

1 Calculate these. Where appropriate, give your answer to 2 dp.

  a $(5.1 + 3)^2 + 7$

  b $20 \div 4 + (10 \div 2)^2$

  c $\dfrac{3^2 + 1}{2^2 + 1}$

  d $\dfrac{\sqrt{15 - 6}}{3^2}$

  e $28 - 1.4^2 \times 5$

  f $63 \times (5.8 - 0.3)^2$

  g $\dfrac{11 + 4}{20 - 7}$

  h $\dfrac{(5 + 8)^2}{(11 - 4)^2}$

2 Use a calculator to calculate these.
Express the remainder as a whole number.

  a $78 \div 7$ **b** $286 \div 23$ **c** $936 \div 29$

  d $1045 \div 48$ **e** $2868 \div 35$ **f** $3999 \div 45$

3 **a** Eggs are packed into boxes of six. How many boxes are needed
to pack 1430 eggs? How many eggs will be left over?

> Make sure your answers make sense in the context of the question.

  b Three friends share £10. How much do they each receive?

  c Nine farmers share out 678 cows.
How many do they each receive?

  d Mendip is an engineer. He cuts a 4.5 m length of steel cable
into 13 equal sized pieces. How long is each piece?

  e Victor takes 30 minutes to run 25 laps of a track.
How long does he take to run each lap?

4 **a** A fig weighs 120 g. A packet of figs costs £3.75 for 1 kg.
How much does one fig cost?

  b A taxi firm charges £1.42 for the first mile and then 46 p
for each additional mile. Naomi is charged £17.52.
How long was her journey?

  c A packet of six Choco bars costs £0.89.
A packet of 12 Choco bars with an extra two bars free
costs £1.69. A packet of 24 Choco bars costs £3.30.
Which packet is the best value for money?

> **Did you know?**
>
> One fig can contain up to 1600 seeds!

a Follow these instructions.
Then subtract 144 from the answer you get.
Read the result carefully. The first two digits will
be your age and the second two digits give the
month of your birth

b Investigate how this puzzle works.

> 1. Type your age in years into a
>   calculator press =
> 2. Multiply your answer by 25 press =
> 3. Add 36 to your answer press =
> 4. Multiply by 4 press =
> 5. Add the number of your month of birth
>   (Jan = 1; Feb = 2; ...) press =

- Know the metric units of measurements and use them to read a scale

Keywords
Approximate   Mass
Area   Measure
Capacity   Time
Estimate   Unit
Length   Volume

- You **measure** different types of quantities using different **units**. Each type of quantity has units of different sizes, from small to large.

> **SMALL** ——————→ **LARGE**
>
> **Length** millimetres (mm) centimetres (cm) metres (m) kilometres (km)
> **Mass** grams (g) kilograms (kg)
> **Capacity** millilitres (ml) centilitres (cl) litres
> **Area** square millimetres (mm²) square centimetres (cm²) square metres (m²)
>   square kilometres (km²)
> **Time** seconds (s) minutes (min) hours (h) days weeks months years decades
>   centuries millennia.

- You can use an **approximate** measure to **estimate** the size of an object.

A standard door is about 2 m tall. You could use this fact to help you estimate the height of your classroom

- You use different types of instruments for measuring different types of quantities.

  For example, you use a ruler for measuring lengths and a clock for measuring time.

- When reading a scale on a measuring instrument, first work out what the divisions on the scale represent.

example

Write the reading on each of these scales.

a
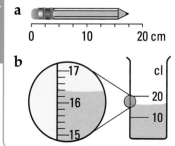

0   10   20 cm

b

a 17.5 cm

The pencil is between 10 and 20 cm long.

Four spaces represent 10 cm.

Each space represents 10 ÷ 4 = 2.5 cm.

b 16.4 cl

There are between 16 and 17 cl of liquid.

Five spaces represent 1 cl.

Each space represents 1 ÷ 5 = 0.2 cl.

Exercise 7g

1 Estimate the size of each of these measurements.
Use the approximations to help you.

Measurement

a Height of a 6-year-old child
b Mass of an adult male
c Distance from home to school
d Height of the school
e Area of your exercise book
f Capacity of a school bag
g Area of your garden
h Mass of a lorry

> **Useful approximation**
> Height of a door = 2 m
> Height of a house = 10 m
> Mass of 1 bag of sugar = 1 kg
> Mass of a small car = 1 tonne
> Capacity of a glass = 250 ml
> Area of a postcard = 100 cm²
> Area of a football pitch = 7500 m²
> Time to walk 1 km = 15 mins

2 Write the reading on each of these scales.

a

b

c

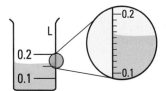

3 Write an estimated reading for each of these scales.

a

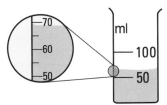

b

c

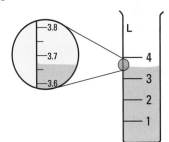

4 Anna takes 23 minutes to walk to school in the morning and
27 minutes in the evening to walk home. She walks for about
3 hours at the weekend. Without using a calculator, work out
how much time she spends walking in 1 week.

problem

a The maximum load in a lift is 300 kg. Mike loads
the lift with 50 boxes of paper, and goes in the lift
himself. Mike weighs 82 kg. Each box of paper
weighs 4.4 kg. Is it safe for Mike to use the lift?

b Invent a similar problem of your own using
other measures.

- Change from one metric unit to another
- Know some imperial units and how to change them to metric units

Keywords
Conversion factor
Convert
Imperial
Measure
Metric
Unit

- You can **convert** between different **metric units** of the same type.

Length	Area	Capacity and Volume	Mass	Time
1 cm = 10 mm	1 cm² = 100 mm²	1 cl = 10 ml	1 kg = 1000 g	1 minute = 60 seconds
1 m = 100 cm	1 m² = 10 000 cm²	1 litre = 100 cl	1 tonne = 1000 kg	1 hour = 60 minutes
1 km = 1000 m	1 ha = 10 000 m²	1 litre = 1000 ml		1 day = 24 hours
	1 km² = 1 000 000 m²	1 litre = 1000 cm³		1 week = 7 days
		1 ml = 1 cm³		1 year = 365 days

- You should know the relationships between metric and **imperial** units.

Length	Capacity	Mass
1 m ≈ 3 feet	1 gallon ≈ 4.5 litres	1 kg ≈ 2.2 pounds
1 inch ≈ 2.5 cm		1 ounce ≈ 30 g

- To convert between units, multiply or divide by the **conversion factor**.

example

a Convert 0.78 km to metres.

b Convert 36 litres to gallons.

a

$$\times 1000$$
$$1 \text{ km} = 1000 \text{ m}$$
$$\div 1000$$

$$0.78 \text{ km} = 0.78 \times 1000 \text{ m}$$
$$= 780 \text{ m}$$

b

$$\times 4.5$$
$$1 \text{ gallon} \approx 4.5 \text{ litres}$$
$$\div 4.5$$

$$36 \text{ litres} \approx 36 \div 4.5 \text{ litres}$$
$$\approx 8 \text{ gallons}$$

Exercise 7h

1 Convert these metric measurements to the units indicated in brackets.

a 35 m (cm)   **b** 16 cm (mm)

c 2.56 km (m)   **d** 9 cm² (mm²)

e 8 m² (cm²)   **f** 7 km² (m²)

g 16.4 cl (ml)   **h** 2.05 litres (cl)

i 12.5 litres (ml)   **j** 0.64 tonnes (kg)

k 1.5 ha (m²)   **l** 0.038 litres (ml)

2 Convert these metric measurements to the units indicated in brackets.

a 560 cm (m)   **b** 5 mm (cm)

c 140 m (km)   **d** 700 mm² (cm²)

e 20 000 cm² (m²)   **f** 50 000 m² (ha)

g 400 ml (litres)   **h** 25.4 cl (litres)

i 340 000 ml (litres)   **j** 980 kg (tonnes)

k 5 m (km)   **l** 760 g (kg)

3 Convert these measurements of time into the units indicated in brackets.

a 5 min (s)   **b** 8 hours (min)

c 11 days (hours)   **d** 6 weeks (days)

e 720 seconds (min)   **f** 450 min (hours)

g 174 hours (days)   **h** 31 days (weeks)

4 Convert these units into the units indicated in brackets.

a 6 gallons (litres)   **b** 5 kg (pounds)

c 12 inches (cm)   **d** 5 m (feet)

e 45 litres (gallons)   **f** 35 cm (inches)

5 Give your answer to each of these calculations in the most appropriate units.

a A machine cuts a 1.8 m length of metal into 250 identical pins. How long is each pin?

b A litre of petrol costs 92.6p. Approximately how much would 1 gallon of petrol cost?

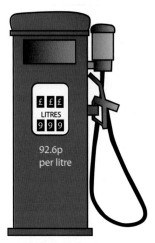

7a

1 Round each of these numbers to the nearest
   i whole number   **ii** tenth   **iii** hundredth.
   a a 3.738   **b** 4.418   **c** 5.2854   **d** 9.147
   e 17.638   **f** 27.105   **g** 8.3055   **h** 4.555
   i 34.2468   **j** 7.7005   **k** 3.310 48   **l** 1.181 18

7b

2 Calculate
   a $(6 + 2)^2 + 6 \times 7$ **b** $24 \div 6 + (9 \div 3^2)$
   c $4 \times (8 - 3)^2 \times 3$ **d** $(4 + 6)^2 \times 3 - 14$
   e $35 \div (10 \div 2) + 3$ **f** $(5 + 5^2) \div 5$
   g $(4^2 - 6)^2 - 99$ **h** $(\sqrt{64} - 2^2) \times 4$

3 Calculate
   a $\dfrac{11 + 4}{8 - 5}$ **b** $\dfrac{5^2 - 1}{2^2 + 2}$

   c $\dfrac{120 - 6^2}{(8 - 5)^2 + 12}$ **d** $\dfrac{(7 + 5)^2}{3^2 + 7}$

4 Calculate
   a $5 \times 6 \times 7$ **b** $80 \div 4 \div 2$
   c $7 \times [12 - (5 - 2)]$ **d** $55 \div [19 - (3^2 - 1)]$
   e $9 \times [29 - (27 - 15)]$ **f** $84 \div [32 - (4^2 - 5)]$
   g $90 \div 2 \div 3$ **h** $200 \div (4 \times 2)$

7c

5 Calculate these using a mental method.
   a 30×13 **b** 500×29 **c** 4.8×70 **d** 400×6.2
   e 3.4×11 **f** 5.8×12 **g** 15×7.1 **h** 19×6.9
   i $357 \div 7$ **j** $310 \div 5$ **k** $656 \div 4$ **l** $376 \div 8$
   m 1.6×39 **n** 4.9×21 **o** 31×2.8 **p** 99×3.9

7d

6 Calculate these using an appropriate written method.
   Remember to do a mental approximation first.
   a 18×4.7 **b** 28×5.2 **c** 3.5×48 **d** 7.2×82
   e 7×12.8 **f** 8×63.7 **g** 9×54.8 **h** 8×84.7
   i 12×1.23 **j** 15×37.2 **k** 42×2.75 **l** 64×49.9

7 Calculate these. Give the remainders as whole numbers.

    a $183 \div 15$ **b** $475 \div 18$ **c** $740 \div 21$ **d** $680 \div 28$

8 Calculate these. Give your answers as decimals to 1 or 2 decimal places.

    a $33.6 \div 7$ **b** $51.2 \div 8$ **c** $85.8 \div 6$ **d** $416.7 \div 9$

    e $25 \div 4$ **f** $64.45 \div 5$ **g** $111.9 \div 6$ **h** $113.89 \div 7$

9 Use a calculator to work out these calculations. Where appropriate, give your answers to 2 decimal places.

    a $(7 + 8.2) \div 7$ **b** $89 - 2.4^2 \times 8$

    c $43 \times (6.7 - 2.8)^2$ **d** $(5 + 8.3) \times 22$

    e $\dfrac{13 + 15}{14 - 9}$ **f** $\sqrt{10^2 - 8^2}$

    g $\dfrac{36 \times 8}{27 \times 5}$ **h** $\dfrac{(4 + 9)^2}{(17 - 11)^2}$

10 Use a calculator to work out these calculations. Express the remainders as whole numbers.

    a $136 \div 8$ **b** $475 \div 13$ **c** $613 \div 18$ **d** $925 \div 19$

    e $843 \div 24$ **f** $999 \div 25$ **g** $2000 \div 30$ **h** $5065 \div 37$

11 Write down the readings on each of these scales.

    a   **b**   **c**

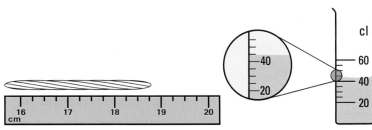

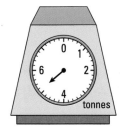

12 Convert these measurements to the units indicated in brackets.

    a 2.8 m (cm)   **b** 0.156 km (m)   **c** 3 cm² (mm²)   **d** 12.25 cl (ml)

    e 4.2 tonnes (kg)   **f** 5 ha (m²)   **g** 5250 cm (m)   **h** 28.4 mm (cm)

    i 2000 mm² (cm²)   **j** 454 g (kg)   **k** 30 cl (litres)   **l** 0.000 45 km (mm)

    m 100 cm (inches)   **n** 30 kg (pounds) **o** 15 feet (m)   **p** 15 litres (gallons)

7 Summary

Key indicators

- Multiply and divide a HTU number by a TU number **Level 5**
- Read and interpret scales on measuring equipment **Level 5**
- Use metric and imperial units of measurement **Level 5**

Level 5

1. When Hannah walks, she covers 50 centimetres every step.
   How many steps will she take during a walk of 1 kilometre?

Rashid's answer ✔

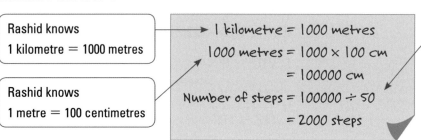

Rashid knows
1 kilometre = 1000 metres

Rashid knows
1 metre = 100 centimetres

1 kilometre = 1000 metres
1000 metres = 1000 × 100 cm
           = 100000 cm
Number of steps = 100000 ÷ 50
           = 2000 steps

Every 50 cm is a step and
so Rashid divides by 50

Level 5

2. Lisa uses a grid to multiply 23 by 15.

×	20	3
10	200	30
5	100	15

200 + 100 + 30 + 15 = 345

Answer = 345

Now Lisa multiplies two different numbers.
Complete the grid, and then give the answer below.

×		40	3
30			
	600		18

Key Stage 3 2007 3–5 Paper 1

8 Data

Probability

Insurance can protect you from losing everything in a disaster. If you are insured and a disaster affects your property, the insurance company will pay for repairs. Insurance companies use probability to calculate how much of a risk there is for fire, flood and theft.

What's the point? If you live next to a river that floods every year, there is a high probability that it will flood again. You will have to pay more for insurance than people who live further away from the river.

✓ Check in

1 Write the decimal number that each arrow is pointing to.

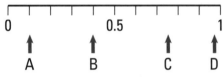

2

6	10	13	14	17	23	28	30

Which of these numbers are

a multiples of 5 (Hint: in the 5 times table)   b multiples of 7

c factors of 30 (Hint: will divide into 30 exactly)   d prime?

3 Work these out, giving each answer in its simplest form.

a $\dfrac{1}{5} + \dfrac{2}{5}$ b $\dfrac{2}{7} + \dfrac{3}{7}$ c $\dfrac{9}{16} - \dfrac{1}{16}$ d $\dfrac{4}{9} - \dfrac{1}{9}$

e $\dfrac{1}{2} - \dfrac{1}{3}$ f $\dfrac{1}{8} + \dfrac{3}{4}$ g $\dfrac{2}{3} - \dfrac{2}{9}$ h $\dfrac{3}{10} + \dfrac{1}{4}$

Level 4

Level 5

Level 6

8a The probability scale

- Describe probabilities in words
- Put probabilities on the probability scale from 0 to 1
- Find the probability of an event not happening

Keywords
Certain   Impossible
Chance   Probability
Evens

- **Probability** is a measure of how likely something is to happen.

- It is measured on a scale from 0 (when something is **impossible**) to 1 (when it is **certain**).

Money doesn't grow on trees.   You could toss a heads or a tail.   The sun will set every day.

Impossible	Evens	Certain
0 or 0%	0.5 or $\frac{1}{2}$ or 50%	1 or 100%

- If the probability of an event happening is p, the probability of it not happening is $1 - p$.

  If the probability of winning a prize in a tombola is 0.2, the probability of not winning a prize is $1 - 0.2 = 0.8$.

Probabilities can be written as decimals, percentages or fractions.

- P(A) means 'the probability that A happens'.

example

The probabilities for a number of events are given here. Place the letters for each of the events on a 0–1 probability scale.

	Event	Probability
A	The first digit in a set of random numbers is 3	0.1
B	Two heads show when two fair coins are tossed.	0.25
C	The score when a six-sided dice is thrown is 7.	0
D	Susie passes her driving test first time.	0.6
E	Susie fails her driving test first time.	0.4

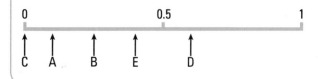

$$P(E) = 1 - P(D)$$
$$= 1 - 0.6$$
$$= 0.4.$$

Exercise 8a

1 Copy the probability scale and mark on it where you would find events which are
  a certain   b evens chance
  c very unlikely   d unlikely.

0   0.5   1
└─────────────────────────┴─────────────────────────┘

2 The probability of event A happening is 0.3.
  What is the probability that A does not happen?

3 a Draw a probability scale and mark on it the probability of each of these events.

  P(A) = 0.7   P(B) = 0.1   P(C) = 0.5   P(D) = 1

  b Describe P(D) in words.

4 Show the likelihood of each of these events happening on a probability scale.

  a It will rain in your area sometime tomorrow.
  b A slice of bread which is dropped will land butter side down.
  c The defending men's champion will lose in the first round at Wimbledon next year.
  d The song which is number one in the charts today will still be number one in two months' time.
  e It will rain in your area sometime in the next week.
  f If you toss a coin twice, you will get two heads.
  g It will rain in your area sometime in the next year.

---

discussion

How likely do you think each of these events is?

a In a group of 15 people who don't know one another, at least two share a birthday.
b In a National Lottery draw (where 6 numbers are chosen at random from 1–49), at least two of the numbers are adjacent numbers (e.g. 22 and 23).
c Haley's Comet will be in the sky on the night of a lunar eclipse.

Research these events using the Internet.
You may be surprised at how likely or unlikely they are!

8b Equally likely outcomes

- Find probabilities of events which are equally
  likely to happen

Keywords
Equally likely   Outcome
Event   Trial
Experiment

- The possible results of an **experiment** or **trial** are known
  as outcomes. In many situations, all the **outcomes** are
  equally likely.

Rolling a dice is an example of a trial.
There are six outcomes: 1, 2, 3, 4, 5 and 6.
If the dice is fair, the outcomes are equally likely.

- Any one outcome or combination of outcomes is known
  as an **event**.

The probability of an event occurring $= \dfrac{\text{The number of ways the event can happen}}{\text{The total number of possible outcomes}}$

When rolling a dice, 'Roll a 3' and 'Roll an even number' are both events.
There is only one way to throw a 3, so $P(3) = \dfrac{1}{6}$.
There are three ways to throw an even number (2, 4 and 6), so
$P(\text{even}) = \dfrac{3}{6} = \dfrac{1}{2}$.

example

There are 28 students in class 7C. 17 are girls, including twin sisters.
The class chooses one student to attend a special occasion
by drawing names from a hat at random.

Find the probability that the person chosen is
a one of the twins   **b** a girl   **c** a boy.

Always give your answer in
its simplest form.

a $P(\text{a twin}) = \dfrac{2}{28} = \dfrac{1}{14}$ There are 2 twins.

b $P(\text{girl}) = \dfrac{17}{28}$ There are 17 girls.

c $P(\text{boy}) = \dfrac{11}{28}$ There are $28 - 17 = 11$ boys.

You could work out part **c**
by calculating
$$P(\text{boy}) = 1 - P(\text{girl})$$
$$= 1 - \tfrac{17}{28}$$
$$= \tfrac{11}{28}$$

- If you want to compare probabilities, it is often easier to
  use decimals or percentages rather than fractions.
    $P(\text{girl}) = \dfrac{17}{28} = 0.61$ (to 2 dp)

Exercise 8b

1 For each of these events, are the outcomes equally likely?

  a In tennis, when the men's defending champion plays a
    qualifier at Wimbledon, he can only win or lose.

  b You toss two coins and count the number of heads – you can
    only get 0, 1 or 2 heads.

  c A bag of sweets contains 4 toffees, 4 chocolates and
    4 fruit sweets.

    i You pick a sweet at random.

    ii You look in the bag to choose a sweet.

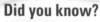

2 A spinner has five sections of equal size. Two are red, one is
  yellow, one is green and one is blue. What is the probability
  that the spinner lands on

  a green

  b red

  c not blue

  d not red?

3 The letters of the word PROBABILITY are written on separate
  cards. One card is chosen at random. What is the chance that
  it shows

  a the letter Y

  b the letter I

  c a vowel

  d a letter in the second half of the alphabet

  e a letter which does not appear in the word ABILITY?

challenge

The numbers 1 to 30 are written on separate cards and one
card is chosen at random.

a If x is the number on the card chosen, which of these
  events are equally likely?

  i $P(x$ is even) and $P(x$ is odd)

  ii $P(\frac{x}{3}$ gives an answer with remainder 0),

    $P(\frac{x}{3}$ gives an answer with remainder 1) and

    $P(\frac{x}{3}$ gives an answer with remainder 2)

b When the number is divided by n, the remainders
  0, 1, 2, ... $n - 1$ are equally likely. Find all possible
  values of n.

- Know what 'mutually exclusive' events are and find their probabilities
- Know that the total is 1 for probabilities of mutually exclusive events

Keywords
Event
Experiment
Mutually exclusive
Outcome

- **Mutually exclusive outcomes** or **events** can only occur separately, not at the same time.

The events 'Roll a 2' and 'Roll an odd number' are mutually exclusive because 2 is not an odd number.
The events 'Roll a 2' and 'Roll a factor of 6' are not mutually exclusive because 2 is a factor of 6.

- If events A and B are mutually exclusive,
  P(A or B) = P(A) + P(B).

This works for any number of events.

P(roll a 4 or roll an odd number) = P(roll a 4) + P(roll an odd number) = $\frac{1}{6} + \frac{3}{6} = \frac{4}{6}$
There are 4 ways of throwing a 4 or an odd number: 1, 3, 4 and 5.

- If the events are not mutually exclusive, you cannot add the probabilities.

There are five ways of getting an odd number or a factor of 6 : 1, 2, 3, 5, 6
So P(roll an odd number or a factor of 6) = $\frac{5}{6}$

However, P(roll an odd number) + P(roll a factor of 6)
$$= \frac{3}{6} + \frac{4}{6} = \frac{7}{6}$$
$\frac{5}{6} \neq \frac{7}{6}$ and a probability greater than 1 is impossible.

Always check whether events are mutually exclusive – don't just assume they are.

- The sum of all possible mutually exclusive events is 1.
  P(1) + P(2) + P(3) + P(4) + P(5) + P(6) = $\frac{1}{6} + \frac{1}{6} + \frac{1}{6} + \frac{1}{6} + \frac{1}{6} + \frac{1}{6} = 1$

example

The probability that a team wins a home soccer match is 0.6, and the probability of a draw is 0.3.
What is the probability that the team loses the match?

. . . .

The team must either win, lose or draw and it will do just one of these things, so the sum of the probabilities of these three mutually exclusive events is 1.

P(lose) = 1 − (0.6 + 0.3) = 0.1

Don't assume that mutually exclusive events are equally likely. They may not be, as here.

Exercise 8c

1 A spinner has 10 sections of equal size. Four are red, three are green and three are blue. What is the probability that the spinner shows red or green?

2 Eggs are classed as small, medium or large. For a particular hen, the probability that an egg she lays is small is 0.3, and the probability that it is large is 0.2. What is the probability that she lays a medium-size egg?

3 The numbers 1 to 20 are written on a set of cards and one card is chosen at random. For the number on the chosen card, events are defined as

   A: it is odd
   B: it is divisible by 2
   C: it is prime
   D: it is divisible by 8
   E: it is divisible by 3
   F: it is divisible by 6

p. 230

Which of the following pairs of events are mutually exclusive? For those pairs which are not, give at least one value which shows they are not.

   a A, B   **b** A, C   **c** B, C
   d B, D   **e** C, D   **f** E, F

4 Zadie throws an ordinary dice. For the number she rolls, events are defined as

   A: it is at least 3
   B: it is no more than 2
   C: it is exactly 4
   D: it is more than 4
   E: it is not 3
   F: it is at least 4

List all the pairs of events which are mutually exclusive.

challenge

a For each of the pairs of events in question **3**, work out the probability that at least one of the events occurs.
b How do these probabilities compare to the sum of the probabilities of the two events?

8d Experimental probability

- Use experiments to find the experimental probability of an event

Keywords
Estimate   Experimental
Experiment   probability
            Trial

If you throw a drawing pin in the air, you know that it will land with the point up or down, but the two outcomes are not equally likely.

You can **estimate** the probability that a drawing pin will land with the point up by throwing one in the air and recording how it lands a large number of times.

- **Experimental probability** is the proportion of times an event occurs during a large number of **trials**, or repetitions of an **experiment**.

- The more trials you carry out, the more likely your experimental probability is to be accurate.

example

Laura throws a drawing pin in the air 20 times.
It lands point up 6 times.
Joanne throws a drawing pin in the air 100 times.
It lands point up 43 times.
a Find P(point up) **i** based on Laura's results
                    i based on Joanne's results.
b Who is correct? Explain your answer.

. . . .

a **i** P(point up) $= \frac{6}{20} = 0.3$ **ii** P(point up) $= \frac{43}{100} = 0.43$
b Joanne has done more trials than Laura, so her estimate should be more accurate, but you don't know for sure.

If Joanne did another 100 trials, the pin is unlikely to land point up exactly 43 times again.

Kate records her coin tosses in this table.

Number of Tosses	Heads	Experimental Probability	Actual Probability
10	6	$\frac{6}{10} = 0.6$	$\frac{5}{10} = 0.5$
100	53	$\frac{53}{100} = 0.53$	$\frac{50}{100} = 0.5$
1000	511	$\frac{511}{1000} = 0.511$	$\frac{500}{1000} = 0.5$

As you carry out more trials, your estimated probability gets closer to the actual probability.

Exercise 8d

1 **a** David draws 10 lines which he thinks are 20 cm long. He measures each one and finds that 4 are shorter than 20 cm. Estimate the probability that his next line is shorter than 20 cm.

  b Michael draws 100 lines which he thinks are 20 cm long. 28 of the lines are shorter than 20 cm. Estimate the probability that his next line is shorter than 20 cm.

2 A traffic warden checks whether cars have a valid parking ticket displayed. She records a Y when there is a ticket displayed and N when there is not. Use her results to estimate the probability that the next car she checks will have a valid parking ticket.

3 The table shows a record sheet which is suitable for estimating the probability of scoring a 6 when a dice is thrown.

  a Make your own table with the same headings. Write the numbers 1 to 30 in the 'Trial' column.

  b Throw a dice 30 times and record the scores in the 'Outcome' column.

  c Complete the 'Running total' column. Each time there is a 6 in the 'Outcome' column, the running total increases by 1.

  d Complete the 'Proportion of 6s' column. Divide the number in the 'Running total' column by the number in the 'Trial' column.

  e Based on your results, estimate P(6).

Trial	Outcome	Running total of 6s	Proportion of 6s
1	3	0	0
2	2	0	0
3	6	1	0.333...
4	3	1	0.25
5	1	1	0.2
6	6	2	0.333...

investigation

Compare your estimate from question **3** with others' in your class.

a Are all the estimates the same?

b Would you expect the estimates to be the same?

c Would you expect to get the same estimate if you repeated the experiment with the same dice?

d Would using a different dice make a difference?

- Compare results found from using theoretical and experimental probabilities

Keywords
Bias
Estimate
Experimental probability
Relative frequenc
Theoretical probabili

- You can check whether something is performing as expected by comparing **experimental probability** with **theoretical probability**.

example

Anji throws a dice 30 times and gets a 1 eight times. Is the dice **biased**?

. . . .

The theoretical probability that a dice will show 1 is $\frac{1}{6}$.

So, on average, a fair dice will show a 1 five times in 30 throws ($30 \times \frac{1}{6} = 5$). However, 30 throws is not a large number, so sometimes a dice will show more than five 1s, and sometimes less. If Anji had thrown a 1 nineteen times in 30 throws you could have been pretty sure something was unusual about the dice, but 8 out of 30 is not so unusual.

Experimental probability is based on an experiment. Theoretical probability is calculated using mathematical reasoning.

Bias means 'lack of randomness'. A biased dice is more likely to show some scores than others.

- In some situations, you will need to decide how accurate you need your **estimate** to be.

  The more trials you carry out, the more reliable your estimate will be.

example

A knitting machine in a factory usually produces no more than 2% of jumpers which are defective. A manager sees that a batch of 20 jumpers has 2 defectives. Should she stop production and have the machine examined?

. . . .

2 out of 20 is 10%, which is quite a lot more than 2%.

However, you can't expect 2% of the jumpers in each batch to be defective, because 2% of 20 is 0.4 and you can't have a partly defective jumper.

She should check more jumpers as they are produced, and call the engineer only if the proportion defective remains higher than normal.

Exercise 8e

1 a If a fair dice is thrown 50 times, about how many of each number would you expect to see?

b Three dice, A, B and C, were each thrown 50 times and the results recorded. Do you think any of the dice were biased? Explain your reasoning.

A

5	4	2	6	3
3	3	2	3	5
4	2	4	6	3
3	4	6	3	2
3	4	1	2	1
5	3	3	3	3
2	1	4	3	3
3	3	3	3	3
5	3	3	3	1
3	2	3	4	2

B

5	4	2	1	2
6	2	6	6	2
4	6	2	3	2
3	5	1	5	1
3	1	6	2	6
5	2	3	5	4
3	1	6	2	3
2	6	2	2	5
6	6	5	4	4
6	4	5	6	3

C

4	3	1	1	5
4	1	5	4	3
6	4	3	3	4
1	4	6	1	5
2	5	4	3	6
2	3	5	5	5
5	6	1	5	3
4	2	1	5	6
5	5	5	3	6
1	4	2	6	4

2 A 1p and a 2p coin are tossed together. The possible outcomes (writing the result of the 1p first) are TT, TH, HT, HH so, if the coins are fair, the probability of getting two heads will be $\frac{1}{4}$.

a If you toss two fair coins 20 times, about how often will you see two heads?

b How many times would you have to see a pair of heads in 20 goes for you to feel the coins were not fair?

c Toss two coins 20 times and count how often you see two heads.

investigation

a In a list of random digits, all 10 digits (0, 1, ... 9) are equally likely to appear in any position. What is the probability that any digit is followed by a repeat of itself?

b Use your calculator random number generator to create a list of 60 random digits. How often is a digit followed by another the same?

c Do you think your calculator is producing genuinely random numbers?

8a

1 P(A) = 0.2, P(B) = 0.9, P(C) = 0.5, P(D) = 0

  a Draw a probability scale and mark on it

  i P(B)   **ii** P(not A)   **iii** P(C)

  b Describe the chance of D not happening in words.

8b

2 For each of these events, are the outcomes equally likely?

  a I buy a raffle ticket – it either wins a prize or it doesn't.

  b A Premier League team has to play a team from League 2 in the 3rd round of the F A Cup. The Premier League team can win, lose or draw the match.

3 The letters of the word UNIVERSITY are written on separate cards. One card is chosen at random.
What is the probability that it shows

  a the letter Y

  b the letter I

  c a vowel

  d a letter in the second half of the alphabet

  e a letter which does not appear in the word OXFORD?

8c

4 The numbers 1 to 20 are written on a set of cards and one card is chosen at random.
For the number on the card which is chosen, events are defined as

  A: it is even

  B: it is divisible by 3

  C: it has exactly 2 factors

  D: it is divisible by 10

  E: it is divisible by 5

  F: it is divisible by 6

Which of the pairs of events below are mutually exclusive?
For those pairs which are not, give at least one value which shows they are not.

  a A, B   **b** A, C   **c** B, D

  d B, E   **e** C, D   **f** E, F

5 A bag has blue, red and green discs in it. A disc is chosen at random from the bag. The probability that it is red is 0.2 and the probability that it is green is 0.5. What is the probability that it is blue?

6 A fisherman records whether or not he catches any fish when he visits a particular river. He records Y when he catches at least one fish and N when he does not catch any fish. Use his results to estimate the probability that he catches no fish the next time he visits that river.

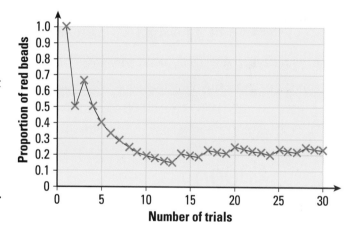

N	N	N	Y	N
N	N	Y	N	Y
N	Y	N	Y	N
Y	N	N	N	N

7 A bag has coloured beads in it. A number of people choose one bead from the bag without looking into the bag. Whether the bead is red or not is recorded and the bead is put back into the bag.

The graph shows the proportion of red beads drawn over the first thirty trials of this experiment.
Estimate the probability that the next person will draw a red bead from the bag.

8 Two dice were each thrown 100 times and the tables show the results. Do you think either of the dice were biased? Explain your reasoning.

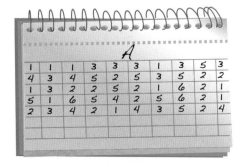

A

1	1	1	3	3	3	1	3	5	3
4	3	4	5	2	5	3	5	2	2
1	3	2	2	5	2	1	6	2	1
5	1	6	5	4	2	5	6	2	1
2	3	4	2	1	4	3	5	2	4

B

1	5	1	1	1	1	1	3	1	1	3
4	3	1	2	6	2	2	6	6	1	5
1	3	1	1	1	6	2	1	1	6	4
1	1	1	2	1	3	3	1	1	1	1
4	2	1	3	6	4	4	1	4	1	1

Maths Life

Charity Costs

Some of the money you give to a charity goes towards the charity's running costs. Without this money, the charity couldn't exist to help anyone at all!

Use Donation amounts
− Running costs
Money to help out
to find the missing
information about
these charities

Sports Day a success!

Donation target was £3000!

Let the children play!

Earley Sports Club	Donations	Costs	Balance
Collection boxes 1 − 10	£550		£550
Collection boxes 11 − 20	£600		
5 Cheques	£2000		
100 Posters for £0.50 each		£50	
25 Boxes for £2 each		£50	£3050
Sports kit		£1200	
Food and drink		£800	£1050
Prizes		£500	
		Left over	

We need
£3000
for a Sports Day!

Donate here!

Saturday 23 June at 2:30pm
*Food and drink
provided*

SALTAIRE DOG SHELTER
be a dog's best friend

Home
About us
The dogs
Adopt a dog
How to help
Links

It costs £300 a day to care for the dogs at Saltaire dog shelter. You can help. Click here to donate today!

Donate

Come to our spectacular fundraising party next week! Click here for more information.

Party!

There are 50 dogs at the shelter.

SALTAIRE DOG SHELTER

Yearly Costs	
Food	£15 000
Shelter	£18 000
Staff	£65 000
Medicine	£11 500
Total	

What is the cost per dog per year?

Party Animal!

Saltaire Dog Shelter raised £120 000 at a fundraising party held last week.

This money will allow the shelter to continue caring for pets waiting for a home.

Fight Childhood Cancers

Donations				
Number of people who pledged	£5		per month	Total per year
545	x	£5	x	12 months

Costs	
TV advert	£2000
Text fees	£350
Office supplies	£500
Payroll	£20 000
Total costs	

Goal: give the scientists £10 000

ust £5 a month to *fight* hildhood cancers. Text now!

hildhood Cancers

Msg
Did the charity make its goal?

Cancel   Send

Fight Childhood Cancers
234 The Way
Londontown
London XY1 2Z3

To the St George Hospital Cancer Research Centre,

For the 2009/2010 financial year, we promise to fund your research by £ ____.

Keep up the good work!

CHolloway

Claire Holloway
Director

Key indicators

- Understand and use the probability scale from 0 to 1 **Level 5**
- Find and justify probabilities **Level 5**
- Estimate probabilities from experimental data **Level 5**
- Know the sum of probabilities of all mutually exclusive outcomes is 1 **Level 6**

Level 6

1 There are many coloured counters in a bag. There are five different colours. There are the same number of red counters as blue counters. One counter is taken out at random. The table shows some of the probabilities. Calculate the probability of picking a red counter.

Colour	Probability
Green	0.35
Orange	0.25
Yellow	0.1
Blue	
Red	

Kamal's answer ✔

Kamal knows the probabilities add to 1

Kamal knows the probabilities of red and blue are equal

0.35 + 0.25 + 0.1 = 0.7
1 − 0.7 = 0.3
0.3 ÷ 2 = 0.15
Probability of a red counter
is 0.15

Kamal checks the probabilities add to 1
0.35 + 0.25 + 0.1 + 0.15 + 0.15 = 1

Level 5

2 The diagram shows five fair spinners with grey and white sectors. Each spinner is divided into equal sectors.

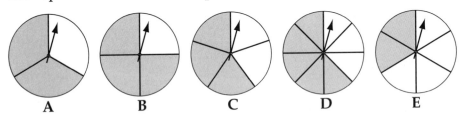

A   B   C   D   E

I am going to spin all the pointers.

a For one of the spinners, the probability of spinning grey is $\frac{3}{4}$. Which spinner is this?

b For two of the spinners, the probability of spinning grey is more than 60%, but less than 70%. Which two spinners are these?

Key Stage 3 2007 3–5 Paper 2

9 Shape

2-D shapes and construction

In ancient times, people navigated by looking at the stars. They would find the North Star in the sky and then judge the angle from the horizon to the star. Their position in relation to the star showed them which way to go.

What's the point? One way of doing this is to put your arm straight out in front of you and make a fist with your thumb on top. Count how many fists you can line up until your fist aligns with the North Star. Multiply the number of fists by 10° to find how many degrees of latitude you are north of the equator.

 **Check in**

Level 3

1 Match these cards with the object below.

[Cube]   [Sphere]   [Cylinder]   [Cuboid]

   a House brick   **b** Glue stick   **c** An orange   **d** Dice

Level 5

2 **a** Draw these angles accurately using a protractor.
   i 90°   **ii** 125°   **iii** 60°   **iv** 315°
  b Match each angle with one of these cards below.

[acute]   [reflex]   [right]   [obtuse]

9a Properties of triangles

- Recognise and name different kinds of triangles

You can use your knowledge of the properties of triangles to find out missing information.

Keywords
Equilateral   Scalene
Isosceles   Triangle
Right-angled

- A **triangle** is a 2-D shape with three sides and three angles.

The angle sum of a triangle is 180°.

Equilateral	Isosceles	Scalene	Right-angled
	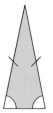	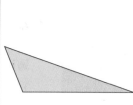	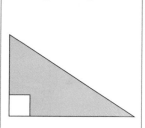
3 equal angles 3 equal sides	2 equal angles 2 equal sides	No equal angles No equal sides	One 90° angle

example

State whether each of these triangles is equilateral, isosceles, scalene or right-angled.

a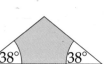

b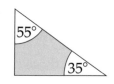

c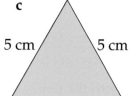

d 55° 35°

a Isosceles   The third angle is 180 − (38 + 38) = 180 − 76 = 104°
The triangle has two equal angles, and therefore two equal sides, so it is isosceles.

b Scalene   The triangle has no equal sides, and therefore no equal angles, so it is scalene.

c Equilateral   The triangle has three equal sides, and therefore three equal angles, so it is equilateral.

d Right-angled   The third angle is 180 − (55 + 35) = 180 − 90 = 90°
The triangle has a right angle.

Exercise 9a

1 State whether each of these triangles is equilateral, isosceles, scalene or right-angled. Explain your answers.

a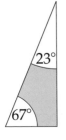

b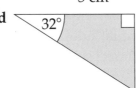
48 mm
65 mm
48 mm

c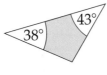

d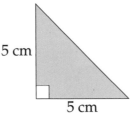

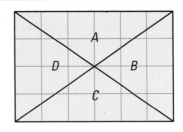
2 Each of these triangles falls into more than one category. State which categories each triangle belongs in. Explain your answers.

a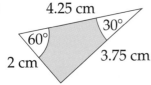
4.25 cm
30°
60°
2 cm
3.75 cm

b
5 cm
5 cm

c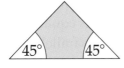
45°   45°

d
32°

e What do you notice about the categories?

Four triangles A, B, C and D are formed by the diagonals of a rectangle.
Copy the diagram on square grid paper and cut out the four triangles.
Arrange all four triangles to make two different isosceles triangles.

A
D   B
C

- Recognise and name different kinds of quadrilaterals
- Know some of their properties

Keywords
Parallel
Quadrilateral
Triangle

- A **quadrilateral** is a 2-D shape with four sides and four angles.

The angle sum of a quadrilateral is 360°.

Square	Rectangle	Rhombus	Parallelogram
	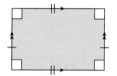		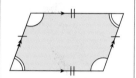
4 right angles 4 equal sides 2 sets parallel sides	4 right angles 2 sets equal sides 2 sets parallel sides	2 pairs equal angles 4 equal sides 2 sets parallel sides	2 pairs equal angles 2 sets equal sides 2 sets parallel sides

Trapezium	Isosceles trapezium	Kite	Arrowhead
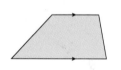	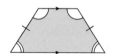		
1 set parallel sides	2 pairs equal angles 1 set equal sides 1 set parallel sides	1 pair equal angles 2 sets equal sides No parallel sides	1 pair equal angles 2 sets equal sides No parallel sides

example

Use two identical isosceles triangles to make
a a rhombus   b a kite   c a parallelogram.

a   b   c

Exercise 9b

1 The rectangle is made from three shapes, *A*, *B* and *C*.

  a Draw the rectangle on square grid paper and cut out the shapes *A*, *B* and *C*.

  b Give the mathematical name of shapes *A*, *B* and *C*.

  c Arrange all three shapes to make

    i an isosceles triangle

    ii a kite

    iii a parallelogram.

  Draw a sketch of each arrangement.

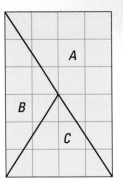

You are allowed to turn the shapes over.

2 List all the quadrilaterals that have

  a four right angles

  b four equal sides

  c one pair of parallel sides

  d two pairs of equal angles.

Did you know?

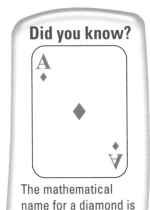

The mathematical name for a diamond is a rhombus.

investigation

The diagonals of a rectangle bisect each other

A rectangle has perpendicular sides

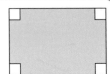

Copy the table and add these shapes in the correct place.

Kite   Square   Rhombus   Parallelogram

Isosceles trapezium

Explain how you decided where to put each shape.

	Diagonals	
	bisect each other	don't bisect each other
Perpendicular sides	rectangle	
No perpendicular sides		

- Recognise and name different kinds of 3-D solids
- Know some of their properties

Keywords
Cross-section Pyramid
Edge 3-D
Face Vertex
Prism

- A solid is a three-dimensional (**3-D**) shape.
  Prisms and **pyramids** are examples of solids.

 p. 276

- A prism has a constant **cross-section**.

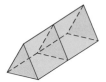

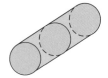

Triangular prism   Circular prism or cylinder

The cross-section names the prism.

- A pyramid tapers to a point.

Square-based pyramid   Circular-based pyramid or cone

The base names the pyramid.

- A **face** is a flat surface of a solid.
  An **edge** is the line where two faces meet.
  A **vertex** is a point at which three or more edges meet.

A cuboid has
6 faces,
8 vertices and
12 edges.

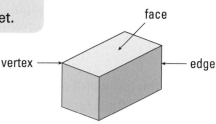

vertex ──→   face   ←── edge

example

A cube is made from four pink squares and two green squares.
The opposite faces are the same colour.
a Find the number of edges where a pink face meets a pink face.
b Find the number of edges where a pink face meets a green face.

....

a 4 edges   **b** 8 edges

Exercise 9c

1 Copy and complete the table for these 3-D shapes.

a   **b**   **c**

d   **e**   **f**

	Name of solid	No. of faces (*f*)	Number of vertices (*v*)	Number of edges (*e*)
a				
b				
c				
d				
e				
f				

Write down a relationship between *f*, *v* and *e*.

2 A tetrahedron is made from three red and one green equilateral triangles.
Find the number of edges where
a a red face meets a red face   **b** a red face meets a green face.

3 A hollow cube is made from 12 straws. One straw is marked *AB*.
Find the number of straws that
a are parallel to *AB*
b are perpendicular to *AB* and meet *AB*
c are not parallel to *AB* and do not meet *AB*.

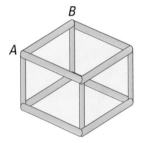

Ryan is slicing cubes of cheese for a snack.
a Describe the shapes of the cut surface for each cube.
b Is it possible to cut a surface which is square?
Illustrate your answer.
c Is it possible to cut a surface which is triangular?
Explain your answer.

9d Constructing bisectors

- Use ruler and compasses to draw angle bisectors and perpendicular bisectors

Keywords

Arc   Compasses
Bisect   Construct
Bisector   Perpendicular

- Bisect means cut in two.
  - An angle **bisector** cuts an angle exactly in half.
  - The **perpendicular** bisector of a line cuts the line exactly in half and is at right angles to the line.

Perpendicular means 'at right angles'.

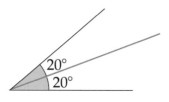

The **pink line** bisects the angle of 40°.

The **pink line** bisects the black line.

- You use **compasses** to **construct** an angle bisector.

Construct means 'draw accurately'.

angle *AOC* = angle *COB*

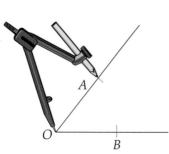

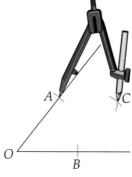

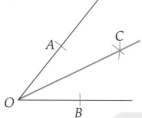

Use compasses to draw an **arc** on each line.

Draw arcs from *A* and *B* that intersect at *C*.

Draw a line for *O* to *C* and beyond.

Do not rub out your construction lines.

- You use compasses to construct a line bisector.

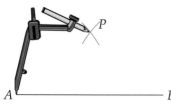

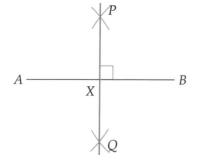

AX = *XB*
PQ is perpendicular to *AB*.

Draw arcs from *A* and *B* above and below the line.

Draw a line from *P* to *Q*.

Exercise 9d

1 a Draw a line *AB*, so that *AB* = 4.8 cm.
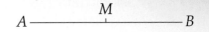
  b Using compasses, construct the perpendicular
    bisector of *AB*.
  c Label the midpoint of *AB* as *M*.
  d Measure the length of *AM*.

2 a Use a protractor to draw an angle *AOB* of 74°.
  b Using compasses, construct the bisector of angle *AOB*.
  c Label the bisector *OC*.
  d Measure the angles *AOC* and *COB*.

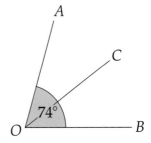

3 Draw these angles, then construct the angle bisector for each.
  a 120°   **b** 36°   **c** 96°
  Use a protractor to check your answers.

4 a Draw a line *AB* = 64 mm.
  b Using compasses, construct the perpendicular bisector of *AB*.
  c Mark the midpoint of *AB* as *X*.
  d Using compasses, construct an angle of 45° at *X*.

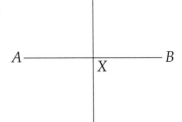

5 a Draw any large triangle.
  b Construct the angle bisector for each of the three angles.
    What do you notice?

6 a Draw any large triangle.
  b Construct the perpendicular bisector for each of the three sides.
    What do you notice?

The diagram shows the construction of the angle
bisector of the angle *AOB*.
  a Give the mathematical name of the
    quadrilateral *AOBC*.
  b Explain why this construction gives
    the angle bisector.

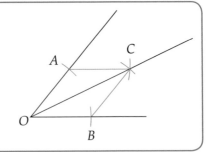

- Use ruler and protractor to draw triangles accurately

Keywords
Construct   Ruler
Protractor   Triangle

- You can construct a **triangle** using a **protractor** and a **ruler**.

It is only possible to draw one triangle when you know

- two angles and the included side (ASA)
- two sides and the included angle (SAS)

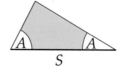
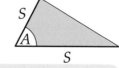

Included means 'in between'.

example

Construct triangle *DEF* using ASA.

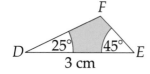

- -

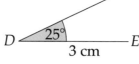

Draw the base line of 3 cm using a ruler.

Draw an angle of 25° at *D* using a protractor.

Draw an angle of 45° at *E* using a protractor to complete the triangle.

Check your diagram by calculating and then measuring the third angle. 25° + 45° = 70°
Angle *F* should be 180° − 70° = 110°   (The angle sum of a triangle is 180°.)

example

Construct triangle *PQR*, with *PQ* = 3.5 cm, *PR* = 2.5 cm and angle *P* = 55° using SAS.

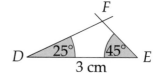

- -

First **sketch** the triangle.
Then carry out the construction.

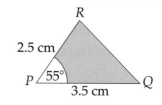

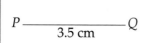

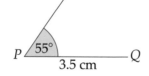

Draw the base line of 3.5 cm using a ruler.

Draw an angle of 55° at *P* using a protractor.

Mark 2.5 cm from *P* and draw *RQ* to complete the triangle.

p. 274

Exercise 9e

1 Construct these triangles (ASA).
State the type of each triangle.

a

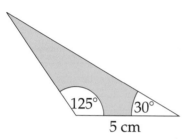

125° 30°
5 cm

b

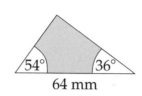

54° 36°
64 mm

c

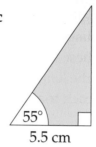

55°
5.5 cm

2 Construct these triangles (SAS).
State the type of each triangle.

a

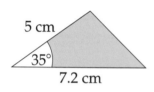

5 cm
35°
7.2 cm

b

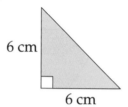

6 cm

6 cm

c

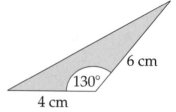

6 cm
130°
4 cm

3 Construct each of these triangles. Draw a sketch first.
  a *ABC*, where angle *A* = 38°, angle *B* = 60° and *AB* = 6 cm
  b *DEF*, where angle *D* = 90°, *DE* = 5 cm and *DF* = 5 cm
State the type of each triangle.

4 Construct these triangles.
You will need to calculate the unknown angles before you
start the construction.

a

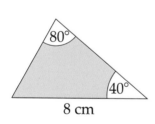

80°
40°
8 cm

b

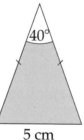

40°

5 cm

c

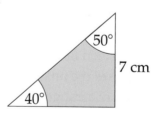

50°
7 cm
40°

  a Construct the rhombus *ABCD*.
  b Measure the lengths of the diagonals of the rhombus.
  The diagonals meet at *X*.
  c Measure the angle *AXB*.

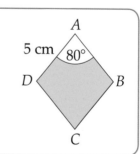

A
5 cm 80°
D B
C

9a

1 You are given five equal lengths of plastic.
The lengths can be joined together only at their ends.
Draw diagrams to show triangles that can be made
using these lengths of plastic. You do not have to
use all the lengths for each triangle.
Name each triangle.

9b

2 Calculate the value of the unknown angles in these
parallelograms.

> The opposite angles of a
> parallelogram are equal.

a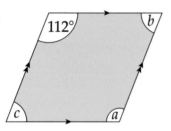

b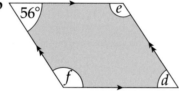

c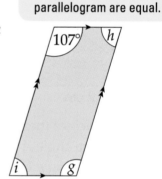

9c

3 A tetrahedron is made from two pink and two green
equilateral triangles.
a Find the number of edges where a pink face meets a pink face.
b Find the number of edges where a pink face meets a green face.
c Find the number of edges where a green face meets a
green face.
d Are the answers the same if these pink and green triangles
are arranged differently?

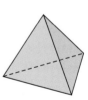

4 Draw these angles, then construct the angle bisector for each.

  a 148°   **b** 56°   **c** 84°

> Check your constructions by measuring the angles with a protractor.

5 Draw and label these lines, then construct the perpendicular bisector of each line.

  a AB = 5.5 cm   **b** CD = 45 mm   **c** EF = 6.8 cm

> Check your constructions by measuring the angle at the midpoint and measuring the distance to the midpoint of each line.

6 The diagram shows the construction of the perpendicular bisector of the line AC.

  a Give the mathematical name of the quadrilateral $ABCD$.

  b Explain why this construction gives the perpendicular bisector.

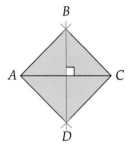

7 Construct each of these triangles.

> You will need to calculate the unknown angle(s) before you start the construction.

a 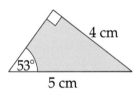   **b** 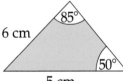   **c**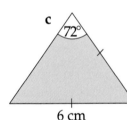

8 Draw a sketch and then construct each of these triangles.

  a ABC, where BC = 45 mm, angle ABC = 55° and angle BCA = 40°

  b DEF, where angle E = 30°, DE = 6 cm and EF = 8 cm

  c GHI, where HI = 35 mm, angle H = 90° and angle I = 60°

Key indicators
- Classify quadrilaterals by their geometric properties **Level 6**
- Use compasses to do standard constructions **Level 6**

Level 5

1 *A* and *B* are fixed points on the grid.
The point *C* can move.

a What type of triangle is *ABC*, when *C* is at (2, 4)?
The point *C* moves so that triangle *ABC* is isosceles.

p. 156

b State the coordinates of 3 possible points for *C*.
c What do you notice about these points?

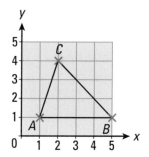

Bill's answer ✔

Bill makes sure
length $AC =$ length BC

a Scalene
b (3, 2) (3, 3) (3, 4)
c The x coordinate is always 3.

Bill notices that the lengths of all 3 sides are not equal

The order of the coordinates is (*x, y*)

Level 6

2 The shapes below are drawn on square grids.

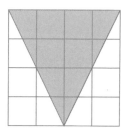

Shape **A**

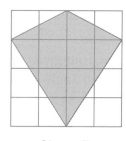

Shape **B**

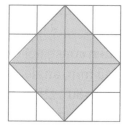

Shape **C**

a Is shape A an equilateral triangle? Yes/No
Explain your answer.
b Is shape B a kite? Yes/No
Explain your answer.
c Is shape C a square? Yes/No
Explain your answer.

Key Stage 3 2004 4–6 Paper 1

10 Algebra

Integers, functions and graphs

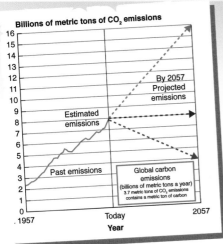

By using a graph to show the global carbon emissions, scientists can see relationships and also predict what might happen next. The red line shows future emissions, if the current rate is continued. If you go up from today's date to the line and then over from the line to the emissions, you can read the emissions level for today.

What's the point? If you see graphs like this on TV or in newspapers, you need to be able to read the maths to understand what it says.

Check in

1 Copy and complete each table for the given function.

a
Multiply by 4 and add 3	
Input	Output
2	
5	
	31
	39

b
Multiply by itself and subtract 5	
Input	Output
3	
	4
6	
	95

2 Write the coordinates of the vertices of these shapes.

a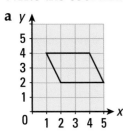

b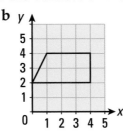

c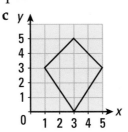

d Name each of these quadrilaterals.

3 Find all the prime numbers below 30.

4 On axes labelled from -10 to 10, plot the following points and join them in order. What do you find?

(10, 4) (4, 9) (-1, 4) (-1, 0) (-6, 0) (-6, –5) (0, -5) (0, -1) (3, -1) (3, -5) (10, -5) (10, 4)

• Find squares and square roots of whole numbers with and without a calculator

Keywords
Square
Square root

• A **square** number is the result of multiplying a number by itself.

$1 \times 1 = 1$ $2 \times 2 = 4$ $3 \times 3 = 9$ $4 \times 4 = 16$

• A square number is written with a raised 2.
$5^2 = 5 \times 5 = 25$

example

Calculate each of these.
a 7^2 **b** 9^2 **c** 10^2

. . . .

a $7^2 = 7 \times 7 = 49$ **b** $9^2 = 9 \times 9 = 81$ **c** $10^2 = 10 \times 10 = 100$

• The opposite of square is **square root**.
$5^2 = 25$ $\sqrt{25} = 5$

• A positive number has two square roots.
$6 \times 6 = 36$ and $-6 \times -6 = 36$
So the square roots of 36 are 6 and -6
• The symbol $\sqrt{}$ is only used for the **positive** square root.
$\sqrt{36} = 6$

You can write ± 6 to mean $+6$ and -6

• You can work out square numbers and square roots using your calculator.

$\sqrt{289} =$ [√] [2] [8] [9] [=] [17]

$23^2 =$ [2] [3] [x²] [=] [529]

Check whether you need to press the 'square root' button on your calculator before or after you enter the number.

Instead of using a calculator, you can make an **estimate**.

example

Estimate the square root of 150.

. . . .

$12^2 = 144$ and $13^2 = 169$, so $\sqrt{150}$ is between 12 and 13, but closer to 12. A good estimate would be 12.3 (or -12.3).

Check using your calculator.
$\sqrt{150} = 12.247\ 448\ 71\ldots$

Exercise 10a

1 Without using a calculator, write the value of each number.

   a 8^2 **b** 13^2 **c** $\sqrt{121}$ **d** $\sqrt{196}$

2 Use your calculator to find each of these.

   a 42^2 **b** 13.7^2 **c** $\sqrt{2601}$ **d** $\sqrt{887}$

3 Without using a calculator, write the value of each number.

   a 17^2 **b** 40^2 **c** $(-8)^2$ **d** $\sqrt{2500}$

4 **a** Estimate the value of $\sqrt{130}$.

   b Use your calculator to find $\sqrt{130}$.
      How close was your estimate?

   c Repeat parts **a** to **b** for $\sqrt{200}$.

5 Explain why $\sqrt{-144}$ has no answer.

6 **a** Find the missing digits in this product.

      $576 = 2\square \times \square\square$

   b Use your answer to explain why 576 is a square number.

   c Use your answer to write down $\sqrt{576}$ without using a
      calculator.

7 Two friends, Dania and Jemisha, answer some
   questions about powers and roots.
   Whose answer is correct in each case?
   Explain why.

Question	Dania's answer	Jemisha's answer
$(-9)^2$	81	-81
$\sqrt{144}$	12	± 12

8 **a** Without a calculator, find $\boxed{?}$ given that $\boxed{?}^2 = 2304$

   b Explain why $\boxed{?}$ could not be a whole number if $\boxed{?}^2 = 413$

---

challenge

$2^2 + 3^2 = 13$.

   a Find 10 two-digit prime numbers that can be written as the
      sum of two square numbers.

   b Find as many two-digit numbers that can be written as the
      sum of two square numbers in two different ways as you can.

10a² Cubes, cube roots and indices

- Find cubes, cube roots and powers of whole numbers with and without a calculator

Keywords
Cube
Cube root
Indices

- A **cube** number is the result of multiplying a number by itself and then by itself again.

1

2

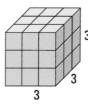
3

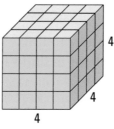
4

$1 \times 1 \times 1 = 1$ $2 \times 2 \times 2 = 8$ $3 \times 3 \times 3 = 27$ $4 \times 4 \times 4 = 64$

- A cube number is written with a raised 3.
  $5^3 = 5 \times 5 \times 5 = 125$

- You can work out cube numbers using your calculator.

  $11^3 = $ [1] [1] [x^3] [=] 1331

  You may need to press SHIFT, or the FUNCTION key, to find a cube number.

- The opposite of cube is **cube root**.
  The cube of 2 is 8.   The cube root of 8 is 2.
  $2^3 = 8$ $\sqrt[3]{8} = 2$

- A positive number has one positive cube root.
  A negative number has one negative cube root.
  $2 \times 2 \times 2 = 8$ but $\text{-}2 \times \text{-}2 \times \text{-}2 = \text{-}8$

- You can work out cube roots using your calculator.
  $\sqrt[3]{2197}$ [$\sqrt[3]{}$] [2] [1] [9] [7] [=] 13

  All calculators are different. Check how to work out cube roots on your calculator.

- x^2 and x^3 are examples of **indices**. The small, raised number tells you how many times x is multiplied by itself.
  $3^4 = 3 \times 3 \times 3 \times 3 = 81$
  $4^{10} = 4 \times 4 \times 4 \times 4 \times 4 \times 4 \times 4 \times 4 \times 4 \times 4 = 1\ 048\ 576$

- You can work out indices using your calculator.
  $2^7 = $ [2] [x^y] [7] [=] 128

  The indices key on your calculator may be different.

Exercise 10a²

1 Without using a calculator, write down the value of each of these numbers.

   a 4^3 **b** 10^3 **c** $\sqrt[3]{27}$ **d** $\sqrt[3]{125}$

2 Use your calculator to find each of these.

   a 7^3 **b** 15^3 **c** $\sqrt[3]{6859}$ **d** $\sqrt[3]{9261}$

3 Without using a calculator, write down the value of each of these numbers.

   a 8^3 **b** 20^3 **c** $(-3)^3$ **d** $\sqrt[3]{27\,000}$

4 Is this statement true or false?

$$\sqrt{16} = \sqrt[3]{64}$$

Explain your answer.

5 Use your calculator to find each of these.

   a 3^5 **b** 5^3 **c** 2^{10} **d** 8^8

6 Two friends, Ben and Rick, answer some questions about powers and roots. Whose answer is correct in each case? Explain why.

Question	Ben's answer	Rick's answer
$\sqrt[3]{-125}$	-5	Cannot be done
4^3	12	64
3^6	216	729
-2^5	-32	32

challenge

A bacteria reproduces by splitting in two. These new bacteria then each split into two and the process continues.

a If there is one bacterium on a surface at 9 a.m. and a split occurs every hour, how many bacteria will there be by 9 a.m. the following day? How can you use your calculator keys to help you decide?

b Can you write a formula connecting B (the number of bacteria) and n (the number of hours after 9 a.m.)?

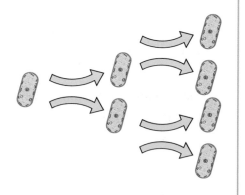

10b Factors and multiples

- Use factors and multiples to find the HCF and LCM of numbers

Keywords

Factor   Multiple
HCF   Product
LCM

- A **factor** of a number is any number that divides into it without leaving a remainder.
  The factors of 12 are 1, 2, 3, 4, 6 and 12.
  $1 \times 12 = 12$ $2 \times 6 = 12$ $3 \times 4 = 12$

1 and 12, 2 and 6,
3 and 4 are factor pairs.

- A **multiple** of a number is any number that it divides into exactly.
  The multiples of 12 are 12, 24, 36, 48, 60, … and so on.

- The **highest common factor (HCF)** of two numbers is the largest number that is a factor of both the numbers.

- The **lowest common multiple (LCM)** of two numbers is the smallest number that is a multiple of both the numbers.

---

example

a i   Find all the factors of 18 and 30.
  ii   Find the highest common factor of 18 and 30.
b i   Find the first 10 multiples of 6 and 15.
  ii   Find the lowest common multiple of 6 and 15.

· ·

a i

Number	Factor pairs	Factor list
18	$1 \times 18, 2 \times 9, 3 \times 6$	1, 2, 3, 6, 9, 18
30	$1 \times 30, 2 \times 15, 3 \times 10, 5 \times 6$	1, 2, 3, 5, 6, 10, 15, 30

  ii   The HCF is 6.   6 is the largest number that appears in
                                      both lists of factors.

b i

Number	First ten multiples
6	6, 12, 18, 24, 30, 36, 42, 48, 54, 60
15	15, 30, 45, 60, 75, 90, 105, 120, 135, 150

  ii   The LCM is 30.   30 is the smallest number that appears
                                       in both lists of multiples.

p. 232

Exercise 10b

1 Write down all the factors of each of these numbers.
   a 20   **b** 14   **c** 36   **d** 50   **e** 64

2 Write down the first five multiples of each of these numbers
   a 10   **b** 7   **c** 13   **d** 24   **e** 99

3 Copy and complete the table for these pairs of numbers.

	Numbers	Factor pairs	Factor list	HCF
Example	10	$1 \times 10, 2 \times 5$	1, 2, 5, 10	5
	35	$1 \times 35, 5 \times 7$	1, 5, 7, 35	
a	12			
	30			
b	18			
	45			
c	15			
	50			

4 By writing down the first 10 multiples of each number given, find the lowest common multiple of each of these pairs of numbers.
   a 4 and 7   **b** 4 and 10   **c** 8 and 20   **d** 12 and 14

5 **a** **i** Show that 60 has 12 factors.
      ii Find three other numbers below 100 with 12 factors.
   b Two numbers have a HCF of 6 and an LCM of 72.
     What are the numbers?

6 Decide whether each statement is true or false.
Explain your answers.
   a Odd numbers have no even factors.
   b Any multiple of 6 is also a multiple of 2 and of 3.
   c The largest factor of any number is itself.
   d No number has exactly three factors.

investigation

Explain why any square number will have an odd number of factors, but all other numbers have an even number of factors.

10c Prime factors

- Write any whole number as the product
  of its prime factors

Keywords
Decomposition
Factor
Prime

- A prime number is a number with exactly two factors,
  1 and the number itself.

  1 is not a prime number because it has only one factor.
  The first ten prime numbers are 2, 3, 5, 7, 11, 13, 17, 19, 23 and 29.

- Any number can be written as a product of its
  prime factors.

- Prime factor **decomposition** involves breaking a number
  down into pairs of factors, until you reach prime numbers.

36 can be written as 6 $\times$ 6.

6 is not prime. It can be written as 2 $\times$ 3.

2 and 3 are both prime numbers.

$$36 = 2 \times 2 \times 3 \times 3$$
$$= 2^2 \times 3^2$$

- You can use the prime factors of a number to work out
  its other, non-prime, factors.

example

Using prime factor decomposition, explain why 6 is a factor of 174 but 9 is not.

174 can be written as 6 $\times$ 29.

6 can be written as 2 $\times$ 3.

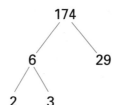

29 is a prime number.

2 and 3 are both prime numbers.

$$174 = 2 \times 3 \times 29$$

Since 2 is a factor and 3 is a factor, then 2 $\times$ 3 = 6 is also a factor. 6 $\times$ 29 = 174
If 9 were a factor, the prime factors of 174 would have to include 3 $\times$ 3, which
is not true.

Algebra Integers, functions and graphs

Exercise 10c

1 Write each of these numbers as the product of its prime factors.
   a 40   **b** 56   **c** 120
   d 250   **e** 360   **f** 990

2 By writing 420 as the product of its prime factors,
   decide which of these numbers are factors of 420.
   12   15   28   35   60

3 **a** Find the largest prime number between 100 and 200.
   b Find as many two-digit prime numbers that remain prime
      when the digits are reversed as you can.

4 Amy finds that the prime number decomposition of a number
   leads to $2^2 \times 3 \times 5^2$. What number is Amy working with?

5 Decide whether each of these statements is true or false.
   Explain your answer.
   a There are no even prime numbers.
   b There are no square numbers that are prime.

6 The product of my age and that of my niece is 408.
   Using prime factor decomposition, decide how old we might
   both be.

7 **a** Write 729 as a product of its prime factors.

   b Use your answer to **a** to explain why 729 is a square number
      with a square root of $3 \times 3 \times 3 = 27$.

   c Use prime factor decomposition to find the square roots of
      i 441   **ii** 576   **iii** 1024

investigation

10d Coordinates

- Plot points on axes using coordinates in all four quadrants

Keywords
Coordinates · Vertices
Origin · x-axis
Perpendicular · y-axis
Quadrant

- You can fix the position of points on a grid using **coordinates**.

- The grid is divided into four **quadrants** by two **perpendicular** axes. The horizontal axis is the **x-axis**. The vertical axis is the **y-axis**.

- The coordinates of a point are written (x, y).
  (2, 1) means 2 along the x-axis and 1 up the y-axis.

- The point of intersection of the axes is called the **origin** (0, 0).

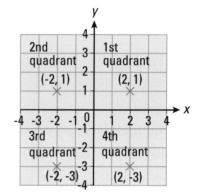

example

Write down the coordinates of the points on the grid.

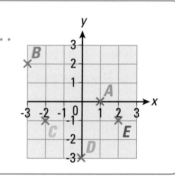

A is (1, 0)

B is (-3, 2)

C is (-2, -1)

D is (0, -3)

E is (2, -1)

example

Three **vertices** of a quadrilateral are (2, 3), (-1, 2) and (-1, 0).
Give the coordinate of the fourth point, if the quadrilateral is
a a kite
b an isosceles trapezium
c a rhombus.

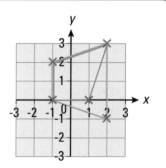

a (1, 0)   The kite is drawn on the grid in blue.
b (2, -1)   The isosceles trapezium is drawn on the grid in green.
c Impossible, as the distances between the given points are not equal.

Exercise 10d

1 Write down the coordinates of the points on the grid.

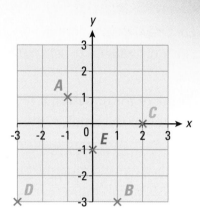

2 Copy the grid and plot the points (2, 3), (0, 3) and (-2, -1).
These points are three vertices of a quadrilateral. Give the coordinates of the fourth point, if the quadrilateral is
a a kite   **b** a parallelogram
c an isosceles trapezium.

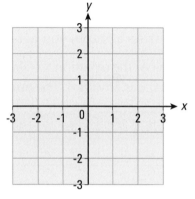

3 A landscape gardener designs gardens using a grid system. She plots the position of a rectangular flower bed, as shown. She wants to plant a rose at the centre of the flower bed. Find the coordinates of the point of intersection of the diagonals.

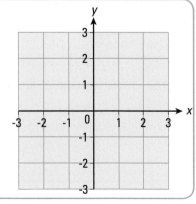

a Plot and join the points A (0, 3) and B (-3, 0).
b Plot the point C (3, 3).
c List the coordinates of possible points D, so that AB is parallel to CD.
d What do you notice about the x and y values of your answers?

challenge

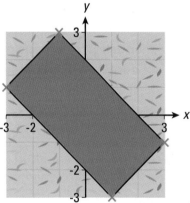

• Draw graphs of lines which have equations where
  x is constant or *y* is constant

Keywords
Equation
Horizontal
Vertical

Think of the **equation** $y = 3$ as a function.
Whatever the input, *x*, the output, *y*, is always 3.

x	-1	0	1	2	3	4	5
y	3	3	3	3	3	3	3

The table gives coordinate pairs: (-1, 3), (0, 3),
(1, 3), (2, 3), (3, 3), (4, 3) and (5, 3). If you plot these
points on a graph, you get a horizontal line.

Think of the equation $x = 4$ as a function. The
input, *x*, is always 4. The output can be any number.

x	4	4	4	4	4	4	4
y	-1	0	1	2	3	4	5

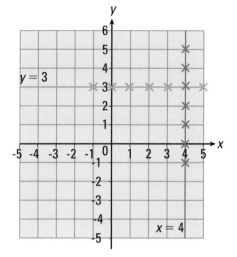

If you plot the points (4, -1), (4, 0), (4, 1), (4, 2), (4, 3),
(4, 4) and (4, 5) on a graph, you get a vertical line.

Remember that coordinates
are always written with the
x value first, (*x*, *y*).

• An equation of the form $y = $ a number always gives a
  horizontal line. An equation of the form $x = $ a number
  always gives a vertical line.

On the graph $y = 3$, the
y-coordinate is always 3.

On the graph $x = 4$, the
x-coordinate is always 4.

example

Write down the equation of each of these lines.
. . . .

Line A $x = 4$
  The line is vertical and the *x*-coordinate is always 4.
Line B $y = 7$
  The line is horizontal and the *y*-coordinate is always 7.
Line C $y = 2\frac{1}{2}$
  The line is horizontal and the *y*-coordinate is always $2\frac{1}{2}$.
Line D $x = -1$
  The line is vertical and the *x*-coordinate is always -1.

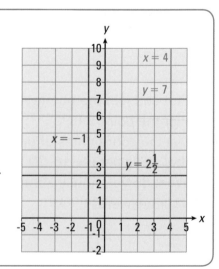

Exercise 10e

1 **a** Is the graph of each of these functions horizontal, vertical or neither?

    i $x = 2$ **ii** $y = 2x - 1$ **iii** $y = 4$

    iv $x = -3$ **v** $y = 2\frac{1}{2}$ **vi** $y + 4 = 0$

  b For those which are horizontal or vertical, draw the graph on axes labelled from -5 to 5.

> Remember to label the axes *x* and *y*.

2 Write down the equation of each line.

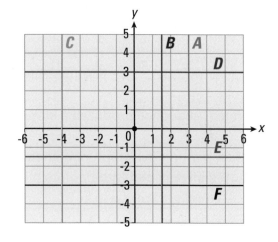

3 Richard draws four lines on a set of axes. The lines create a square of side length 4 units. What lines might you plot if you wanted to create

  a a square of length 5 units

  b a rectangle with dimensions 3 units by 4 units

  c a rectangle with area 24 units²

  d a capital letter E with lines 1 unit wide?

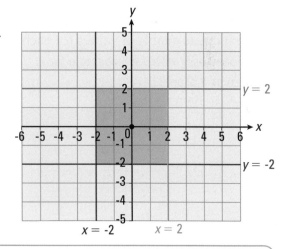

investigation

a Draw the graphs of each of these pairs of functions.

> Intersect means 'cross'.

  i $x = 4$ and $y = 3$ **ii** $x = -3$ and $y = 5$

  iii $y = -1$ and $x = 2$ **iv** $y = -2$ and $x = -4$

b At what coordinate does each pair of graphs intersect?

c What do you notice?

- Draw graphs of straight lines using their equations

Keywords
Diagonal
Intersect
Linear

p. 22

You already know that, for a **linear** sequence, the difference between successive terms is constant.

- The outputs of a linear function form a linear sequence.

  $y = 2x + 3$ is a linear function.

  The difference between successive y values is 2.

x	1	2	3	4	5
y	5	7	9	11	13

A linear function contains x and y. It does not involve any terms with powers (e.g. x^2).

- A linear sequence produces a sloping straight-line graph.

- When plotting the graph of a linear function, you should always plot three points.

Two points should be enough, but a third acts as a check – if the three points are not in a straight line, you have made a mistake!

example

a Plot the graphs $y = 4x - 2$ and $y = 2x + 6$ on the same axes.
b Write down the coordinate at which they **intersect**.
. . . .

Intersect means 'cross'.

a First create a table of values for each function.

Choose easy values to substitute for x, such as 1, 2 and 3.

$y = 4x - 2$

x	1	2	3
y	2	6	10

$y = 2x + 6$

x	1	2	3
y	8	10	12

Form coordinate pairs:
$y = 4x - 2 \rightarrow$ (1, 2), (2, 6), (3, 10)
$y = 2x + 6 \rightarrow$ (1, 8), (2, 10), (3, 12)
Plot the coordinate pairs one function at a time.
Connect the points for each function with a straight-line to graph the function.

b The graphs intersect at (4, 14).

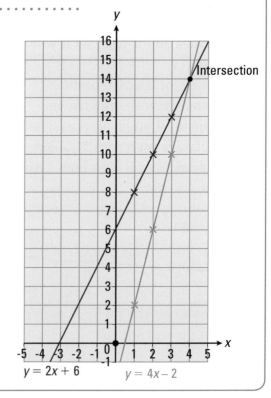

Exercise 10f

1 Is the graph of each of these functions a sloping straight line or not?

a $y = 2x - 1$ **b** $x = 2$ **c** $y = x$

d $y = 3x + 1$ **e** $y = 5x - 6$ **f** $x = 2$

g $y = 3(x - 2)$ **h** $y = -3$ **i** $x + y = 5$

j For those which are sloping straight lines draw the graph on axes labelled from -10 to 10.

2 Here are two lists showing linear equations and the coordinates of a point that lies on each one. Match the equation with the coordinate that lies on its graph.

Equation	Coordinate
$y = 3x - 2$	$(5, 14)$
$y = 2x + 4$	$(1, -2)$
$x + y = 9$	$(4, 0)$
$y = 6x - 8$	$(3, 7)$
$y = 9(x - 4)$	$(6, 3)$

3 Marcus and Cristina both open a bank savings account. Marcus's bank rewards him by putting £100 into his account as long as he puts in £20 a month. Cristina's bank rewards her with £50 as long as she saves £25 a month.

a Use a graph to show how much each student will have each month between now and two years' time.

b When do they have the same amount?

c Who will save up more?

d Can you think of an equation that the bank could use to model the savings in each account?

a Using suitable graphical software or a graphical calculator, plot each of these graph groups on one axes.

b Decide what is the same and what is different about the graphs in each group.

c Look at the equations of the graphs in each group. Explain your answers to part **b** by referring to the equations.

d Use your results to predict what $y = 10x - 2$ will look like. Check your prediction.

Group 1
$y = 2x + 1$
$y = 3x + 1$
$y = 4x + 1$
$y = 5x + 1$

Group 2
$y = 2x + 1$
$y = 2x + 2$
$y = 2x + 3$
$y = 2x - 2$

Group 3
$y = 2x + 1$
$y = -2x + 1$

• Find the equation of a graph of a straight line

Keywords
Equation   Linear
Horizontal   Vertical

p. 262

• You can find the **equation** of a graph by thinking of the graph as many points with coordinates that follow a pattern. This pattern can then be expressed as an equation.

The equation of a **vertical** line is x = a number.

The equation of a **horizontal** line is y = a number.

The equation of a sloping straight-line line contains both x and y.

To find the equation of a line, write the coordinates of some points that lie on the line and see if you can spot a pattern. Write the pattern in words first, then form an equation.

example

a Write five coordinates that lie on each of these lines.

b Use your answer to part **a** to find the equation of each line.

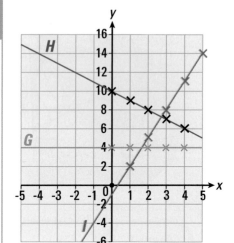

Remember that coordinates are always written with the x value first, (x, y).

Keep things simple by avoiding negative coordinates, if possible.

G **a** (0, 4), (1, 4), (2, 4), (3, 4) and (4, 4)

   b The second coordinate is always 4. So $y = 4$.

H **a** (0, 10), (1, 9), (2, 8), (3, 7) and (4, 6)

   b The two coordinates add to give 10. So $x + y = 10$.

I **a** (1, 2), (2, 5), (3, 8), (4, 11) and (5, 14)

   b The second coordinate is one less than treble the first.
   So $y = 3x - 1$.

The y-coordinates of a **linear** graph form a linear sequence. If the y-coordinates go up in 3s, the pattern is connected to the 3 times table.

Exercise 10f²

1 Match each coordinate set with the pattern it follows and
its equation.

Coordinates	Pattern in words	Equation
(1, 3), (2, 6), (3, 9)	The difference between the two numbers is 4.	$y = 3x$
(1, 7), (2, 6), (3, 5)	The second number is always 5.	$x + y = 8$
(1, 5), (2, 6), (3, 7)	The sum of the two numbers is 8.	$y - x = 4$
(1, 5), (2, 5), (3, 5)	The second number is treble the first.	$y = 5$

2 **a** Write down five coordinates that lie on each of
these lines.

b Use your answer to part **a** to find the equation
of each line.

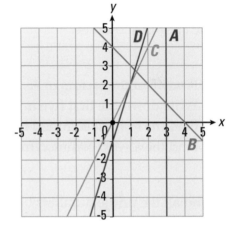

3 A mobile phone company sent out these bills to
customers on its 'Prime Time' package.

Prime Time

Name: Mr R Mann
Time: 10 mins
Cost: £9

Prime Time

Name: Miss V Hill
Time: 20 mins
Cost: £13

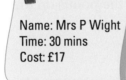

Prime Time

Name: Mrs P Wight
Time: 30 mins
Cost: £17

Prime Time

Name: Mrs A Yates
Time: 1 hour
Cost: £29

a Plot a graph of these bills, where x = time in minutes and y = cost in pounds.
b Find the equation that the mobile phone company uses to bill its customers.
c Explain how this billing method works.

experiment

a Take a beaker of water and record its temperature.
Heat the water steadily and record its temperature every
30 seconds until it boils.
b Plot your results on a graph.
c Suggest an equation for this heating process.

10a

1 Without using a calculator, write down the value of
   a 11^2 **b** $\sqrt{81}$

2 **a** Estimate $\sqrt{55}$.
   b Use your calculator to check how close you are.

10a²

3 Without using your calculator, write down the value of
   a 5^3 **b** $\sqrt[3]{8}$

4 Alex says that 2^5 is 10. Explain his mistake and state what the answer should be.

10b

5 **a** Find all of the factors of 45.
   b Write down the first five multiples of 13.
   c Find the highest common factor of 12 and 20.
   d Find the lowest common multiple of 8 and 10.

10c

6 Find all the prime numbers between 40 and 60.

7 Write each of these numbers as a product of its prime factors.
   a 45   **b** 120   **c** 250   **d** 360   **e** 1240

10d

8 Write the coordinates of the points on the grid.

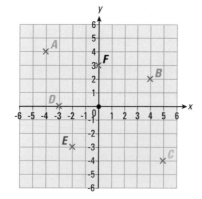

10e

9 Plot each of these graphs on the copy of the same set of axes from question 8.
   a $y = 5$ **b** $x = 2$ **c** $y = -3$ **d** $x = 1.5$

10 Using axes of your choice, plot each of these graphs on a separate diagram.

    a $y = 2x$ **b** $y = x + 1$

    c $y = 3x - 1$ **d** $x + y = 7$

11 Is this statement true or false?

    The point $(3, 7)$ lies on the graph $y = 2x + 1$.

    Explain your answer.

12 Find the equation of the graph on which each of these sets of coordinates lie.

a

x	1	2	3	4	5
y	5	10	15	20	25

b

x	1	2	3	4	5
y	5	5	5	5	5

c

x	1	2	3	4	5
y	4	5	6	7	8

d

x	1	2	3	4	5
y	7	9	11	13	15

13 Match each graph with its equation.

    $y = x$ $x = -1$ $y = 3x - 3$

    $x + y = 9$ $y = 2x + 4$

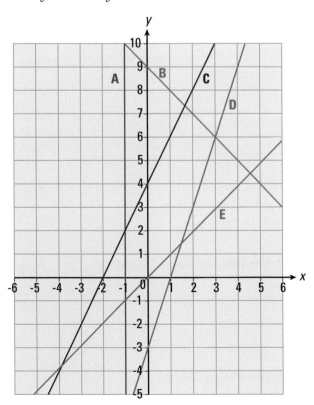

10 Summary

Key indicators
- Plot the graphs of simple linear functions **Level 5**
- Plot the graphs of linear functions, for example $y = 4x + 2$ **Level 6**

Level 6

1 a Michelle says 3^4 is the same as 4^3.
Is she correct?
Explain your answer.
b 6^5 is 7776. Calculate 6^7.

Zak's answer ✔

$$\begin{array}{r} 7776 \\ 6\times \\ \hline 46656 \end{array} \qquad \begin{array}{r} 46656 \\ 6\times \\ \hline 279936 \end{array}$$

a $3^4 = 3 \times 3 \times 3 \times 3 = 81$
$4^3 = 4 \times 4 \times 4 = 64$
Michelle is not correct.
b $6^7 = 6^5 \times 6 \times 6$
$= 7776 \times 6 \times 6$
$= 279936$

Zak knows 3^4 means
$3 \times 3 \times 3 \times 3$ or 9×9
Zak calculates 16×4

Level 6

2 The graph shows a straight line.

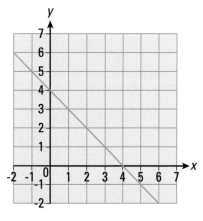

a Fill in the table for some of the points on the line.

(x, y)	(,)	(,)	(,)
$x + y$			

b Write an equation of the straight line.
c On the graph, draw the straight line that has the equation
$x + y = 6$.

Key Stage 3 2004 4–6 Paper 2

Percentages, ratio and proportion

Baked beans are one of the healthiest foods you can eat. One serving can contain 5% of your daily fibre, 23 % of your daily protein and 13 % of your daily calcium intake. They also have a high proportion of healthy carbohydrates.

What's the point? Food products must contain nutritional guidance on their label. You need to understand percentages to make informed choices about your diet.

 **Check in**

Level 4

1 A recipe for 10 rich scones uses 200 g of flour. Without using a calculator, work out the amount of flour needed to make

 a 20 scones   **b** 5 scones **c** 1 scone **d** 12 scones

2 In class 7C there are 3 boys for every 5 girls. There are 15 girls in class 7C. Work out the number of boys.

Level 5

3 Copy and complete these fraction and percentage equivalences.

 a $\dfrac{3}{4} = \dfrac{75}{100} = \square\%$ **b** $\dfrac{9}{10} = \dfrac{\square}{100} = \square\%$ **c** $\dfrac{2}{5} = \dfrac{\square}{100} = \square\%$

 d $\dfrac{11}{20} = \dfrac{\square}{\square} = \square\%$ **e** $\dfrac{7}{25} = \dfrac{\square}{\square} = \square\%$ **f** $\dfrac{21}{20} = \dfrac{\square}{\square} = \square\%$

- Change fractions, decimals and percentages into each other

Keywords
Decimal   Percentage
Fraction   Proportion

- A **proportion** is a part of the whole. You can use **percentages**, **fractions** and **decimals** to describe proportions.

These are the results of a Year 7 survey to find the average time spent on different activities during a typical school day. How much of the day is spent at school?

Activity	Time (h)
Sleeping	8
School	⑥
Eating	2
Homework	1.5
TV	3.5
Other	3
Total	㉔

Proportion of time spent at school $= \frac{6}{24}$

$$\frac{6}{24} = \frac{1}{4} = \frac{25}{100}$$

÷6   ×25

÷6   ×25

Simplify the fraction by ÷ 6.
Find an equivalent fraction out of 100 to give a percentage.

A Year 7 student spends a $\frac{1}{4}$, or 25%, of the day at school.

- You can compare any proportions by first writing them as fractions and then converting them to percentages.

A football manager wants to know who of two footballers is better at taking penalties.
Tyrone Shannon has scored 17 out of 24 penalties.
Steve St Clement has scored 11 out of 15 penalties.
Who is the best penalty taker?

Tyrone Shannon

$\frac{17}{24} = 17 \div 24$

$= 0.70833 \times 100\%$

$= 70.8\%$ (to 1 dp)

Steve St Clement

$\frac{11}{15} = 11 \div 15$

$= 0.73333 \times 100\%$

$= 73.3\%$ (to 1 dp)

Convert to a decimal by dividing the numerator by the denominator, then multiply by 100 to convert to a percentage.

Steve St Clement is better at taking penalties by 2.5%.

Exercise 11a

1 Write the proportion of each shape that is shaded.
Write each of your answers as a fraction in its simplest
form and a percentage (to 1 dp).

a   b   c

2 Answer these questions without using a calculator.
Express each of your answers as a fraction in its simplest
form and a percentage (to 1 dp).
a Harvey scores 42 out of 60 in his German test.
What proportion of the test did he answer correctly?
b Class 7C has 32 pupils. 20 of these pupils are boys.
What proportion of the class are girls?

3 Here are the exam results of some pupils in maths,
English and science.

Pupil name	Maths (40 marks)	English (50 marks)	Science (60 marks)
Ali	24	28	26
Bart	10	14	15
Chloe	19	31	22
Dan	38	40	48
Eva	7	15	12

In which subject did each student do best?
Explain your answers.

4 A football manager is comparing two footballers to see who
is better at taking penalties. Xang-Xua takes 20 penalties and
scores 17 times. Zinadine takes 15 penalties and scores
12 times. Which footballer is better at taking penalties?
Explain your answer.

Javed says that at his school there are more girls in every
class than at Gavin's school.
At Javed's school there are 1250 pupils and 723 of the pupils are girls.
At Gavin's school there are 1100 pupils and 685 of the pupils are girls.
Is Javed correct? Explain your answer.

- Find the values of quantities when they change in direct proportion to each other
- Use the unitary method with direct proportion

Keywords
Direct proportion
Unitary method

- Two quantities are in **direct proportion** if, when one of them increases, the other also increases by the same proportion.

The cost of text messages is in direct proportion to the number of text messages.

5 text messages cost 5 × £0.08 = £0.40
50 text messages cost 50 × £0.08 = £8.00

> **Text message charges**
> 1 text message £0.08
> 5 text messages £0.40
> 50 text messages £4.00

- You can solve simple problems involving direct proportion by multiplying or dividing both quantities by the same number.

example

Two pizzas cost £15. What is the cost of three pizzas?

. . . .

The number of pizzas has been multiplied by 1.5.
So you need to multiply the cost of the pizzas by 1.5.
Three pizzas cost £22.50.

×1.5 (2 pizzas   £15
       3 pizzas   £22.50) ×1.5

- You can also solve problems involving direct proportion by using the **unitary method.**

The unitary method involves finding the value of one unit of a quantity.

example

a 10 voice minutes cost 35p. What is the cost of 18 voice minutes?
b 3 cans of cola contain 417 calories. How many calories are there in 5 cans of cola?

. . . .

a Find the cost of 1 voice minute by dividing by 10. Then multiply the cost of 1 voice minute by 18.
18 voice minutes cost 63p.

÷10 (10 voice minutes   35p
      1 voice minutes   3.5p) ÷10
×18 (18 voice minutes   63p) ×18

b Find the calories in 1 can by dividing by 3. Then multiply the calories in 1 can by 5.
5 cans of cola contain 695 calories.

÷3 (3 cans of cola   417 calories
     1 can of cola   139 calories) ÷3
×5 (5 cans of cola   695 calories) ×5

Exercise 11b

1 Here are three offers for voice minutes on a mobile phone. In which of these offers are the numbers in direct proportion? In each case explain and justify your answers.

a

Voice minutes	Cost (£)
1	£0.05
5	£0.50
20	£1.00

b

Voice minutes	Cost (£)
5	£0.19
25	£0.95
100	£3.80

c

Voice minutes	Cost (£)
20	£0.90
50	£2.10
100	£3.70

2 Use direct proportion to solve these problems.

a Three bars of chocolate cost £1.40.
What is the cost of six bars of chocolate?

b 400 g of cheese contains 148 g of fat.
How many grams of fat are there in 600 g of cheese?

c 20 text messages cost 90p.
What is the cost of 50 text messages?

d A recipe for two people uses 250 g of potato.
How much potato is needed for three people?

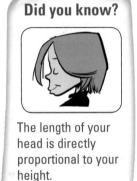

Did you know?

The length of your head is directly proportional to your height.

3 Use direct proporation to solve these problems.

a 5 litres of water costs £1.35. What is the cost of 8 litres?

b £1 is worth 10.80 Danish Kroner.
How much is £2.50 in Danish Kroner?

c 24 litres of petrol costs £21.72.
What is the cost of 38 litres of petrol?

d 200 voice minutes cost £4.40.
What is the cost of 45 voice minutes?

e There is a total of 1280 MB of memory on five identical memory sticks. How much memory is there on 11 memory sticks?

f A recipe for five people uses 800 g of rice. How much rice is needed to make the recipe for eight people?

activity

a Copy and complete this conversion table.
b Find five real-life distances given in miles or kilometres (e.g. from Paris to London) and use your table to convert them to kilometres or miles.

Miles	Kilometres (km)
1	
	4
5	8
10	
16	
	150

- Simplify ratios and use ratios in problems and with maps

Keywords
Compare   Scale
Ratio   Simplify

- You can **compare** the size of two or more quantities by writing them as a **ratio**.

  2 pink beads to 1 blue bead = 2 : 1

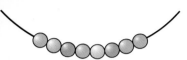

- You **simplify** a ratio by dividing both parts of the ratio by the same number.

---

example

Write each of these ratios in its simplest form.

a 45 : 150   **b** 9 : 18 : 36   **c** 2 m : 50 cm

. . . .

First find the largest number that divides into all parts of the ratio.

a
$\div 15 \begin{array}{c} 45 : 150 \\ 3 : 10 \end{array} \div 15$

b
$\div 9 \begin{array}{c} 9 : 18 : 36 \\ 1 : 2 : 4 \end{array} \div 9$

c
$\div 50 \begin{array}{c} 200 : 50 \\ 4 : 1 \end{array} \div 50$

Change both quantities to the same units.

2 m : 50 cm = 200 cm : 50 cm

- You can solve problems involving ratios by multiplying both sides of the ratio by the same number.

---

example

The ratio of boys to girls in a school is 8 : 9. There are 464 boys at the school. How many girls are there?

The ratio tells you that, for every eight boys, there are nine girls.

. . . .

8 has been multiplied by 58 to get 464.
Multiply 9 by 58 to find the number of girls.
There are 522 girls in the school.

boys : girls

$\times 58 \begin{array}{c} 8 : 9 \\ 464 : 522 \end{array} \times 58$

- You use ratios when you are interpreting maps or diagrams drawn to **scale**.

---

example

A map has a scale of 1 : 5000. What distance does 4 cm on the map represent in real life?

The ratio tells you that 1 cm on the map represents 5000 cm in real life.

. . . .

You need to multiply by 4.
Multiply 5000 by 4 to find the distance in real life.
The real-life distance = 20 000 cm = 200 m

map : real life

$\times 4 \begin{array}{c} 1 : 5000 \\ 4 \text{ cm} : 20\,000 \text{ cm} \end{array} \times 4$

Exercise 11 c

1 Write each of these ratios in its simplest form.

   a 4 : 10   **b** 14 : 18   **c** 36 : 132

   d 25 : 175   **e** 6 : 8 : 10   **f** 16 : 40 : 24

   g 60 cm : 1 m   **h** 45 mm : 6 cm   **i** 80p : £2

   j 1700 g : 3 kg   **k** 4 h : 80 min   **l** 75p : £1.75

2 Give your answer as a ratio in its simplest form.

   a A recipe requires 250 g of flour for every 200 g of butter.
      What is the ratio of flour to butter?

   b Sam earns £225 a week. Thelma earns £375 a week. What is
      the ratio of Sam's weekly wage to Thelma's weekly wage?

3 **a** At a swimming club the ratio of boys to girls is 7 : 4.
      There are 56 boys at the club. How many girls are there?

   b In a school the ratio of teachers to students is 3 : 44.
      If there are 1144 students at the school, how many
      teachers are there?

   c The main ingredients in a recipe are mushrooms, kidney
      beans and onions, in the ratio 6 : 5 : 3 by weight. If the
      onions weigh 360 g, how many grams of mushrooms and
      kidney beans are needed?

4 A map has a scale of 1 : 10 000.

   a What is the distance in real life of a measurement of
      7 cm on the map?

   b What is the distance on the map of a measurement
      of 5000 m in real life?

5 A map has a scale of 1 : 25 000.

   a What is the distance in real life of a measurement of
      4 cm on the map?

   b What is the distance on the map of a measurement
      of 2 km in real life?

6 The angles in a triangle are in the ratio 1 : 3 : 6.
   Calculate the size of the three angles.

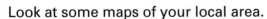

Investigation

Look at some maps of your local area.
What are the scales used on the maps?
Which map shows your local area in more detail?

- Divide a quantity into a given ratio

- You can divide a quantity in a given **ratio** by using the **unitary method.**

  The unitary method finds the value of one unit of a quantity.

- You can check your answer by **simplifying** the two parts of your answer to check the ratio, and then adding the two parts together to check the total.

---

example

Karen and Phil share a 350 g bar of chocolate in the ratio 2 : 5. How much chocolate do they each receive?

· ·

Splitting the chocolate in the ratio 2 : 5 means that the bar has to be divided into 7 equal parts, 2 parts for Karen and 5 parts for Phil.

350 g

$\div 7 \left(\begin{array}{cc} \text{7 parts} & \text{350 g} \\ \text{1 part} & \text{50 g} \end{array}\right) \div 7$

Each of the parts weighs 50 g.

Add the two parts of the ratio to find the number of equal parts.

Karen gets 2 parts.   Phil gets 5 parts.

$\times 2 \left(\begin{array}{cc} \text{1 part} & \text{50 g} \\ \text{2 parts} & \text{100 g} \end{array}\right) \times 2$ $\times 5 \left(\begin{array}{cc} \text{1 part} & \text{50 g} \\ \text{5 parts} & \text{250 g} \end{array}\right) \times 5$

Karen receives 100 g and Phil receives 250 g.
Check your answer by simplifying.

Karen's share : Phil's share

$\div 50 \left(\begin{array}{c} \text{100 g : 250 g} \\ \text{2 : 5} \end{array}\right) \div 50$

Check your answer by adding.
100 g + 250 g = 350 g
Both checks are correct, so the answer is correct.

Exercise 11d

1 Zac picks some strawberries. He shares out 20 strawberries between himself and his brother in the ratio 2 : 3.
How many strawberries do they each receive?

2 Divide each of these quantities in the ratio given in brackets.
   a £80 (3 : 5)   b 85 cm (2 : 3)   c 128 MB (3 : 5)
   d 171 kg (4 : 5)   e 154 seconds (5 : 6)   f £208 (5 : 11)

3 a Brenda downloads 65 music tracks from the Internet. She groups them into pop and rock, and finds that they are in the ratio 5 : 8. How many pop tracks has she downloaded? How many rock tracks has she downloaded?

   b Danielle and Eve eat a bunch of grapes together in the ratio 4 : 5. There are 72 grapes in the bunch.
     How many grapes do they each eat?
   c Felix and Garfield are two cats. They eat 400 g of catfood a day between them in the ratio 7 : 9.
     How much catfood do they each eat in a day?

4 Ciaron is given £46 for his birthday. He decides to spend his money on a top-up card for his mobile phone and a new computer game. The computer game costs more than the top-up card. He spends the money in the ratio 3 : 5.
How much does the computer game cost? Give your answer to an appropriate degree of accuracy.

5 Divide each of these quantities in the ratio given in brackets.
   a 60p (2 : 3 : 7)   b 135 km (2 : 3 : 4)
   c 256 MB (1 : 2 : 5)   d 3410 g (2 : 4 : 5)

6 In a school census, Kieran counts the number of boys, girls and adults at his school, and he finds that they are in the ratio 6 : 7 : 1. There are 1190 people at Kieran's school.
How many adults are there at Kieran's school?

challenge

Gordon is a gardener. He makes a compost heap from paper, old vegetables and horse manure in the ratio 3 : 4 : 1. He has 10 kg of old vegetables.
a How much paper does he need?
b How much horse manure does he need?
c What is the total weight of his compost heap?

- Know the difference between ratio and proportion
- Know how to find and use ratios and proportions in problems

Keywords
Proportion
Ratio

- It is important to understand the relationship between ratio and proportion.

example

On this 1 m ruler, 40 cm is painted pink, 50 cm is painted blue and 10 cm is painted yellow.

Find **a** the ratio of pink : blue : yellow
      b the proportion of the stick that is each colour.

For every 4 cm of pink there is 5 cm of blue and 1 cm of yellow.

a   pink : blue : yellow
        40 cm : 50 cm : 10 cm

         ÷10 ⟍   ⟋ ÷10

           4   :   5   :   1

b   ÷20
            $\frac{40}{100} = \frac{2}{5}$
                   ÷20

$\frac{2}{5}$, or 40%, of the rule is pink.

The whole ruler is 40 cm pink + 50 cm blue + 10 cm yellow = 100 cm long.
40 cm is shaded pink.

- You can divide a quantity in a given ratio by using the relationship between ratio and proportion.

	pink : blue : yellow	
Ratio	4 : 5 : 1	
Proportion	$\frac{4}{10}$ $\frac{5}{10}$ $\frac{1}{10}$	

- A ratio compares the size of the parts.

- Proportion compares the size of the part with the whole.

example

Karen, Phil and Gerry share a 350 g bar of chocolate in the ratio 2 : 1 : 4. How much chocolate did Karen receive?

There are 2 + 1 + 4 = 7 equal parts altogether.
Splitting the chocolate in the ratio 2 : 1 : 4 means that Karen receives $\frac{2}{7}$ of the chocolate, Phil receives $\frac{1}{7}$ of the chocolate and Gerry receives $\frac{4}{7}$ of the chocolate.

Karen receives $\frac{2}{7}$ of 350 g = $\frac{2 \times 350}{7} = \frac{700}{7} = 100$ g

Think of multiplying by $\frac{1}{7}$ as dividing by 7.

Exercise 11e

1 For each of these diagrams, write
  i the ratio of yellow pieces to blue pieces (in its simplest form)
  ii the proportion of the shape shaded yellow (as a fraction in its simplest form).

a

b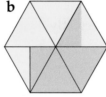

c

2 Calculate
  a $\frac{2}{5}$ of 15 MB
  b $\frac{3}{8}$ of £32
  c $\frac{4}{5}$ of $80
  d $\frac{1}{4}$ of 48 min
  e $\frac{7}{9}$ of 207 m
  f $\frac{2}{7}$ of 364 days

3 a Divide £90 in the ratio 3 : 2.
  b Divide 208 cm in the ratio 3 : 5.
  c Divide 369 pupils in the ratio 2 : 7.
  d Divide £2.86 in the ratio 2 : 7 : 4.
  e Divide 1800 in the ratio 1 : 2 : 6.
  f Divide £448 in the ratio 5 : 2 : 7.

4 In a class of 30 pupils, there are 18 girls.
  a Write the ratio of boys to girls in the class.
  b Write the proportion of the class who are boys.

5 Harvey shared some money between his two children, Velma and Madison. He gave $\frac{5}{8}$ of the money to Madison. What is the ratio of Madison's money to Velma's money?

6 a At a skiing club the members are classified as beginner, intermediate and advanced. The ratio of beginners : intermediates : advanced is 4 : 3 : 2. There are 72 members of the club. How many intermediate skiers are there?

  b To make brown paint you mix 13 litres of green paint with 6 litres of red paint and 1 litre of blue paint. How many litres of each colour do you need to make 10 litres of brown paint?
  c Vasquez, Pia and Carlos share £10 in the ratio 6 : 8 : 11.

puzzle

Two runners start running a race around a 400 m track. One runner is much faster than the other runner. The ratio of their speeds is 5 : 7. At what distance into the race does the faster runner overtake the slower runner?

11a

1 Answer these questions without using a calculator.
Express each of your answers as a fraction in its lowest
form and as a percentage.
   a Jayne scores 35 out of 40 in her English test.
      What proportion of the test did she answer correctly?
   b Class 7C has 36 pupils, of which 27 are boys.
      What proportion of the class are boys?

2 Lola put £230 into a savings account. After one year the
   interest was £11. Angelina put £400 into a savings account.
   After one year the interest was £19. Who had the better rate of
   interest? Explain your answer.

11b

3 Use direct proportion to solve these.
   a 30 text messages cost £1. What is the cost of 15 text messages?
   b Three litres of fruit juice costs £2.10. What is the cost of five litres?
   c £1 is worth 2.2 Swiss Francs. How much is £4.50 in
      Swiss Francs?
   d Liam's computer can download 3.6 MB of data in 30 seconds.
      How much data can the computer download in 12 seconds?
   e 50 voice minutes costs £1.20. What is the cost of
      85 voice minutes?
   f A recipe for eight people uses 1 kg of potatoes. How much
      potato is needed to make the recipe for six people?

11c

4 Write each of these ratios in its simplest form.
   a 6 : 10   b 14 : 21 : 35   c 18 : 27
   d 56 : 28 : 42 e 45 cm : 1 m   f 88p : £2
   g 36p : £2.16   h 1100 g : 2 kg   i 2 h : 90 min

5 a At a music club the ratio of boys to girls is 3 : 5.
      There are 15 boys at the club. How many girls are there?
   b A model ship is built to a scale of 1 : 24.
      The real ship is 38.4 m long. How long is the model?

6 A map has a scale of 1 : 2000.
   a What is the distance in real life of a measurement of 6 cm on the map?
   b What is the distance on the map of a measurement of 200 m in real life?

7 Divide each of these quantities in the given ratio

    a £70   3 : 4   **b** 240 cm   5 : 7

    c 90p   2 : 3 : 4   **d** 38 km   4 : 7 : 8

    e 512 MHz 1 : 3 : 4   **f** 2.8 kg   1 : 2 : 4

8 a Celia is given £65 for her birthday. She decides to spend her
    money on a top-up card for her mobile phone and a new
    DVD. The DVD costs less than the top-up card. She spends
    the money in the ratio 3 : 10. How much does the DVD cost?

   b Tom, Aftab and Neil play for the same rugby team. In a
    game, Tom scores 6 points, Aftab scores 10 points and Neil
    scores 14 points. They win the game and decide to share a
    150 g bar of chocolate in the ratio of the points they scored.
    How much chocolate does each boy receive?

   c Two horses eat 4 kg of food a day between them in the
    ratio 3 : 5. How much food do they each eat in a day?

9 Simon leaves some money to his three grandchildren.
  Dervla receives £24, Caitlan receives £30 and Claire receives £36.

   a Write the ratio of
    Dervla's money: Caitlan's money: Claire's money.

   b Write the proportion of the money that Simon gave
    to Claire.

10 In a school of 480 students, there are 248 girls.
   a Write the ratio of boys to girls in the school.
   b Write the proportion of the students who are boys.

11 Catherine shares out some strawberries between
  herself and her two friends, Samina and Skye.
  Catherine gets six strawberries, Samina gets eight
  strawberries and Skye gets ten strawberries.

   a Write the ratio of Catherine's share to Samina's
    share to Skye's share of the strawberries.

   b Write the proportion of the strawberries that
    Samina received.

Key indicators
- Compare percentages, fractions and decimals **Level 5**
- Solve problems using ratio and direct proportion **Level 6**

Level 6

1 Part of a recipe for apple crumble is shown. The recipe serves 2 people. Calculate the quantities of apples, flour and butter needed for 5 people.

Apple crumble
Serves 2 people
150 g of apples
180 g of flour
50 g of butter

Vishal's answer ✔

Vishal finds what 1 person needs first

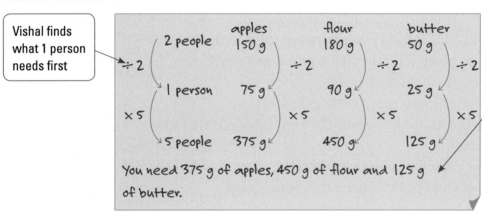

Vishal checks that flour is the largest answer and butter is the smallest answer

Level 6

2 a In this design, the ratio of grey to black is 3 : 1

What percentage of the design is black?

b In this design, 60% is grey and the rest is black.

What is the ratio of grey to black?
Write your ratio in its simplest form.

Key Stage 3 2007 4–6 Paper 1

12 Algebra

Expressions and equations

People have always asked questions to find out answers. Now we use search engines on the Internet to find answers. In fact, Google receives 37 billion search requests each month!

What's the point? You discover the unknown when you solve an equation.

✓ Check in

1 Evaluate each of these expressions.

   a $-2 + 10$ **b** $-4 - 8$ **c** $9 - -4$ **d** $-3 + -10$

   e -4×6 **f** $-15 + \sqrt{9}$ **g** 2×-8 **h** $18 - \sqrt{16}$

2 Match these expressions in words with one given in symbols.

Words	Symbols
I think of a number, double it and add 5	$x^2 + 5$
I think of a number, multiply it by itself, then add 5	$2(x + 5)$
I think of a number, multiply it by 5 then square it	$5x^2$
I think of a number, add 5 then double it	$(5x)^2$
I think of a number, multiply it by itself then by 5	$2x + 5$

3 Simplify each of these expressions where possible.

   a $4x + 9y + 2x - y$ **b** $3x^2 + 5x + 7x$ **c** $10ab + 2ba$

   d $14m + 7$ **e** $5t - t$ **f** $x^2 + x^2$

4 Expand these expressions, simplifying where possible.

   a $3(x + 9)$ **b** $5(y - 4)$ **c** $m(m + 3)$

   d $x(y + z)$ **e** $2(x + 9) + 4(x - 2)$

Level 5

Level 6

- Substitute numbers into an expression to find its value

Keywords
BIDMAS   Expression
Evaluate   Substitute

p. 86
- If you know the value of an unknown, you can **substitute** it into an **expression** to work out the expression's value.

---

example

Evaluate

a $3(a - 7)$ when $a = 9$

b $3m - 2n$ when $m = 6$ and $n = -4$.

· ·

a $3(a - 7) = 3 \times (9 - 7)$

$= 3 \times 2$

$= 6$

b $3m - 2n = 3 \times 6 - 2 \times (-4)$

$= 18 - (-8)$

$= 18 + 8$

$= 26$

Evaluate means 'work out the value of'.

Remember **BIDMAS** – make sure you do the calculations in the correct order.

In part **b**, n is negative, so you will need to take great care.

- Squaring a negative number gives a positive answer.

$(-4)^2$ means $(-4) \times (-4) = 16$.

- Cubing a negative number gives a negative answer.

$(-4)^3$ means $(-4) \times (-4) \times (-4) = -64$.

---

example

Find the value of **a** $2y^2$ and **b** $y^3 + 2$, given that $y = -3$.

· ·

a I think of a number, square it, then multiply by two.

$2y^2 = 2 \times (-3)^2$

$= 2 \times 9$

$= 18$

b I think of a number, cube it, then add two.

$y^3 + 2 = (-3)^3 + 2$

$= -27 + 2$

$= -25$

Write negative numbers in brackets.

Exercise 12a

1 Given that $p = 4$, find pairs of expressions with equal values. For the odd one out, suggest your own expression that would give an equal value.

$2p + 4$	$2p^2$	$3(p - 2)$
p^3	$(2p)^2$	$3p - 2$
$4p - 10$	$16 - p$	$4(p + 4)$

2 Given that $a = 3$, $b = -2$ and $c = -5$, find the value of

a $4a + b$ **b** c^2 **c** b^3 **d** $2(a + c)$

e $3(a - b)$ **f** $3a + 2c$ **g** $2b - c$ **h** $4a^2$

i ab **j** $bc + 1$ **k** $ac - 2$ **l** $12 - ac$

3 **a** Evaluate $3(x + 4)$ when $x = 7$.

   b Expand $3(x + 4)$ and substitute $x = 7$ into the resulting expression.

   c Compare your answers to **a** and **b**. What do you notice and why?

   d Repeat parts **a** and **b** for $2(y - 3)$ when $y = -5$.

4 Where possible, simplify each of these expressions by collecting like terms. Then find the value of each expression, given that $m = 4$ and $n = -2$.

   a $2m + 5m - 4m + m$ **b** $2mn + 7nm$

   c $8m + 9n - 6m - 11n$ **d** $3m^2 + 7m + 2m^2 - 4m$

   e $4n + 6$ **f** $n^2 + n^2$

5 **a** Use the formula $C = 50 - 4b$ to find the value of C when b is 3.

   b Explain why this formula can be used to find the change from £50 when books costing £4 each are purchased.

   c Substitute $b = 15$ into this formula. What does your answer mean in real life?

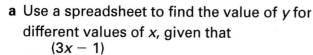

ICT

a Use a spreadsheet to find the value of y for different values of x, given that
$y = \dfrac{(3x - 1)}{x}$.

b Which value of x gives $y = 2.6$?

c Explain why x cannot be equal to zero.

- Simplify simple algebraic expressions and find common factors of expressions

Keywords
Expression   Simplify
Like terms

You already know that you can **simplify expressions** involving addition and subtraction by collecting the **like terms**.

Cannot be simplified	Can be simplified
$6x - 8y$	$6x + 3x - 5x = 4x$
$3m + 5$	$2p + 3q - p + 7q = p + 10q$
$5x + 6x^2$	$x^2 + x^2 = 2x^2$

- You can also simplify expressions involving multiplication.
  - Sometimes all you need to do is remove the $\times$ sign.

    $4 \times w = 4w \qquad p \times q = pq$
  - For more complex expression, deal with the numbers first, then the letters.

    $3p \times 2p \times 5q = 3 \times p \times 2 \times p \times 5 \times q$
    $= (3 \times 2 \times 5) \times (p \times pq)$
    $= 30p^2q$

Remember that you can multiply in any order; the answer will be the same.

example

Find a simplified expression for the area of this pool.

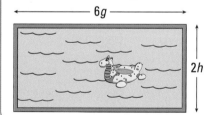

Area = length $\times$ width
$= 6g \times 2h$
$= 12gh$

example

Simplify this expression as fully as possible.

$8w \times 5w \times 7$

. . . .

$8w \times 5w \times 7 = 8 \times w \times 5 \times w \times 7$

$= (8 \times 5 \times 7) \times (w \times w)$ Separate numbers from letters.

$= 280\,w^2$

Exercise 12b

1 Expand and simplify each of these expressions.

a $3(a + 2)$

b $4(m + 1) + 3(m + 2)$

c $x(x + 2) + x(x - 3)$

d $2m(3m + 1)$

e $4g(2g + 7t)$

f $2p(p^2 + 3p)$

2 Decide whether each of these expressions is true or false. Correct those that are false.

$a \times b = ab$	$2m \times 3n = 5mn$	$5r \times 6r = 30r^2$	$5p \times 4q = 5p4q$

$3t \times 4t = 12t$	$2a \times 4ab = 8(ab)^2$	$5p^2 \times 4p = 20p^3$	$3x \times 2y \times 4z = 24xyz$

3 Simplify each of these expressions as fully as possible.

a $3 \times r \times 4 \times t$

b $2t \times 5$

c $3m \times 2n$

d $2a \times 3b \times 5c$

e $3g \times 2g$

f $5ab \times 4cd$

g $2b^2 \times 3b$

h $2d^2 \times 3d^2$

4 Didier got some of his simplification homework wrong. In each case, explain his mistake and write the correct answer.

a $y^2 + y^2 = y^4$ ✗

b $2p \times 3p = 6p$ ✗

c $5m + 1 = 6m$ ✗

d $3p \times 2q = $ Not like terms ✗

e $5x + 2y - 8x + y = 3x + 3y$ ✗

---

puzzle

In each grid, the top tile contains the sum of the two given expressions and the bottom tile their product.

a Copy and complete these grids.

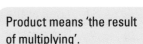

Product means 'the result of multiplying'.

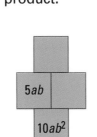

$3x$	$2y$		$4m$	$2n$		x^2	x^2		$5ab$	

$10ab^2$

b Design some grids of your own.

c Would any grids give the same answer in the addition tile as in the multiplication tile?

- Simplify algebraic expressions involving division of expressions

Keywords
Cancelling   *Inverse*
Expression   *Simplify*

Algebraic **expressions** involving division are written as fractions. Like numerical fractions, they can be **simplified** by **cancelling**.

- You can simplify expressions involving division.
  - Sometimes all you need to do is write the expression as a fraction, rather than using the ÷ sign.

    $$6 \div a = \frac{6}{a} \qquad c \div d = \frac{c}{d}$$

  - As with multiplication, deal with the numbers first, then the letters.
  - You can only cancel factors.

    $$\frac{3x^2}{3x} = \frac{x^2}{x}$$

    Look at the numbers first. 3 is a factor of $3x^2$ and can be cancelled.

    $$x = x$$

    Then look at the letters. x is a factor of x^2 and can be cancelled.

    Take care if there is an addition or subtraction sign.

    $$\frac{x+3}{3}$$

    This cannot be simplified.
    3 is not a factor of $x + 3$.

'Multiply by 3' and 'Divide by 3' cancel each other out because division is the **inverse** of multiplication.

'Add 3' and 'Divide by 3' do not cancel each other out because division is not the inverse of addition.

example

Simplify each of these expressions.

a $\dfrac{24a}{3a}$ **b** $\dfrac{12ab^2}{6b}$

. . . .

a $\dfrac{24a}{3a} = \dfrac{8a}{a}$ Look at the numbers first.
3 is a factor of $24a$.

$= 8$ Then look at the letters.
a is a factor of $8a$.

b $\dfrac{12ab^2}{6b} = \dfrac{2ab^2}{b}$ Look at the numbers first.
6 is a factor of $12ab^2$.

$= 2ab$ Then look at the letters.
b is a factor of $2ab^2$.

Exercise 12b²

1 Simplify each of these expressions as fully as possible.

a $6t \div 3$ b $2p \div 12$ c $9b \div 3$ d $\dfrac{6m}{2}$

e $\dfrac{15h}{3h}$ f $\dfrac{20mn}{5n}$ g $\dfrac{12abc}{4bc}$ h $\dfrac{45x^2}{5x}$

2 Explain why $\dfrac{4m}{4}$ simplifies to give m, but $\dfrac{m+4}{m}$ cannot be simplified.

3 Simplify

a $\dfrac{30x + 10}{5}$ b $\dfrac{6y - 9}{3}$ c $\dfrac{10p + 50q}{10}$ d $\dfrac{x^2 + 2x}{x}$

4 Write a simplified expression for each description.

a 12 people win a lottery syndicate. If the prize money is £$36ab$, how much do they each get?

b A rectangle has an area of $18a^2b$ and a height of $6a$. What is its width?

5 Amanda got some of her simplification homework wrong. Mark her work. If an answer is wrong, explain her mistake and write the correct answer.

a $5a \div b = \dfrac{5a}{b}$ b $12 \div 3x = 4x$

c $\dfrac{22p + 4}{2} = 11p + 2$ d $\dfrac{m + 2}{2} = m$

e $\dfrac{5x + 10y}{10} = \dfrac{5x}{10} + 7$ f $\dfrac{18f^3g}{6gh} = \dfrac{2f^3}{h}$

g $\dfrac{25xy^2}{10xy} = \dfrac{5y}{2}$

Find pairs which simplify to give the same expression.

$\dfrac{24ab^2}{8ab}$ $\dfrac{2a+4b}{2}$ $\dfrac{15a^2b}{5a}$ $\dfrac{a+2b}{1}$

$\dfrac{12ab^2}{4b}$ $2(4a+3b)$ $\dfrac{9ab}{3a}$ $\dfrac{16a+12b}{2}$

12c Solving equations

- Solve equations with the unknown quantity on only one side of the equation

- An **equation** is different from an **expression** because it contains an equals sign. The two sides are equal.

- When you **solve** an equation, you find the unknown value. This is called the **solution** to the equation.

- To solve an equation, you need to undo each operation in turn.

  To 'undo' an operation, use the **inverse**.

  Addition and subtraction are inverse operations.

  +2 'undoes' −2 and vice versa.

  Multiplication and division are inverse operations.

  ×3 'undoes' ÷3 and vice versa.

  As in 'pass the parcel', the layer that was added last is the first to be taken off.

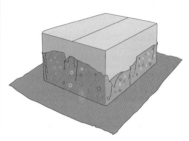

example

Solve the equation $3x - 1 = 20$.

. . . .

$3x - 1 = 20$	The equation reads 'I think of a number, multiply it by 3 and subtract 1 to get 20'.
$3x = 21$	So add 1 ...
$x = 7$	... and divide by 3 on both sides.

Make sure you always do the same to both sides of the equation.

This method also works for equations that look very difficult.

example

Solve the equation $\dfrac{2(3x^2 + 8)}{5} = 8$.

. . . .

$\dfrac{2(3x^2 + 8)}{5} = 8$	The equation reads 'I think of a number, square it, multiply it by 3, add 8, multiply by 2 and divide by 5 to get 8'.
$2(3x^2 + 8) = 40$	Multiply both sides by 5.
$3x^2 + 8 = 20$	Divide both sides by 2.
$3x^2 = 12$	Subtract 8 from both sides.
$x^2 = 4$	Divide both sides by 3.
$x = 2$	Take the square root of both sides.

Taking the square root is the inverse of squaring.

Exercise 12c

1 Solve these equations. You should find each answer somewhere in the coloured panel.

a $x + 2 = 10$
b $y - 4 = 9$
c $2z - 9 = 13$
d $3(a - 2) = 12$
e $\dfrac{b}{2} + 5 = 10$
f $x^2 = 100$
g $\dfrac{2(3x - 1)}{10} = 4$
h $2x^2 = 50$

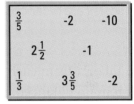

5	11	8
10	6	
13		7

2 Solve these equations. You should find each answer somewhere in the coloured panel.

a $4x + 12 = 8$
b $8(y - 2) = 4$
c $\dfrac{z}{5} + 7 = 5$
d $5p - 1 = 17$
e $3(q + 2) = 7$
f $5(s + 3) + 2 = 7$
g $10m + 6 = 12$
h $x^3 + 9 = 1$

$\frac{3}{5}$	-2	-10
$2\frac{1}{2}$	-1	
$\frac{1}{3}$	$3\frac{3}{5}$	-2

3 Aminah says that $3(x + 4) = 30$ should be solved by first expanding the brackets. Jack says she is wrong. Show that they are both correct.

4 Cristina solved some equations but all of her answers are wrong. Explain her mistake in each case.

a $2x + 3 = 12$
 $2x = 15$
 $x = 7\frac{1}{2}$ ✗

b $2x - 1 = 20$
 $x - 1 = 10$
 $x = 11$ ✗

c $6x - 1 = 2$
 $6x = 3$
 $x = 2$ ✗

d $4x + 5 = -2$
 $4x = 3$
 $x = \frac{3}{4}$ ✗

5 For each of these situations, answer the question by writing and solving an equation.

a When I think of a number, multiply it by 7 and subtract 5, I get 16. What is my number?

b My uncle is three times as old as me and my cousin is one year younger than me. The sum of our ages is 59. How old are we?

challenge

a 'Solve' this equation to find x.

  $t(px - q) + m = r$

b In pairs, make up some similar equations of your own and swap them with each other.

Your answer will not be a number, but will have the other letters in it.

- Solve equations with the unknown quantity on both sides of the equation

Keywords
Equation
Solve

- To **solve** an **equation** with the unknown on both sides, first remove the unknown from one side.

Imagine that the equation $8x + 3 = 2x + 9$ is on a set of scales.

The two sides of the equation are equal, so the scales are balanced.

If you take $2x$ from each side, the scales remain balanced.

If you just took $2x$ from the right hand side, the scales would not remain balanced – the right hand side would be lighter.

- If both the terms containing the unknown are positive, subtract the smaller term from both sides.

- You can then solve the equation in the same way as an equation with only one unknown.

Solve these equations.

a $8x + 3 = 2x + 9$ **b** $4(x - 1) = 2(4x + 8)$

a $8x + 3 = 2x + 9$
    $6x + 3 = 9$ $2x$ is smaller than $8x$, so subtract $2x$.
    $6x = 6$ Subtract 3.
    $x = 1$ Divide by 6.

b $4(x - 1) = 2(4x + 8)$ First expand the brackets.
    $4x - 4 = 8x + 16$ $4x$ is smaller than $8x$, so subtract $4x$.
    $-4 = 4x + 16$
    $-20 = 4x$ Subtract 16.
    $x = -5$ Divide by 4.

Remember: make sure you always do the same to both sides of the equation.

Be careful with negatives. After you subtract $4x$ from both sides, you are left with -4 on the left hand side, not 4.

1 Solve these equations. You should find each answer somewhere in the coloured panel.

3	5	2
23	4	2

   a $7x + 1 = 4x + 7$ b $9y - 3 = 4y + 12$

   c $2z + 19 = 6z + 3$ d $a - 5 = 3a - 9$

   e $3(b + 1) = 4(b - 5)$ f $2(2c + 1) = 5c - 3$

2 Solve these equations.

   a $2x + 5 = 3x - 2$ b $3x + 1 = 5x - 7$ c $4x - 8 = 2x + 6$

   d $4x + 2 = 5x$ e $x + 6 = 7x - 12$ f $2x + 9 = 4x + 3$

   g $2(x - 7) = x - 4$ h $3x - 8 = 2(x + 1)$ i $3x - 7 = x + 11$

   j $5x - 2 = 7x - 6$ k $2x - 1 = 9x - 8$ l $2x - 1 = x + 1$

3 Solve these equations. You should find each answer somewhere in the coloured panel.

-1	-4	$7\frac{1}{2}$
-8	-16	$2\frac{1}{4}$

   a $8x - 1 = 6x + 14$ b $3(y - 4) = 5(y + 4)$

   c $7z - 5 = z - 11$ d $12a + 4 = 10a - 4$

   e $7b - 12 = 3(b - 1)$ f $\frac{3}{4}c + 1 = \frac{1}{4}c - 3$

4 For each of these situations, answer the question by writing and solving an equation.

   a I think of a number, multiply it by 7 and subtract 12 and I get the same answer as when I multiply the number by 2 and add 8. What is my number?

   b The diagram shows a rectangle. What is its length?

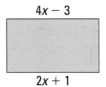

$4x - 3$

$2x + 1$

5 Two equations have been solved and the steps mixed up. Unscramble them.

$2x = 5$	$5x = 2$	$7x - 3 = 2x - 1$	$2x - 1 = 4$

$5x - 3 = -1$	$5x - 1 = 3x + 4$	$x = 2\frac{1}{2}$	$x = \frac{2}{5}$

   a Try out this 'Think of a number' problem, either on your own or in a pair, using different starting numbers.

   b What do you notice? Can you use algebra to explain your findings?

   c Now make up a similar puzzle of your own.

I think of a number,
- add 4
- double it
- add 10
- halve this
- then subtract 9.

12a

1 Given that $p = 4$, $q = -2$ and $r = -3$, evaluate these expressions.

a $3p + 7$ **b** pq **c** q^2 **d** $2q - r$

e $2pqr$ **f** r^3 **g** $\dfrac{qr}{p}$ **h** $\dfrac{p^2}{q}$

2 a Using the formula $C = 20 - 2m$, find the value of C when

i $m = 5$ **ii** $m = 12$ **iii** $m = -3$.

b Explain why the formula could be used to work out the change from a £20 note when some magazines, each costing £2, are purchased. Explain also why, in this case, your answers to parts **a ii** and **iii** no longer make sense.

12b

3 Simplify each of these expressions.

a $3 \times w$ **b** $p \times q$

c $2 \times a \times 3 \times b$ **d** $2m \times 4n$

e $5p \times 5p$ **f** $a \times 3b \times 4c$

g $3ab \times 4b$

4 Expand and simplify each of these expressions.

a $3(2p + 1) + 4(3p + 4)$

b $a(a + 4) + 2a(3a + 1)$

c $5(2x - 1) + 3(4 - 9x)$

d $x(x + 1) + x(2x + 2)$

12b²

5 Simplify each of these expressions.

a $\dfrac{12x}{6}$ **b** $\dfrac{24a}{6a}$ **c** $\dfrac{14abc}{7c}$

6 Explain why $\dfrac{10x}{5}$ can be simplified to $2x$, but $\dfrac{x + 10}{5}$ cannot be simplified to $x + 2$.

7 Explain why each expression simplifies to give $x + 3$.

a $\dfrac{2x + 6}{2}$ **b** $\dfrac{3x + 9}{3}$

c $\dfrac{6x + 18}{6}$ **d** $\dfrac{x + 3}{1}$

8 Solve these equations.

  a $3x - 1 = 8$ **b** $4x + 5 = 17$

  c $2(x - 3) = 8$ **d** $x^2 = 144$

  e $2x^2 = 32$ **f** $\dfrac{p}{4} - 1 = 2$

  g $\dfrac{3(2m - 1)}{9} + 2 = 3$ **h** $4t - 1 = -9$

9 For each of these situations, answer the question by writing and solving an equation.

  a I think of a number, double it and add 5. I get 1. What is my number?

  b I think of a number, subtract 4, multiply it by 3 and add 2. I get 20. What is my number?

  c I think of a number, multiply it by itself and then by 5. I get 80. What is my number?

  d The angles in a triangle are x, $x + 10$ and $x + 20$. What is the size of each angle?

  e The sum of my age five years ago, my age now and my age in four years time is 50. How old am I?

10 Solve these equations.

  a $6x - 2 = 2x + 10$ **b** $5y - 4 = 3y + 12$

  c $4z - 16 = 2z + 2$ **d** $4a + 27 = 9a - 8$

  e $3b - 5 = 7(b + 1)$ **f** $2(c + 4) = 3(c + 5)$

11 For each of these situations, answer the question by writing and solving an equation.

  a I think of a number, multiply it by 3 and subtract 4. This gives me the same answer as when I double the number and add 1. What is my number?

  b I think of a number, subtract 2 and multiply it by 5. This gives me the same answer as when I take 7 from the number and treble it. What is my number?

  c The area of each shape is equal. Find x and, hence, the dimensions of each shape.

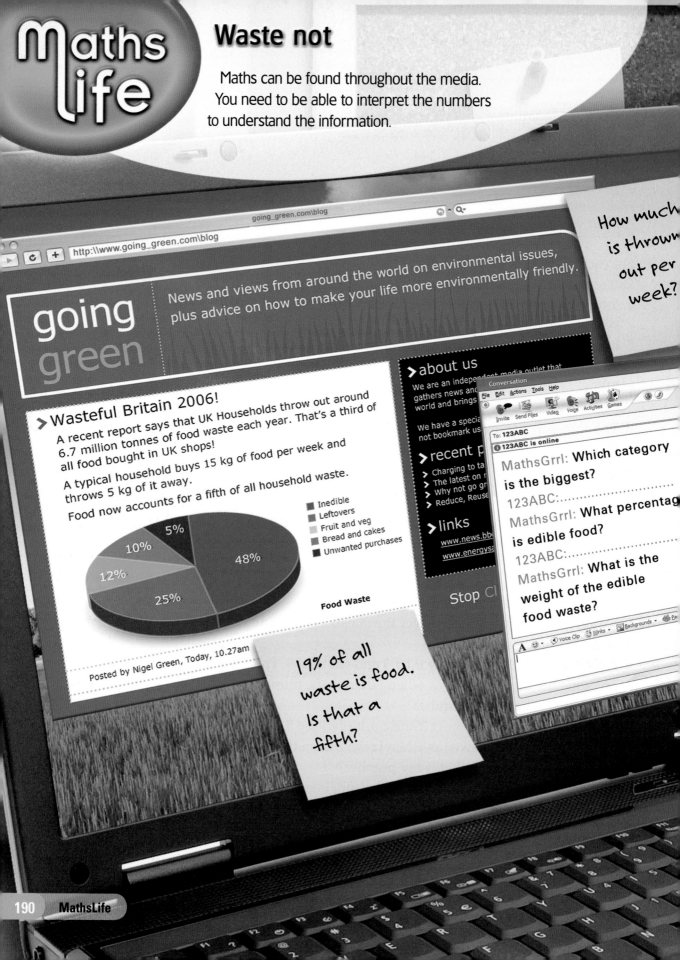

Maths Life

Waste not

Maths can be found throughout the media.
You need to be able to interpret the numbers
to understand the information.

going_green.com\blog

http:\\www.going_green.com\blog

going green

News and views from around the world on environmental issues,
plus advice on how to make your life more environmentally friendly.

> Wasteful Britain 2006!

A recent report says that UK Households throw out around
6.7 million tonnes of food waste each year. That's a third of
all food bought in UK shops!

A typical household buys 15 kg of food per week and
throws 5 kg of it away.

Food now accounts for a fifth of all household waste.

- Inedible
- Leftovers
- Fruit and veg
- Bread and cakes
- Unwanted purchases

5%
10%
12%
25%
48%

Food Waste

Posted by Nigel Green, Today, 10.27am

> about us

We are an independent media outlet that
gathers news and
world and brings

We have a special
not bookmark us

> recent p

- > Charging to ta
- > The latest on r
- > Why not go gr
- > Reduce, Reuse

> links

www.news.bb
www.energysa

Stop Cl

How much is thrown out per week?

19% of all waste is food. Is that a fifth?

Conversation

File Edit Actions Tools Help

Invite Send Files Video Voice Activities Games

To: 123ABC

123ABC is online

MathsGrrl: Which category is the biggest?

123ABC:............

MathsGrrl: What percentag is edible food?

123ABC:............

MathsGrrl: What is the weight of the edible food waste?

A ☺ ▾ Voice Clip Winks ▾ Backgrounds ▾ Pa

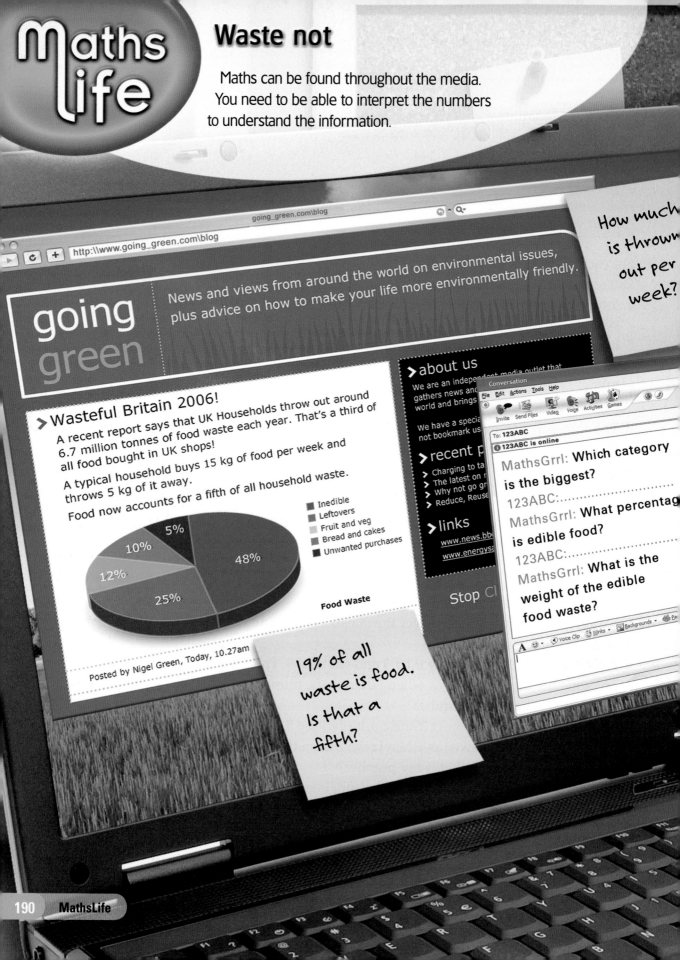

FOOD WASTE

What is the typical household?
I'll ask a random sample of neighbours to find out!

Food Waste questionaire
Number in household ....
Weight of food bought in each week ....
Weight of food thrown out each week ....

Is this a random sample?

Address	#34	#36	#38	#40	#42	#44
People in household	2	4	3	5		1
Weight of food bought	17 kg	28 kg	22 kg	18 kg	34 kg	8 kg
Weight of food thrown out		12 kg		5 kg	14 kg	2 kg
Waste per person	4 kg		3.5 kg		2 kg	

Now fill in the blank grey boxes above using
Total waste ÷ Total number of people = Waste per person

What weight of food did they eat?

What percentage of the food bought did they throw away?

What about composted food waste?

191

12 Summary

Key indicators
- Substitute integers (whole numbers) into simple formulas **Level 5**
- Use letter symbols to represent unknown numbers or variables **Level 5**
- Solve linear equations **Level 6**

Level 5

1 Solve these equations.

    a $4a + 3 = 9$
    b $3b - 1 = 11$

Level 6

    c $3c + 2 = c + 12$

Peter's answer ✔

Peter subtracts 3 from both sides then divides both sides by 4

Peter adds 1 to both sides then divides both sides by 3

Peter subtracts 2 from both sides, subtracts c from both sides then divides both sides by 2

Peter checks the answer:
$3 \times 5 + 2 = 5 + 12$
$15 + 2 = 17$

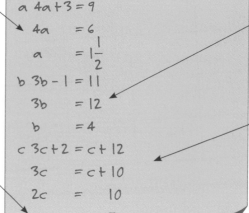

$$a \quad 4a + 3 = 9$$
$$4a \quad = 6$$
$$a \quad = 1\frac{1}{2}$$
$$b \quad 3b - 1 = 11$$
$$3b \quad = 12$$
$$b \quad = 4$$
$$c \quad 3c + 2 = c + 12$$
$$3c \quad = c + 10$$
$$2c \quad = 10$$
$$c \quad = 5$$

2 Look at the cube.
The area of a face of the cube is $9x^2$

    area $= 9x^2$

Write an expression for the total surface area of the cube.
Write your answer as simply as possible.

Key Stage 3 2007 4–6 Paper 1

13 Shape

Transformations and symmetry

Dancers follow precise instructions for how and where they should move across the dance floor. The choreographer writes step notation which tells the dancer what each foot should be doing when and also in what style.

What's the point? The dancers translate across the dance floor like a shape translates across a grid.

✓ Check in

Level 3

1 Jonathan is looking at photographs on a computer. He must click either 'rotate clockwise' or 'rotate anticlockwise' to see the photographs the correct way up. Write the correct instruction for these.

a 　　**b** 　　**c**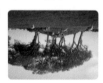

2 Name these quadrilaterals.

a 　　**b** 　　**c** 　　**d**

Level 5

3 Draw a set of axes from -5 to 5.
　a Plot these sets of coordinate pairs and join each set with a straight line.
　　i (-5, 1) (-3, 1) (0, 1) (2, 1) (4, 1)
　　ii (-2, 5) (-2, 2) (-2, -1) (-2, -3) (-2, -4)
　b Write the equations of the lines that you have drawn.
　c Write an alternative name for　　　**i** the *x*-axis　　　**ii** the *y*-axis

193

13a Reflection

- Reflect shapes in mirror lines to find their images

Keywords
Congruent   Object
Equidistant   Reflection
Image   Transformation
Mirror line

- A **transformation** moves a shape to a new position.

- A **reflection** is a type of transformation. Reflection 'flips' an **object** over a **mirror line**, to create an **image**.
The starting shape is called the object.
The image is the shape after the transformation.

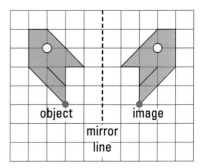

- The object and the image are **equidistant** from the mirror line.   Each dot (•) is 2 units from the mirror line.

- The object and the image are exactly the same size and shape. They are **congruent**.

---

example

Draw the reflection of the pink shape using the mirror line.

Mark each point of the image by counting squares.
For example, from point A to the mirror line is 3 squares down.
So from the mirror line to A′ (the image of A) is 3 squares across.
Then join the points to form the image.

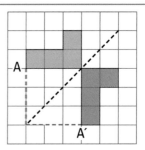

You can rotate the page to make the mirror line vertical.

- When a reflection is drawn on a coordinate grid, you can describe the mirror line using an equation.

---

example

a Reflect the blue shape in the line $x = 0$.
b Mark the equal angles and equal sides on the completed quadrilateral.
c State the name of the quadrilateral.

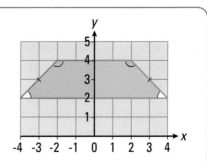

a The line $x = 0$ is the y-axis.
b The object and image are congruent, so the angles and lengths in the image are equal to the angles and lengths in the object.
c Isosceles trapezium.

Exercise 13a

1 Copy each diagram and reflect the shape in the mirror line.

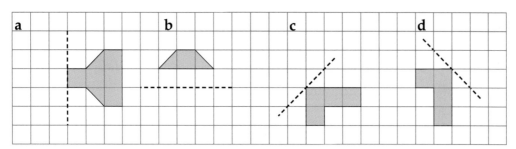

2 Copy this diagram.

    a Reflect the three coloured squares in one of the mirror lines.

    b Reflect the six squares in the other mirror line.

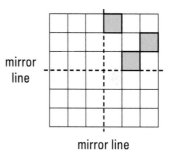

3 For each shape

    i copy the diagram and reflect the shape in the mirror line

    ii mark the equal angles and the equal sides on the completed shape

    iii state the name of the final shape.

a 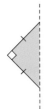   **b**    **c**    **d**

4 **a** Plot and join each of these sets of points in order on the same coordinate grid.

    i (0, 4), (3, 4), (3, 2), (4, 2), (4, 0), (3, 0), (3, -4) and (0, -4)

    ii (0, 1), (1, -1) and (0, -1)

    iii (0, -2), (1, -2), (1, -3) and (0, -3).

    iv (1, 1), (2, 1), (2, 2), (1, 2) and (1, 1).

    b Reflect the shapes using the y-axis as the mirror line.

a Place a mirror on these three squares to form each of these shapes.

b Draw other shapes that can be formed using this method.

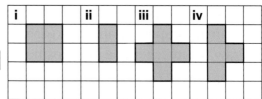

• Rotate shapes about a point to find their images

Keywords
Anticlockwise   Image
Centre of   Object
  rotation   Rotation
Clockwise   Transformati‹
Congruent   Turn

• A **rotation** is a type of **transformation**.

The blades on a wind turbine rotate around a fixed point.

• Rotation **turns** an **object** about a point, called the **centre of rotation**.

The centre of rotation (•) can be …

… on the edge   … inside   … or outside the shape.

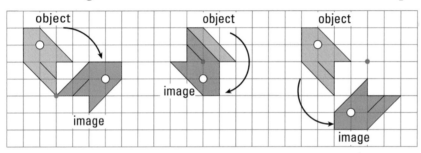

90° **clockwise**   180° clockwise   90° **anticlockwise**

Each point on the object, and its equivalent point on the image, are the same distance from the centre of rotation.

• The object and the **image** are **congruent**.

Congruent means 'exactly the same size and shape'.

• You describe a rotation by giving
  – the centre of rotation
  – the angle of rotation
  – the direction of turn, either clockwise or anticlockwise.

example

Draw the pink triangle after an anticlockwise rotation of 90° about (1, 1).

Lay some tracing paper over the diagram and trace the object.
Put the point of your pencil on the point (1, 1).
Rotate the paper 90° anticlockwise.
Draw the image in the new position.

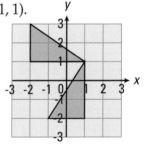

Exercise 13b

1 Copy and rotate each shape through the given angle using the dot as the centre of rotation.

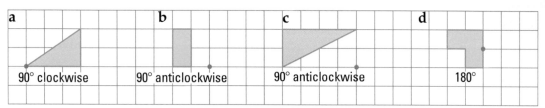

2 a Plot and join the coordinates (3, 0), (0, 0) and (0, 2) to form a triangle.
b State the name of the triangle.
c Rotate the triangle through 90° anticlockwise about (0, 0).
d Give the coordinates of the image.
e State two different transformations that will return the triangle to its original position.

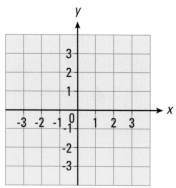

3 i Copy and rotate each triangle through 180°, using the dot as the centre of rotation.
ii Mark the equal angles and the equal sides on the quadrilaterals.
iii Give the name of the quadrilaterals.
State the names of three different types of quadrilaterals that cannot be formed by this method.

a 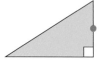   **b**   **c**   **d**

4 a Plot and join the coordinates in order to form a hexagon. (1, 2), (2, 2), (2, 4), (0, 4), (0, 3), (1, 3), (1, 2)
b Rotate the hexagon through 90° clockwise about (1, 1).
c Give the coordinates of the image.
d State two transformations that will return the hexagon to its original position.

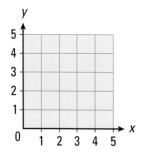

A tile in the shape of a rhombus is shown on isometric paper.
Rotate the tile through 60° or 120° about the vertices to give different patterns.

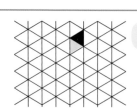

Vertices means 'corners'.

- Know about reflection symmetry and rotational symmetry
- Find all the symmetries of a shape

Keywords
Line of symmetry
Reflection symmetry
Rotate
Rotation symmetry
Symmetry

- A shape has **reflection symmetry** if it has a **line of symmetry**.

- A line of symmetry divides the shape into two identical halves.

You can find the line of symmetry by using a mirror or folding in half.

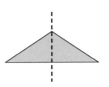 

Using a mirror   Folding

This butterfly has a line of symmetry.

- A shape has **rotation symmetry** if it **rotates** onto itself more than once in a full turn.

- The **order of rotation symmetry** is the number of times a shape looks exactly like itself in a complete turn.

A rectangle has rotation symmetry of order 2.

You can find the order of rotation symmetry using tracing paper.

example

State the order of rotation symmetry for a parallelogram.

Lay a piece of tracing paper over the parallelogram.
Trace the parallelogram.
Using the point of your pencil to hold the tracing paper down at the centre, rotate the tracing paper through 360° and count how many times the parallelogram and the tracing coincide.
The parallelogram has rotation symmetry of order 2.

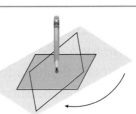

- A shape with rotation symmetry of order 1 has no rotation symmetry.   All shapes will look the same if rotated through 360°.

Exercise 13c

1 Copy each shape and draw the lines of symmetry.

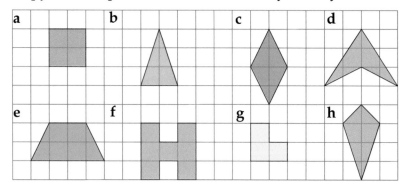

2 Copy each shape and state the order of rotation symmetry.

a   b   c   d

e   f   g   h

Did you know?

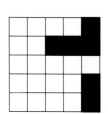

The Isle of Man has this symbol on its flag.

3 Combine these shapes to make
  a three shapes with only reflection symmetry
  b four shapes with only rotation symmetry
  c one shape that has both reflection and rotation symmetry.
  Draw the lines of symmetry on each of your shapes and/or state the order of rotation.

4 This 5 × 5 crossword grid is incomplete.
  Copy and complete the grid so that it has rotation symmetry of order 2.

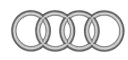

* Translate shapes and describe the size of a translation

Keywords
Congruent   Object
Image   Translation

* A **translation** is a type of transformation.
  A translation slides an **object**.

  The shape has been translated 4 units to the right and 1 up.
  Each vertex moves the same amount in a translation.

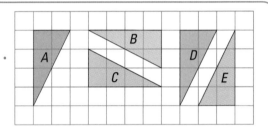

* The object and the **image** are **congruent**.

* You describe a translation by giving
  – the distance moved right or left, then
  – the distance moved up or down.

Congruent means 'exactly
the same size and shape'.

---

example

Which triangle is a translation of
triangle *A*?
· ·

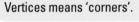

Triangle *D*
In a translation, the image and object look
the same, only the position changes. All the
other triangles have been rotated.

---

example

a Draw the triangle with vertices (3, 1) (3, 3) and (2, 1).
b Translate the triangle by 2 units to the left and 1 unit up.
c Give the coordinates of the vertices of the image.
d State the transformation that would return the
   triangle to its original position.
· ·

Vertices means 'corners'.

a, b Mark each point of the image by counting
     squares 2 left and 1 up. Draw the blue triangle.
c   (1, 2) (1, 4) and (0, 2).
d   A translation of 2 units to the right and 1 unit down.

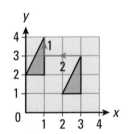

Exercise 13d

1 a Give the mathematical name of the
quadrilaterals in the diagram.
b List the shapes that are translations of shape A.
c List the shapes that are translations of shape B.

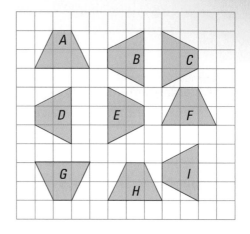

2 Triangle A is translated to triangle B.
a Give the coordinates of the red dot in triangle A.
b Give the coordinates of the red dot in triangle B.
c Describe fully the transformation of triangle A to triangle B.

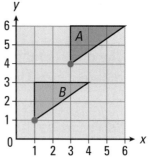

3 Describe these translations.

a C to B	**b** A to D
c D to A	**d** D to E
e A to E	**f** E to A
g B to C	**h** B to A
i E to D	**j** E to C

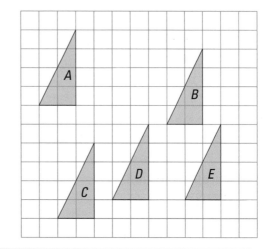

- Enlarge a shape using a positive whole number as a scale factor

Keywords
Enlargement   Scale
Image   factor
Object   Similar

- An **enlargement** is a type of transformation. Enlargement alters the size of an **object**.

- To enlarge an object, you multiply the lengths by the **scale factor**. The angles of the shape do not change.
  The shape has been enlarged by scale factor 2.
  Each length in the **image** is twice as long as the corresponding length in the object.

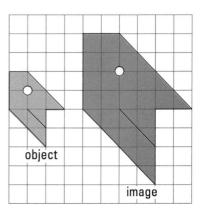

- The object and the image are the same shape but a different size. They are **similar**.

- You describe the size of an enlargement by giving the scale factor.

---

example

The blue triangle is an enlargement of the pink triangle. Calculate the scale factor.

. . . .

$3 \div 1 = 3$ The base of the image is 3 units, the base of the object is 1 unit.

$6 \div 2 = 3$ The height of the image is 6 units, the height of the object is 2 units.

The scale factor is 3.

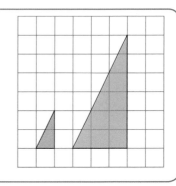

---

example

Draw an enlargement of the pink shape using a scale factor of 2.

. . . .

Start at one corner of the shape and work round, remembering that each length on the image is twice as long as the corresponding length on the object.

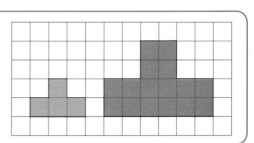

Exercise 13e

1 Here are two triangles.
  a Measure the angles A, D, B, E, C and F.
  b Are the triangles similar?
  c Calculate the scale factor of the enlargement.

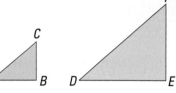

2 Calculate the scale factor of each of these enlargements.

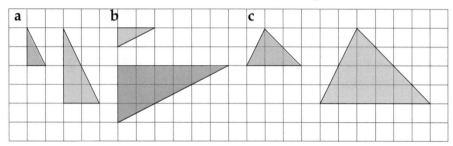

3 Copy these shapes onto square grid paper and
  enlarge each by the given scale factor.

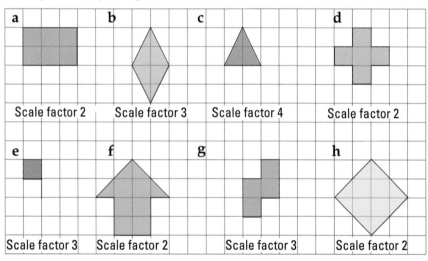

a Scale factor 2   b Scale factor 3   c Scale factor 4   d Scale factor 2

e Scale factor 3   f Scale factor 2   g Scale factor 3   h Scale factor 2

activity

a i   Draw a large triangle.
  ii Mark a point O inside the triangle.
  iii Draw lines from O to the vertices.
  iv Find the midpoint of each line and join these three
      points to form a triangle. This triangle is similar to
      the first triangle.
b Use this method to draw other similar shapes.

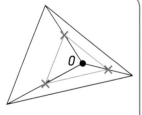

- Use reflections, rotations and translations of a shape to make a tessellation

Keywords
Congruent   Tessellation
Reflection   Transformation
Rotation   Translation

You see tiling patterns in pavements, patios, mosaics and quilts.
This quilt is a repeating pattern of blue squares.

- A **tessellation** is a tiling pattern with no gaps or overlaps.

- You can tessellate shapes using **transformations** – **reflection**, **rotation** or **translation**.

This tessellation is made from a shape reflected in the mirror lines.
The shapes are **congruent**.

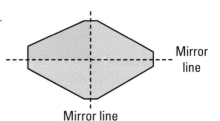

Mirror line

Mirror line

This tessellation is made by rotating a right-angled triangle through 180° about the red dots. The right-angled triangles are congruent.

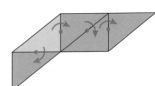

This tessellation is made from repeated translations of a parallelogram.
The parallelograms are congruent.

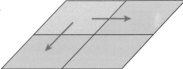

example

An L-shaped tile is made from four squares.
Draw at least three more of these tiles to show that they tessellate.

. . . .

Two of the tiles form a rectangle.
You know that a rectangle tessellates.

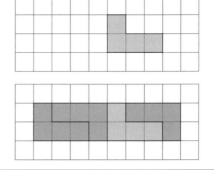

Exercise 13f

1 Copy these shapes onto square grid paper. Tessellate each
  quadrilateral, and state whether you used reflections,
  rotations or translations.

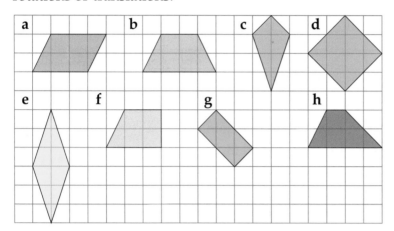

2 Use isometric paper to show tessellations of
  a equilateral triangles
  b regular hexagons
  c equilateral triangles and regular hexagons together
  d rhombuses and regular hexagons together.

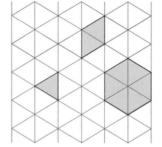

3 Tessellate each triangle by rotating it through 180° about
  the red dots.

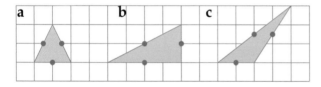

activity

a i Draw a 3 by 2 rectangle.
  ii Remove and translate a triangle.
  iii Remove and translate another triangle.
  iv Add some decorative details.

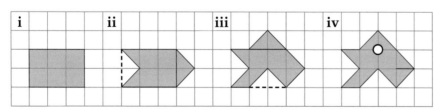

b Show that this shape tessellates using repeated translations.
c Make some tiles of your own using the same method.

1 Copy each diagram and reflect the shape in the mirror line.

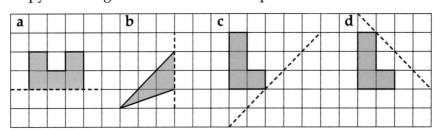

2 a Draw axes from -3 to 3 for both x and y. Plot and join the points given by the coordinates (0, 1), (3, 1) and (3, 3). Label the shape A.

   b i Reflect shape A in the y-axis.

    ii Give the coordinates of the vertices of the image.

   c i Reflect shape A in the x-axis.

    ii Give the coordinates of the vertices of the image.

3 Copy each shape and rotate it through the given angle using the dot as the centre of rotation.

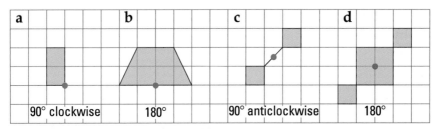

4 a Draw axes from -3 to 3 for both x and y. Plot and join the points given by the coordinates (1, 1), (1, -1), (0, -1) and (0, 1).

   b State the mathematical name of the shape.

   c Rotate the shape through 90° clockwise about (1, 1).

   d Give the coordinates of the vertices of the image.

5 Five squares are joined together to form this pentomino tile.

   a Draw 11 other tiles that can be made using five squares.

   b Copy and complete the table for all 12 tiles.

No symmetry	Only reflection symmetry	Only rotation symmetry	Both reflection and rotation symmetry

6 List the shapes that are translations of the blue shape.

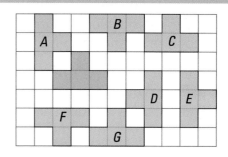

7 On square grid paper draw an *x*-axis from 0 to 15 and a *y*-axis from 0 to 10.

   a Plot each shape on the same grid.

     Shape *A*   (9, 7), (10, 7), (10, 9), (9, 9) and (9, 7)

     Shape *B*   (6, 2), (6, 3), (1, 3), (1, 2) and (6, 2)

     Shape *C*   (12, 1), (11, 3), (11, 1) and (12, 1)

     Shape *D*   (9, 1), (11, 5), (6, 5), (8, 1) and (9, 1)

     Shape *E*   (8, 7), (8, 8), (7, 8), (7, 7) and (8, 7).

   b Give the mathematical name of each shape.

   c Translate each shape on the same grid.

     Shape *A*   6 units to the left and 1 unit down

     Shape *B*   0 units to the right and 7 units up

     Shape *C*   10 units to the left and 6 units up

     Shape *D*   5 units to the left and 4 units up

     Shape *E*   5 units to the left and 1 unit up

8 Copy each letter onto squared grid paper and enlarge it by the given scale factor.

   a

   b

   c
   d

   Scale factor 2   Scale factor 4   Scale factor 3   Scale factor 2

9 Tessellate this shape on square grid paper.

13 Summary

Key indicators
- Recognise line and rotation symmetry of 2-D shapes **Level 5**
- Recognise reflection in mirror lines **Level 5**
- Recognise rotation about a given point **Level 5**

Level 5

1 a Reflect triangle *A* in the mirror line.
You can use a mirror to help you.

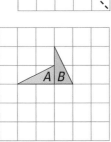

b You can rotate triangle *A* to triangle *B*.
Put a cross on the centre of rotation.
The rotation is clockwise.
What is the angle of rotation?

Kathryn's answer ✔

Kathryn makes the mirror line vertical by moving the page.

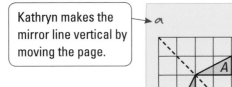

b Clockwise rotation of 90°

Kathryn marks one side of the triangle. The marked side moves through $\frac{1}{4}$ of a full turn.

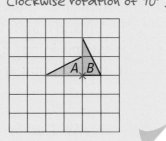

Level 6

2 This pattern has rotational symmetry of order 6.
What is the size of angle *w*?
Show your working.

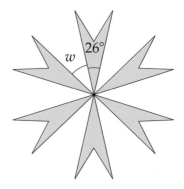

Key Stage 3 2003 4–6 Paper 2

14 Data

Surveys and data

Florence Nightingale was a celebrated nurse during the Victorian era. However, she was also a famous statistician. She is considered the first person to use clearly presented charts and graphs to argue a point. As a result, she improved hygienic conditions in the London hospitals.

What's the point? Clearly presented data backs up your ideas and helps you to get your point across.

 Check in

1 Find the mode or modes of these sets of data.
   a 4, 4, 5, 5, 5, 6, 7, 7
   b 20, 22, 19, 21, 18, 20, 23, 21, 17, 11
   c

Score	6	7	8	9	10
Frequency	7	7	8	10	9

2 a Find the median of these salaries.
     £24 000   £27 000   £20 000   £23 000   £25 000   £40 000
   b Explain what happens to the median value when the person who earns £40 000 has a pay rise which gives him a new salary of £48 000.

3 The total mass of eight 'Beefsteak' tomatoes is 1880 g. Work out the mean mass of these tomatoes.

4 The mean height of a group of five 11-year-old girls is 150 cm. A girl of height 153 cm joins the group. Work out the mean height of the group now.

- Know about primary and secondary data and the difference between them

Keywords

Data
Data-handling cycle
Experiment

Primary
Secondary
Survey

- **Primary data** is data you collect yourself.

   You might carry out a **survey** to collect opinions or measurement, or devise an **experiment**.

- **Secondary** data is data which have already been collected by someone else.

   Sources of secondary data include the internet, newspapers and library archives.

> Secondary data can save a lot of time and effort, but you should use it only if it provides all the information you need, and if you are certain it was collected reliably.

- The **data-handling cycle** shows the stages of statistical enquiry.

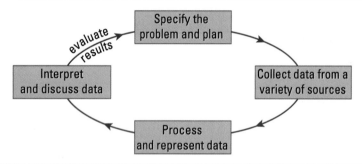

example

Keith wants to know if people's reaction times change as they get older. He decides to measure how long it takes someone to press a button when prompted.

a Is the data he collects primary or secondary data?

b Discuss how he could use the test to collect the information he needs.

. . . .

a Primary data   Keith collects the data himself.

b Keith could either

   1 ask the same people to take the test at age 20, 40 and 60   This is unrealistic.

   2 ask people of different ages to take the test and then look at the averages per group.   This is a realistic plan.

Keith should collect a lot of data to make sure the data is reliable.

Exercise 14a

1 Phil wants to find out what sort of magazine articles students at her school like best. She has collected lots of information. Are these examples of primary or secondary data?

a *Teen!* magazine's report on the results of a reader survey.

b A questionnaire filled in by students at Phil's school.

c The same questionnaire filled in by students at Phil's cousin's school.

2 People who live in a new housing development complain that they cannot get out at the junction, on to the main road, because of the traffic. The council has to decide whether to put in traffic lights or a roundabout at the junction.

a What primary data could they collect?

b What secondary data could they use to help them make the decision?

3 Ella wants to buy a book for her niece, but is not sure what book would be best. She decides to buy whatever is most popular at the moment with teenage girls.

a Where could she go to collect some primary data?

b Where could she look for secondary data?

4 When a car tries to stop quickly it will often leave tyre marks on the road. After road accidents, forensic scientists may try to work out the speed of the car by looking at the length of the tyre marks. Give at least two factors that might affect the length of the tyre marks a car leaves in an emergency stop, apart from the speed of the car.

discussion

Josie is keen to start driving as soon as she is old enough. She wants to know which instructor she should choose in order to have the best chance of passing the test. She decides to go to the two test centres near her home and ask people taking the test for information which might help her. Devise a list of questions she could ask.

- Create a sheet for recording the data needed for an investigation

Keywords
Data
Data-collection sheet
Tally chart

- Before you start to collect **data** you must decide what information you need.

- Your **data-collection sheet** must be easy to complete.

If you are asking people several different questions, make sure that you keep each person's answers together.

example

Arabella wants to know whether boys walk to school more than girls. She asks some of her classmates whether they walk to school or not, and uses this **tally chart** to record her results.

	Boy	Girl
Walk	༎༎ ⏐⏐⏐	⏐⏐⏐
Other	༎༎	⏐⏐⏐⏐

Will Arabella's data give her the information she needs? Explain your answer, and suggest how her data collection could be improved.

• •

No. Arabella hasn't taken into account the fact that whether students walk to school might also be affected by how far they live from the school. She also needs to ask more students, so that her data is more reliable. If she asks an equal number of girls and boys, it will be easier to compare the data.

A better data-collection sheet would look like this.

Name	Boy/girl	Distance to school	Walk to school?
Paulo	B	0.5 km	Y
Sharon	G	2.3 km	N

- When planning what data to collect, think about what graphs or calculations you are going to use to answer your questions.

Arabella could use this comparative bar chart to confirm that students who walk to school live, on average, closer to the school than those who do not walk.

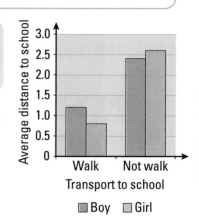

Exercise 14b

1 A teacher in a primary school wants to award a prize to the best student in the class during the year.
He wants to base it on more than just academic work.

Create a data-collection sheet he could use to help him choose the winner.

2 A town is planning to bring in a charge for cars entering the town. They want to know how many cars come in at different times, and how many passengers they carry.

Create a data-collection sheet they could use for this.

3 Tereza wants to know how often people of different ages go to the cinema.

Create a data-collection sheet she could use for this.

4 Your family are moving to a new area. Your parents draw up a data-collection sheet on which they can record the features that are important to them – house price, number of bedrooms, whether there is a garage, how close the local station is, and so on. They also want to know your opinion.

Create your own data-collection sheet with the information you would be interested in.

Your parents have decided to buy a plasma television.

a Use the Internet to look at the specifications of a range of televisions.
What information is included in most of specifications lists?
Is it all relevant or are there some details that don't matter to you?

b Make a data-collection sheet using the information for some of the televisions. Is there anything else you would like to know before making a decision? How would you find it out?

c Decide which plasma television you would buy.

d Now imagine that you have a budget of £750.
Which television would you choose now?
What did you have to compromise on?

- Write questions which are clear, unbiased and easy to answer
- Design a questionnaire for an investigation

Keywords
Bias
Questionnaire
Survey

- When you use a **questionnaire** to collect data
  - think carefully about who to **survey**.
  - ask clear, easy to answer and unbiased questions.
  - test your questionnaire on a few people.

example

Simon wants to investigate theatre attendance in his home town.
He plans to ask 100 people as they leave the local theatre.
How could Simon improve his questionnaire?

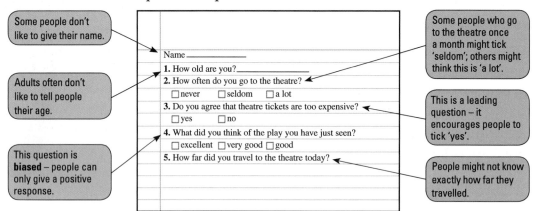

Some people don't like to give their name.

Adults often don't like to tell people their age.

This question is **biased** – people can only give a positive response.

Some people who go to the theatre once a month might tick 'seldom'; others might think this is 'a lot'.

This is a leading question – it encourages people to tick 'yes'.

People might not know exactly how far they travelled.

Name _____
1. How old are you? _____
2. How often do you go to the theatre?
   ☐ never   ☐ seldom   ☐ a lot
3. Do you agree that theatre tickets are too expensive?
   ☐ yes   ☐ no
4. What did you think of the play you have just seen?
   ☐ excellent ☐ very good ☐ good
5. How far did you travel to the theatre today?

If Simon asks only people leaving a theatre, he won't get the opinions of people who never go, perhaps because they think the tickets are too expensive.

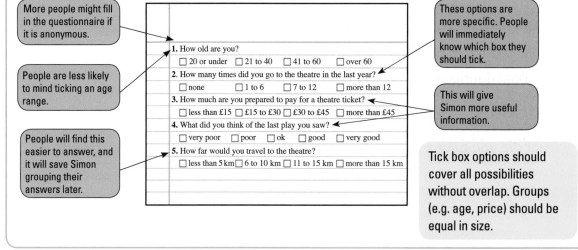

More people might fill in the questionnaire if it is anonymous.

People are less likely to mind ticking an age range.

People will find this easier to answer, and it will save Simon grouping their answers later.

1. How old are you?
   ☐ 20 or under ☐ 21 to 40 ☐ 41 to 60 ☐ over 60
2. How many times did you go to the theatre in the last year?
   ☐ none   ☐ 1 to 6   ☐ 7 to 12   ☐ more than 12
3. How much are you prepared to pay for a theatre ticket?
   ☐ less than £15 ☐ £15 to £30 ☐ £30 to £45 ☐ more than £45
4. What did you think of the last play you saw?
   ☐ very poor   ☐ poor   ☐ ok   ☐ good   ☐ very good
5. How far would you travel to the theatre?
   ☐ less than 5 km ☐ 6 to 10 km ☐ 11 to 15 km ☐ more than 15 km

These options are more specific. People will immediately know which box they should tick.

This will give Simon more useful information.

Tick box options should cover all possibilities without overlap. Groups (e.g. age, price) should be equal in size.

Exercise 14c

1 Write one criticism of each question.

   a Do you agree that the new bus service is excellent?

   b What is your opinion of the new bus service?

      ☐ Excellent   ☐ Very good   ☐ Good

2 A questionnaire on reading habits asked
'How often do you read a magazine?'

   a Write one criticism of the way the question is asked.

   b Rewrite the question in a better form.

3 A fitness club is thinking of opening a new branch in a
neighbouring town. The manager's nephew goes to the
town during half term and asks people in the town centre
if they would ever use a fitness centre.

   a Is this a good way to collect the data?
     Suggest a way to improve it.

   b Suggest how to improve the way the question is asked.

4 Which of these questions might people not be happy
to answer?

   a How much do you earn?

   b Do you like walking?

   c Are you married?

   d How often do you go to the cinema?

   e Have you ever been arrested?

5 A survey asks

> How old are you?
> ☐ under 21   ☐ 21–40   ☐ 40–60

   a Write two criticisms of the options given.

   b Suggest better options.

---

investigation

Find a questionnaire in a newspaper or magazine,
or choose one which has been sent to your home.
Look at the way the questions have been asked.
Could any of them be improved?

- Collect discrete and continuous data in a grouped frequency table
- Find the modal class of a grouped frequency table

- You can use a **grouped frequency table** to make data more manageable.

This grouped frequency table shows the scores of 25 students who took a test with 40 marks.

It is much easier to use than one with 40 separate rows.

Test score	Tally	Frequency
0–10	II	2
11–20	IIII	4
21–30	IHL IHL III	13
31–40	IHL I	6

- The groups are called **class intervals**. They should usually all be equal.

  In this frequency diagram of test scores, each class interval is 10.

- The **modal class** is the class with the highest frequency.

Mr Jackson times the students in class 7C doing a maths puzzle (in seconds to 1 dp).

22.5 12.3 6.3 9.9 29.0 22.2 37.0 17.2 17.2 28.4
37.0 29.7 4.1 28.8 27.0 23.8 14.8 10.0 20.0 33.8
30.1 32.2 20.1 21.6 10.5 23.7 36.7 25.5 18.8 25.6

a Create a grouped frequency table for these data.
b State the modal class.

a The lowest value is 4.1 and the highest is 37.0.
So your table could have four equal class intervals.

Time (seconds)	Tally	Frequency
$0 \le t < 10$	III	3
$10 \le t < 20$	IHL II	7
$20 \le t < 30$	IHL IHL IIII	14
$30 \le t < 40$	IHL I	6

As you record a tally mark for each time, cross it off the list.

$0 \le t < 10$ means that the time is greater than or equal to 0 and less than (but not equal to) 10. The time 10.0 goes in the next group, $10 \le t < 20$.

b The modal class is $20 \le t < 30$.   It has the highest frequency.

Exercise 14d

1 An airline company records the weights of the bags that 30
passengers check in (in kg to 1dp).

7.3	8.2	9.1	9.0	6.2	11.2	7.8	4.3	7.9	12.4
6.1	7.0	8.4	4.9	5.4	11.6	9.4	9.0	6.7	10.5
6.4	7.9	10.8	11.2	13.4	9.5	4.7	5.6	7.1	8.2

a Copy and complete the frequency table.

Weight (kg)	Tally	Frequency
$4 \leq w < 6$		
$6 \leq w < 8$		
$8 \leq w < 10$		
$10 \leq w < 12$		
$12 \leq w < 14$		

b State the modal class.

Bags that weigh less than 10 kg can be checked in free.
Heavier bags cost more.

c How many passengers have to pay for baggage?

2 These are the ages of athletes in a Charity Run.

21	28	58	45	63	47	17	39	24	52
67	47	14	23	31	46	27	33	41	30
22	27	19	55	40	24	16	67		

a Copy and complete the tally chart.

Age	Tally	Frequency
$10 \leq a < 20$		
$20 \leq a < 30$		
$30 \leq a < 40$		
$40 \leq a < 50$		
$50 \leq a < 60$		
$60 \leq a < 70$		

b State the modal class.

c What else does your table tell you about the ages of the runners?

discussion

Think about ways you could use grouped frequency
tables in your life.
Maybe to organise a collection?
Or perhaps to count your pocket money?

- Draw a pie chart by calculating the angle needed for each part of it

Keywords
Frequency
Pie chart
Sector

- In a **pie chart**, each **sector** represents a category of data. The angle of the sector is proportional to the **frequency** of the category.

A sector looks like a slice of a pie.

example

Amanda asked her classmates about their favourite sport. Here are her results.

Sport	Frequency
Tennis	7
Netball	4
Football	8
Hockey	5
Total	24

p. 78

Draw a pie chart to show this information.

Add an extra column to the table for your working out.

Amanda surveyed 24 people in total. Each person is represented by a $\frac{1}{24}$ slice.

There are 360° in a circle, so each person is represented by $\frac{1}{24} \times 360° = 15°$.

7 people are represented by $7 \times 15° = 105°$, and so on.

Sport	Frequency	Angle
Tennis	7	$7 \times 15° = 105°$
Netball	4	$4 \times 15° = \;\;60°$
Football	8	$8 \times 15° = 120°$
Hockey	5	$5 \times 15° = \;\;75°$
Total	24	Check $\quad$ 360°

Favourite sport

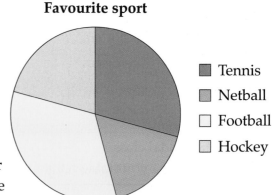

■ Tennis
■ Netball
□ Football
□ Hockey

To draw the pie chart, draw a circle with a pair of compasses. Then draw a line from the centre to the top of the circle. Carefully measure the first angle and draw a line to complete the sector. Then do the second sector, and so on. When you get to the final sector, measure it to make sure you haven't made any mistakes.

Exercise 14e

1 A class votes for who is to represent them on the school council. The table shows the votes for each of the four candidates.

Candidate	Malik	Sofie	Katrina	Callum
Number of votes	5	8	11	6

Draw a pie chart to show the results of the election.

2 The number of times sixth form students in a school have taken a driving test are summarised in the table.

Number of driving tests	None	One	Two	Three or more
Number of students	23	42	14	11

Draw a pie chart to show this information.

3 The table shows information about the maximum temperature in London between October 1st and October 30th 2000.

Maximum temperature (T °C)	Number of days
$10 \leq T < 12$	1
$12 \leq T < 14$	5
$14 \leq T < 16$	18
$16 \leq T < 18$	5
$18 \leq T < 20$	1

Draw a pie chart to show this information.

challenge

The table shows the population of the countries in Britain. The numbers are larger than you have met before.

Country	Population (1000s)
England	50431
Wales	2958
Scotland	5094
N. Ireland	1724
Total	60207

Work out how to calculate the angle for each country, then draw a pie chart to show this information.

- Understand the information given on a frequency diagram

Keywords
Frequency diagram

- A **frequency diagram** represents data visually.

example

The graph shows the number of homes with a TV in the UK over the past 50 years.

a Describe what has happened to TV ownership in the past 50 years.

b i In which 10-year period was there the biggest increase in TV ownership?

ii About how much was the increase?

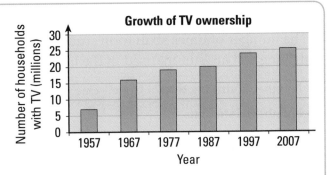

a TV ownership has increased over the past 50 years.
It increased sharply at first, and then more gradually.

b i 1957 to 1967   These two bars have the greatest difference in height.

ii 9 million households   The height of the 1967 bar is about 16 and 1957 bar is about 7.
16 − 7 = 9. Don't forget that the scale is in millions.

example

The graph shows the number of after-school activities attended by the 30 members of class 7C.

Find   a the range
       b the mode
       c the median
       d the mean for these data.

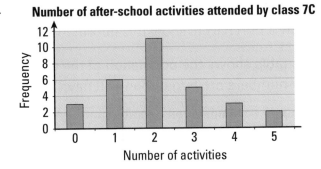

a 5 activities   5 − 0 = 5

b 2 activities   This is the highest bar on the graph.

c 2 activities   The median lies between the 15th and 16th values, which are both 2.

d 2.17 activities (to 2 dp)   Mean = $\dfrac{0 \times 3 + 1 \times 6 + 2 \times 11 + 3 \times 5 + 4 \times 3 + 5 \times 2}{30}$

$= \dfrac{0 + 6 + 22 + 15 + 12 + 10}{30} = \dfrac{65}{30} = 2.166 \ldots$

Exercise 14f

77

1 The graph shows what people in the UK spent their money on in 2001–2002.

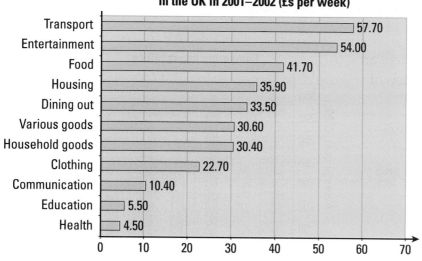

Analysis of average weekly expenditure by households in the UK in 2001–2002 (£s per week)

Category	£ per week
Transport	57.70
Entertainment	54.00
Food	41.70
Housing	35.90
Dining out	33.50
Various goods	30.60
Household goods	30.40
Clothing	22.70
Communication	10.40
Education	5.50
Health	4.50

a How much, on average, does a household spend per week altogether?

b How much more, on average, does a household spend per week on entertainment than on clothing?

c What is the average **yearly** expenditure on health?

2 The graph shows how many TVs the 30 students in Class 7C have at home. Find

a the range

b the mode

c the median

d the mean of this data.

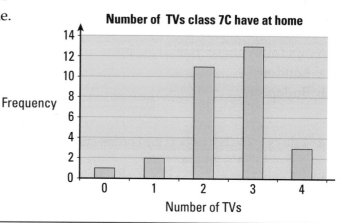

Number of TVs class 7C have at home

Frequency — Number of TVs

investigation

Find out the latest figures for weekly household expenditure, and compare them to the figures for 2001–2002.
Are there any differences in the pattern of spending?

- Understand the information given on comparative bar charts

Keywords
Comparative bar chart
Stacked bar chart

- You can use a **comparative** or **stacked bar chart** to compare different sets of data.

A comparative bar chart gives an immediate visual impression of the data.

This graph clearly shows that house prices in Manchester are cheaper than in Bristol and Newcastle.

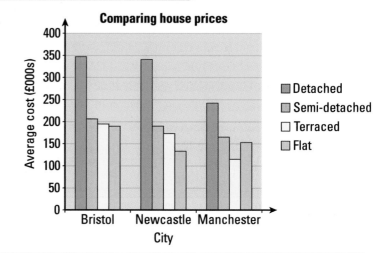

example

This stacked bar chart shows information about the maximum temperature in London and Budapest in April one year.
On how many days was the temperature more than 21 °C in
a London
b Budapest?

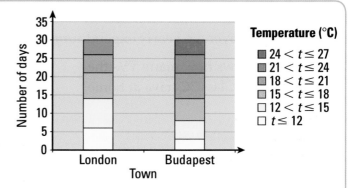

. . . .

a 4 days   The last block in the London stack is $21 < t \leq 24$
$30 - 26 = 4$
b 9 days   The last two blocks in the Budapest stack correspond to temperatures over 21 °C.
$30 - 21 = 9$

Notice that 'hotter' colours have been used for the higher temperatures. It is immediately clear that Budapest is generally hotter than London.

Exercise 14g

1 The graph shows the total number of homes in the UK, and the number of homes with a TV.

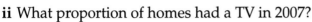

Growth of TV ownership

  a How many more homes with a TV are there in 2007 than there were in 1957?

  b i What proportion of homes had a TV in 1957?

   ii What proportion of homes had a TV in 2007?

  c Describe what has happened to the proportion of homes with a TV between 1957 and 2007.

2 The graph shows the results of a survey on TV viewing habits in April 2002 and April 2007.

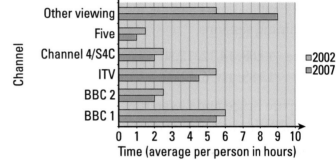

TV weekly viewing summary

  a In 2002, on average how much longer did a person watch BBC1 than BBC2?

  b On average, how much less did a person watch ITV for in 2007 than in 2002?

  c Summarise the change which has taken place in channels people watch between 2002 and 2007.

3 The graph shows what three friends spend their pocket money on in an average month.

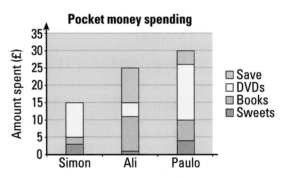

Pocket money spending

  a How much pocket money does

   i Simon **ii** Ali **iii** Paulo

   receive each month?

  b What is the average monthly spend on DVDs for the three friends?

  c Comment on what the graph tells you about their spending habits.

---

discussion

Draw a stacked bar chart to represent the data on weekly viewing figures given in question **2**. Use one stack for 2002 and another for 2007.

Which method of comparison do you prefer?

- Compare two sets of data using an average and the range

p. 70

Keywords

Average   Range

Mean   Spread

Median   Variation

Mode

- When you compare two sets of data, it is sensible to look at an **average** and at a measure of **spread**.
- The **mean**, **median** and **mode** are all averages. It is usually best to use the mean or median.
- **Range** is a measure of spread. It tells you how much **variation** is in the data.

example

The school athletics coach needs to recruit a new member to the school 100 m relay race team. Bruce and Gwen both want the position. Here are their times from their last 10 training sessions.

Bruce   13.08, 14.12, 12.30, 13.01, 14.16, 13.85, 11.96, 12.07, 12.15, 12.45

Gwen   13.98, 13.66, 13.50, 12.91, 13.34, 13.22, 12.40, 12.87, 12.78, 12.55

Compare Bruce and Gwen times.
Who should the coach choose?

. . . .

You could use either the mean or the median, plus the range, to compare Bruce and Gwen's times.

The times are all different, so there is no mode.

Bruce   Mean $= \frac{129.15}{10} = 12.92$ seconds (to 2 dp)

           Median $= \frac{12.45 + 13.01}{2} = \frac{25.46}{2} = 12.73$ seconds

           Range $= 14.16 - 11.96 = 2.2$ seconds

There are 10 times, so the median time is the midpoint of the fifth and sixth values – remember to put the times in order first.

Gwen   Mean $= \frac{131.21}{10} = 13.12$ seconds (to 2 dp)

           Median $= \frac{12.91 + 13.22}{2} = \frac{26.13}{2}$

               $= 13.07$ seconds (to 2 dp)

           Range $= 13.98 - 12.40 = 1.58$ seconds

Using the mean and the range: Bruce has a faster mean time but, because a relay race is a team event, Gwen might be a better choice – she has a smaller range, meaning that she is more reliable.

This sort of question often doesn't have a right and a wrong answer – so make sure you explain your choice.

Exercise 14h

1 Find the median and the range for each of these sets of data.

  a Resting pulse rates of a group of Year 7 students

      61, 71, 80, 66, 68

  b Resting pulse rates of a group of Year 2 students

      93, 78, 81, 81, 71, 95, 82

  c Pulse rates of a group of Year 7 students after running for 5 minutes

      113, 147, 127, 139, 122, 135, 119

  d Compare the three sets of data using the range and the median.

2 The length of time between eruptions of a geyser is recorded (in minutes).

      62, 88, 63, 93, 57, 87, 56, 91

  a Calculate the mean time between eruptions, and the range of the times between eruptions.

Another geyser has a mean of 75 minutes between eruptions and a range of 8 minutes.

  b Compare the distribution of times between eruptions for the two geysers.

Did you know?

Old Faithful Geyser in Yellowstone National Park can shoot up to 32 000 litres of boiling water to a height of 55 metres.

---

challenge

A psychologist is interested in seeing whether various factors make a difference to the time people take to react to a noise stimulus. She measures the reaction times (in hundredths of a second) of different groups of people under different conditions.

a Find the median reaction time for each of the groups, and the range of times.

  i Normal conditions

    16, 19, 15, 19, 22, 17, 16, 17, 21, 18, 17

  ii Using their non-writing hand to react

    19, 22, 23, 19, 17, 24, 27, 21, 18

  iii Blindfolded

    20, 21, 18, 19, 23, 21, 24, 18, 17, 22, 19, 23, 20

  iv After two alcoholic drinks

    22, 19, 14, 21, 15, 26, 23, 19, 24

b Compare the four groups using the range and the median.

14a

1 Natasha wants to know whether people watch digital TV channels more than the BBC, ITV, Channel 4 and Five
  a How could she collect some primary data?
  b Where could she look for secondary data?

14b

2 Francis wants to compare the effectiveness of the schools in his area. Write down at least three pieces of information he might find useful.

14c

3 A questionnaire on exercise habits asks 'How often do you go to the gym?'
  a Make a criticism of the way the question is asked.
  b Rewrite the question in a better form.
  c Raymond plays chess. He took the questionnaire to people at the chess club. Is this a good way to collect the data? Suggest a way to improve it.

14d

4 A soccer coach records his players' times to run a drill.
  a Construct a tally chart and frequency table to show these data.
  b State the modal class.

20.6	22.1	20.3	19.7
22.8	24.0	21.3	18.9
24.3	20.4	20.8	23.4
24.2	26.5	19.9	23.1
24.1	20.4	21.3	22.8
21.7	17.5	19.4	16.9
24.1	18.3	22.1	19.4
17.8	21.3		

14e

5 A focus group is asked to choose one of four models to appear on the front cover of a magazine. The table shows how they voted. Draw a pie chart to show the results of the voting. Show how you calculate the angles.

Model	Votes
Louise	12
Laura	4
Joanne	9
Carole	11

6 The graph shows the results of
a survey on TV viewing
habits in April 2007.

   a Which of the main channels
   listed is watched least?

   b These are the weekly
   average times. What is
   the total daily average
   time spent watching TV?

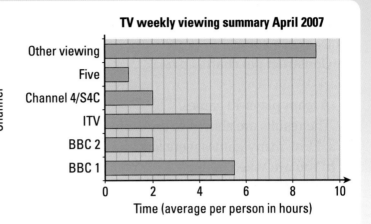

7 The graph shows the percentages of adults in different age groups
who owned mobile phones in 2001 and 2003.

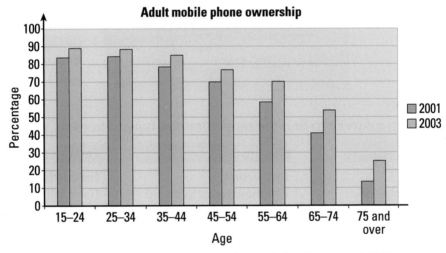

   a What percentage of 45–54 year olds owned a mobile phone in 2001?

   b How much did this increase by between 2001 and 2003?

   c Describe the change in ownership of mobile phones between 2001 and 2003.

8 Here are the times of the athletes
who finished the 100 metre
Olympic final in Australia.

Compare the men's and
women's times.

Men's times (seconds)	
9.87	10.09
9.99	10.13
10.04	10.17
10.08	

Women's times (seconds)	
10.75	11.20
11.12	11.22
11.18	11.29
11.19	

14 Summary

Key indicators

- Compare two simple distributions using range and one of mode, median or mean **Level 5**
- Design a survey or experiment **Level 6**
- Construct pie charts **Level 6**

1 A team plays 40 games.

The results are shown in the table.

Won	22
Drawn	7
Lost	

a How many games were lost?

b You are asked to draw a pie chart of the results.
Calculate the angles in the pie chart.

Bashira's answer ✔

Bashira knows the angles at a point add to 360°

a $40 - (22 + 7) = 11$

b $360° \div 40 = 9°$ per game

Won is $22 \times 9° = 198°$

Drawn is $7 \times 9° = 63°$

Lost is $11 \times 9° = \dfrac{99°}{360°}$

Bashira checks the angles add to 360°

2 Some pupils plan a survey to find the most common type of tree in a wood.

Design 1

Instruction:
Write down the type of each tree that you see.

For example:
Elm, oak, oak, oak, sycamore, ash, …

Design 2

Instruction:
Use these codes to record the type of each tree that you see.

Ash	A
Birch	B
Elm	E
Oak	O
Sycamore	S

For example:
E, O, O, O, S, A, …

Design 3

Instruction:
Use a tally chart to record the type of each tree that you see.

For example:

Type of tree	Tally
Ash	I
Birch	
Elm	I
Oak	III
Sycamore	I
Other	

The pupils will only use one design.

a Choose a design they should not use.
Explain why it is not a good design to use.

b Choose a design that is the best.
Explain why it is the best.

Key Stage 3 2003 3–5 Paper 2

Calculations

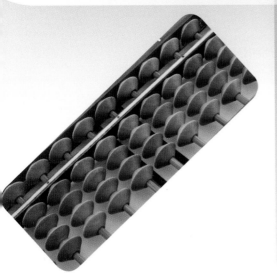

A soroban is a Japanese abacus. A soroban works by keeping track of the numbers in a calculation through the placement of beads on a series of wires. School children in Japan still learn calculation skills by using a soroban.

What's the point? A calculator is a modern day tool to help which you can use to help with your calculations.

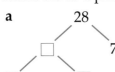 **Check in**

1 Copy and complete this grid in order to calculate 428×67.

×	400	20	8
60			
7			

$428 \times 67 =$

2 **a** Change these mixed numbers to improper fractions.

   i $1\frac{1}{3}$ **ii** $1\frac{4}{9}$ **iii** $2\frac{5}{8}$ **iv** $4\frac{3}{4}$

   b Change these improper fractions to mixed numbers.

   i $\frac{11}{8}$ **ii** $\frac{7}{2}$ **iii** $\frac{18}{5}$ **iv** $\frac{77}{10}$

3 Copy and complete these factor trees to write each of these numbers as a product of its prime factors.

a   28   **b** 126

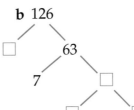

28 =   126 =

- Find the factors of a whole number
- Use divisibility tests to find factors and to test for prime numbers

Keywords
Divisibility
Factor
Prime

- A **factor** of a number is any number that divides into it without leaving a remainder.

- You can use simple **divisibility** tests to help you find all the factors of a number.

example

Find all the factors of 106.

Factor	Divisibility test	Is it a factor of 106?
2	The number ends in 0, 2, 4, 6, or 8	Yes : 106 ends in a 6
3	The sum of the digits is divisible by 3	No : 1 + 0 + 6 = 7
4	The last two digits are divisible by 4	No : 06 is not divisible by 4
5	The number ends in 0 or 5	No : 106 ends in 6
6	The number is divisible by 2 and 3	No : not divisible by 3
7	There is no test for 7	No : 106 ÷ 7 = 15 r 1
8	Half of the number is divisible by 4	No : 53 is not divisible by 4
9	The sum of digits is divisible by 9	No : 1 + 0 + 6 = 7
10	The number ends in 0	No : it ends in 6

$1 \times 106 = 106$ $\qquad$ $2 \times 53 = 106$

The factors of 106 are 1, 2, 53 and 106.

- A **prime** number is a number with exactly two factors, 1 and the number itself. You can work out whether a number is prime by checking for divisibility by primes.

example

Are these prime numbers? $\quad$ **a** 51 $\quad$ **b** 53

a 51 is not a prime number.
$\quad$ 2 is not a factor
$\quad$ 3 is a factor

You can stop as soon as you find a factor.

b 53 is a prime number.
$\quad$ 2 is not a factor
$\quad$ 3 is not a factor
$\quad$ 5 is not a factor
$\quad$ 7 is not a factor

You can stop at 7 because $7^2 = 49$.

Exercise 15a

1 Write all the factors of

    a 42   **b** 80   **c** 64   **d** 92   **e** 88

2 Identify which of the numbers in the box are multiples of

    a 23

    b 17

    c 29

253	377	391
400	493	667

3 Use the divisibility tests to answer each of these questions. Explain your answers.

    a Is 5 a factor of 125?   **b** Is 3 a factor of 142?

    c Is 7 a factor of 104?   **d** Is 11 a factor of 231?

    e Is 2 a factor of 458?   **f** Is 6 a factor of 102?

    g Is 2 a factor of 136?   **h** Is 9 a factor of 513?

4 Write down all the factors of

    a 160   **b** 264

    c 325   **d** 224

    e 432   **f** 270

5 a Find all 12 factors of 60.

    b Find three more numbers less than 100 with exactly 12 factors.

6 Use the divisibility tests to see which of these are prime numbers. Explain your answers.

    a 95   **b** 61

    c 37   **d** 109

    e 112   **f** 129

7 Use your calculator to find the first prime number greater than 2000.

You can check whether a number divides by 6 by using the divisibility tests for 2 and 3.

a Investigate numbers that are multiples of 15. Do they all divide by 5 and 3?

b Use your findings to write down and explain a divisibility test for 15.

c Invent some more divisibility tests for other numbers larger than 10.

- Write a number as the product of its prime factors
- Use prime factors to find the HCF and LCM of two numbers

p. 152

- You can find the **HCF** and the **LCM** of a set of numbers by using **prime factors**.

example

Find the HCF and LCM of 36 and 60.

Write both numbers as the product of their prime factors.

| 2) 36 |
| 2) 18 |
| 3) 9 |
| 3) 3 |
| 1 |

| 2) 60 |
| 2) 30 |
| 3) 15 |
| 5) 5 |
| 1 |

$36 = 2 \times 2 \times 3 \times 3$
$ = 2^2 \times 3^2$

$60 = 2 \times 2 \times 3 \times 5$
$ = 2^2 \times 3 \times 5$

In this method, you find the prime factors by repeatedly dividing by the lowest prime factor you can. You might prefer the method you learnt in Chapter 10.

Multiply the prime factors they have in common.
They have $2 \times 2 \times 3$ in common.
HCF of 36 and 60 $= 2^2 \times 3$
$ = 12$

Multiply the highest power of each of the prime factors.
You need 2^2, 3^2 and 5.
LCM of 36 and 60 $= 2^2 \times 3^2 \times 5$
$ = 180$

- You can cancel a fraction to its **simplest form** by dividing the numerator and denominator by the HCF.

    The HCF of 20 and 36 is 4. The fraction cannot be cancelled further.

$$\frac{20}{36} = \frac{5}{9}$$
$\div 4$ ... $\div 4$

- You can add or subtract fractions with different denominators by first writing them as equivalent fractions with the **lowest common denominator.**

    $\frac{3}{8} + \frac{5}{12} = \frac{9}{24} + \frac{10}{24} = \frac{19}{24}$ 24 is the LCM of 8 and 12.

When you rewrite a fraction as an equivalent fraction with a different denominator, remember to multiply the numerator and denominator by the same number.

Exercise 15b

1 Find the HCF of

   a 8 and 12   **b** 25 and 40   **c** 60 and 96

   d 36 and 48   **e** 84 and 144   **f** 100 and 180

   g 9, 12 and 15   **h** 16, 40 and 56

2 Find the LCM of

   a 8 and 12   **b** 20 and 35   **c** 30 and 45

   d 36 and 90   **e** 56 and 136   **f** 48 and 108

   g 6, 8 and 12   **h** 15, 20 and 35

3 Write each of these fractions in its simplest form.

   a $\dfrac{12}{18}$ **b** $\dfrac{25}{30}$ **c** $\dfrac{24}{32}$

   d $\dfrac{27}{45}$ **e** $\dfrac{30}{48}$ **f** $\dfrac{72}{80}$

   g $\dfrac{175}{245}$ **h** $\dfrac{117}{169}$ **i** $\dfrac{480}{1080}$

4 Work out each of these, giving your answer as a fraction in its simplest form.

   a $\dfrac{4}{5} - \dfrac{3}{15}$ **b** $\dfrac{5}{9} + \dfrac{1}{6}$ **c** $\dfrac{3}{4} + \dfrac{1}{6}$

   d $\dfrac{3}{10} + \dfrac{4}{15}$ **e** $\dfrac{3}{8} - \dfrac{1}{12}$ **f** $\dfrac{1}{9} - \dfrac{1}{12}$

   g $\dfrac{7}{15} + \dfrac{5}{12}$ **h** $\dfrac{7}{20} - \dfrac{3}{16}$ **i** $\dfrac{3}{14} + \dfrac{7}{10}$

5 In a 10 000 m race the lead runner runs at 69 seconds per lap. The slowest runner runs at 72 seconds per lap. After how many laps will the lead runner overtake the slowest runner?

investigation

a Copy and complete this table.

b Write down anything you notice about the numbers in your table.

c Write down a quick way to find the LCM if you know the HCF.

Numbers	Product	HCF	LCM
6 and 4	24	2	12
8 and 12			
10 and 15			
6 and 9			
12 and 16			
12 and 15			
14 and 21			
16 and 24			

- Multiply decimal numbers mentally using several methods

Keywords
Division   Halve
Double   Multiplication
Factor

There are lots of mental strategies you can use to help you work out **multiplications** and **divisions** in your head.

p. 4

- You can use your knowledge of place value to multiply or divide any number by 0.1 and 0.01.

example

Calculate   **a** 4.8×0.1 **b** $0.96 \div 0.01$

a $4.8 \times 0.1 = 4.8 \div 10$
$= 0.48$

b $0.96 \div 0.01 = 0.96 \times 100$
$= 96$

> Multiplying by 0.1 is the same as dividing by 10.

> Dividing by 0.01 is the same as multiplying by 100.

- You can think of numbers as pairs of **factors** and carry out two simple multiplications or divisions instead of one difficult one.

example

Calculate   **a** 21×0.04 **b** $435 \div 15$

a Think of 0.04 as 4×0.01
$21 \times 0.04 = 21 \times 4 \times 0.01$
$= 84 \times 0.01$
$= 0.84$

b Think of 15 as 5×3
$435 \div 15 = 435 \div 5 \div 3$
$= 87 \div 3$
$= 29$

> In part **a**, multiply by 4 first. Then multiply by 0.01.

> In part **b**, divide by 5 first. Then divide by 3.

- You can use **doubling** and **halving** to make the calculations easier.

example

Calculate   **a** 8×7.5 **b** 2.4×4.5

a $8 \times 7.5 = 4 \times 15$
$= 60$

b $2.4 \times 4.5 = 1.2 \times 9$
$= (1.2 \times 10) - (1.2 \times 1)$
$= 12 - 1.2$
$= 10.8$

> Double one number and halve the other.

> Think of 9 as $10 - 1$.

Exercise 15c

1 Calculate these mentally.

   a -3 + -6   **b** -13 + 28   **c** -6 − -8

   d -53 − -21   **e** 230 + 480   **f** 6.8 + 3.7

   g 0.56 − 0.39   **h** 0.024 + 0.075   **i** 3.6 + 5.9

2 Calculate these mentally.

   a $\sqrt{12 \times 3}$ **b** $\sqrt{35 + 14}$

   c $(7 + 5)^2$ **d** $(13 - 9 + 5)^2$

   e $\sqrt{117 - 36}$ **f** $(4 + 3 \times 2)^2$

3 Calculate these mentally.

   a 30×60 **b** 50×70 **c** 400×9

   d 200×70 **e** $1200 \div 60$ **f** $6300 \div 70$

   g $12 \div 0.1$ **h** 260×0.01 **i** $0.8 \div 0.01$

4 Calculate these mentally.

   a $156 \div 6$ **b** $420 \div 15$ **c** 0.6×21

   d 0.03×15 **e** 0.8×12 **f** 0.05×22

   g $144 \div 18$ **h** $252 \div 12$ **i** 2.2×18

5 Calculate these mentally.

   a 12×1.3 **b** 75×29 **c** 15×3.2

   d $185 \div 12$ **e** $170 \div 15$ **f** $200 \div 18$

   g 6.4×2.5 **h** 22×3.1 **i** 5.5×6.2

6 Use an appropriate mental method to solve each of these problems.

   a Callum puts 4.5 kg of bottles into the recycling skip every week.
      What weight of bottles does he recycle in a year?

   b Naheeda puts 12 photos onto her computer.
      The photos take up 228 MB on her hard drive.
      About how much memory is taken up by each photo?

   c Manuel runs at 4.3 m per second for 199 seconds.
      How far does he run?

---

puzzle

Here are two calculations. Some of the digits have been covered up. Find the digit covered by each of the boxes.

   a 2 ☐ 2 ÷ 1 ☐ = ☐ 1   **b** ☐.3 × 1 ☐ = ☐ 2 ☐.5

- Multiply decimal numbers using the grid method and the standard method

- If a **multiplication** involves **decimals**, you can change the calculation into an **equivalent** whole number calculation by multiplying by a power of 10.

- You should always **estimate** the answer first.

Dave plays £1.92 per day for his school meal. In March he has a school meal on 23 days of the month. How much money does he spend on his school meals in March?

First estimate the answer.

$23 \times 1.92 \approx 20 \times £2 = £40$

This is the grid method.

Next, change the calculation to an equivalent whole number calculation.

$23 \times 1.92 = 23 \times 192 \div 100$

Now do the calculation.

$23 \times 192 = 2000 + 1800 + 300$
$+ 270 + 40 + 6$
$= 4416$

So the total cost of Dave's school meals in March is $4416 \div 100 = £44.16$.

✕	100	90	2
20	20×100 $= 2000$	20×90 $= 1800$	20×2 $= 40$
3	3×100 $= 300$	3×90 $= 270$	3×2 $= 6$

Calculate 21.6×5.3.

First estimate the answer.

$21.6 \times 5.3 \approx 22 \times 5 = 110$

This is the standard method.

Next, change the calculation to an equivalent whole number calculation.

$21.6 \times 5.3 = 216 \times 53 \div 100$

Now do the calculation.

$216 \times 53 = 11\,448$

So $21.6 \times 5.3 = 11\,448 \div 100$
$= 114.48$

$$\begin{array}{r} 216 \\ \times\ 53 \\ \hline 648 \\ +10800 \\ \hline 11448 \end{array}$$

Exercise 15d

1 Calculate

  a 16 × 35   **b** 49 × 54   **c** 68 × 32

  d 64 × 49   **e** 73 × 55   **f** 9 × 336

  g 478 × 7   **h** 8 × 879   **i** 134 × 67

> Remember: always do a mental approximation first.

2 Calculate

  a 8 × 3.26   **b** 9 × 4.65   **c** 7 × 6.92

  d 5 × 4.48   **e** 8 × 26.3   **f** 6 × 54.5

  g 8 × 37.1   **h** 9 × 68.4

3 Calculate

  a 15 × 2.44   **b** 13 × 3.76   **c** 49 × 4.71

  d 68 × 3.96   **e** 58 × 4.54   **f** 78 × 6.08

  g 89 × 5.94   **h** 85 × 8.09

4 Calculate

  a 3.6 × 35.4   **b** 7.3 × 26.7   **c** 4.5 × 58.3

  d 7.2 × 51.6   **e** 6.3 × 76.3   **f** 9.3 × 50.2

  g 4.6 × 83.5   **h** 7.8 × 30.6

5 **a** Ashleigh buys 8 CDs. Each CD costs £9.29. How much does she spend in total?

  b Karen delivers 68 boxes of exercise books to her local school. Each box weighs 6.82 kg. What is the total weight of boxes she has delivered to the school?

  c Ralph buys 4.6 kg of sweets for a party. The sweets cost £4.90 for 1 kg. How much money does Ralph spend on sweets for the party?

  d 1 litre of diesel costs 88.6 pence. Jameela's drive to work each day uses 3.8 litres of fuel. How much money does the fuel cost for her journey?

investigation

Here is a list of five numbers.

   13   15.6   11   5.7   6.3

a Multiply the first two numbers together.

  Multiply the second and third numbers together.

  Multiply the third and fourth numbers together.

  Multiply the fourth and fifth numbers together.

  Add together the four answers to get a total.

b Re-arrange the numbers and repeat this process to get a new total.

c What is the largest total you can make?

- Divide a decimal number using written methods including short division

Keywords
Divide
Estimate
Remainder

- When you **divide** a number there is sometimes a **remainder** left over. You can write a remainder as a whole number or you can use a decimal.

- You can think of division as repeated subtraction.

- You should always **estimate** the answer first.

example

Calculate   **a** $107.1 \div 17$ **b** $92.5 \div 16$
Give your answer to 1 decimal place if appropriate.

a $107.1 \div 17 \approx 120 \div 20 = 6$ **b** $92.5 \div 16 \approx 90 \div 15 = 6$

$$\begin{array}{r} 107.1 \\ -102.0 \\ \hline 5.1 \\ -5.1 \\ \hline 0.0 \end{array}$$ $17 \times 6 = 102$

$17 \times 0.3 = 5.1$

$$\begin{array}{r} 92.50 \\ -80.00 \\ \hline 12.50 \\ -11.20 \\ \hline 1.30 \\ -1.28 \\ \hline 0.02 \end{array}$$ $16 \times 5 = 80$

$16 \times 0.7 = 11.2$

$16 \times 0.08 = 1.28$

Work out your answer to 2 decimal places so you can round it to 1 at the end.

$107.1 \div 17 = 6 + 0.3$
$\qquad = 6.3$

$92.5 \div 16 = 5 + 0.7 + 0.08 \; r0.02$
$\qquad = 5.78 = 5.8 \text{ (to 1 dp)}$

- You can also use the method of short division.

example

Calculate $11 \div 7$, giving your answer to 3 decimal places.

$11 \div 7 \approx 1.5$

$$7 \overline{) 11.\overset{4}{0}\overset{5}{0}\overset{1}{0}\overset{3}{0}} = 1.5714$$

$11 \div 7 = 1 \, r \, 4$
$40 \div 7 = 5 \, r \, 5$
$50 \div 7 = 7 \, r \, 1$
$10 \div 7 = 1 \, r \, 3$
$30 \div 7 = 4 \, r \, 2$

Add four zeros to make your calculation easier.

You need to give your answer to 3 decimal places, so you can stop when the answer has 4 decimal places.

$11 \div 7 = 1.571 \text{ (3 dp)}$

Exercise 15e

1 Calculate

   a 174 ÷ 6   **b** 231 ÷ 7   **c** 216 ÷ 8   **d** 333 ÷ 9

   e 486 ÷ 18   **f** 442 ÷ 17   **g** 806 ÷ 26   **h** 1023 ÷ 33

2 Calculate

   a 43.8 ÷ 6   **b** 57.6 ÷ 8   **c** 65.8 ÷ 7   **d** 79.2 ÷ 9

   e 91.8 ÷ 17   **f** 91.8 ÷ 18   **g** 75.2 ÷ 16   **h** 91.2 ÷ 19

   i 58.5 ÷ 15   **j** 61.2 ÷ 17   **k** 58.8 ÷ 21   **l** 82.8 ÷ 23

3 Calculate these. Where appropriate, give your answer as a decimal
to 2 decimal places.

   a 107 ÷ 8   **b** 134 ÷ 7   **c** 88 ÷ 6   **d** 65 ÷ 9

   e 85.6 ÷ 14   **f** 93.7 ÷ 15   **g** 87.5 ÷ 16   **h** 95.4 ÷ 17

   i 98.2 ÷ 13   **j** 46.8 ÷ 18   **k** 32.8 ÷ 19   **l** 44.2 ÷ 16

4 Calculate these. Where appropriate, give your answer as a decimal
to 3 decimal places.

   a 12 ÷ 7   **b** 19 ÷ 3   **c** 15 ÷ 8   **d** 12 ÷ 5

   e 25 ÷ 11   **f** 19 ÷ 12   **g** 18 ÷ 13   **h** 23 ÷ 14

5 a What is 999 ÷ 37?

   b What is the remainder when 1000 is divided by 37?

   c What is first multiple of 37 larger than 1000?

6 For each of these questions, give your answer rounded
to 2 decimal places, as appropriate.

   a Bernice runs 100 m in 13 seconds.
      What is her average speed in metres per second?

   b Jevon sells a number of items on an auction website for
      £82.56. He shares this equally between his two sisters,
      three brothers and himself. How much do they each receive?

   c Dillon downloads a file at 18 kB per second. The file is 96.5 kB
      in size. How many seconds does it take to download the file?

> You can think of Bernice's
> speed as how far she will
> travel in 1 second.

---

puzzle

Baked beans come in three different sized tins.

a Which size of tin is the best value for money?

b Explain and justify your answer.

100 g
16 p

250 g
37 p

450 g
69 p

Calculator methods

- Decide how best to use the display on a calculator after doing a division

- You can use a calculator to convert between units of **time**.

example

Convert 1000 minutes into hours and minutes.

$1000 \div 60 = 16.666...$ Divide by 60 (1 hour = 60 minutes).
This is 16 hours and 0.666... of an hour.

$0.666... \times 60 = 40$ Change the decimal part to a whole number by multiplying it by 60.

1000 minutes = 16 hours and 40 minutes

- When you work out a division using a calculator and the answer is not a whole number, you must decide how to write and interpret the answer:
  - give a remainder as a decimal or fraction
  - round up or down
  - give to a suitable degree of accuracy

example

a A shopkeeper has 100 packets of crisps to be packed into special multi-packs each containing 9 packets. How many multi-packs will she fill?

b The shopkeeper shares 100 club points between 9 shoppers. How many points will each shopper receive?

a $100 \div 9 = 11.111...$
This tells us that the shopkeeper will fill 11 multi-packs, with 0.111... of a multi-pack left over.
0.111... of a multi-pack is $0.111... \times 9$ packets ≈ 1 packet.
So the shopkeeper will fill 11 multi-packs with 1 packet of crisps left over.

b Each person receives 11 whole points and 0.111... of a point.
You can give the remainder as a fraction. $0.111... = \frac{1}{9}$
So each person receives $11\frac{1}{9}$ points.

Exercise 15f

1 Use your calculator to work out these divisions. Give the remainder part of the answer in the form specified in brackets.

  a £100 ÷ 9   (a decimal to 2 dp)

  b 48 cats ÷ 5   (a whole number remainder)

  c 52 pies ÷ 6   (a fraction)

  d 55 hours ÷ 4   (a fraction)

  e 22.7 kg ÷ 50   (a decimal to 3 dp)

2 Convert these measurements of time to the units given in brackets.

  a 188 minutes (hours and minutes)

  b 8.2 hours (hours and minutes)

  c 2000 hours (days and hours)

  d 300 days (weeks and days)

  e 3500 seconds (minutes and seconds)

  f 2500 minutes (hours and minutes)

  g 35 000 days (years and days)

3 Convert these measurements of time to the units given in brackets.

  a 35 000 minutes (days, hours and minutes)

  b 100 000 seconds (days, hours, minutes and seconds)

  c 50 000 000 seconds (years, weeks, days, hours, minutes and seconds)

4 Give your answer to each of these questions in a form appropriate to the situation.

  a Johnny has 113 CDs. He packs them into bundles of 15. How many bundles of 15 can he make?

  b A lottery syndicate wins £123 567.89. There are 17 people in the syndicate. How much do they each receive?

  c 58 chocolate bars are shared between eight people. How much chocolate does each person receive?

  d A ski lift can carry 78 people. How many journeys does the ski lift take to carry 1000 people?

puzzle

Irene buys seven items in a shop. They cost
88p, 92p, £1.02, 68p, 86p, £1.00 and 99p.
She gives the shop assistant £10 and is given £2.88 in change.
Irene immediately thinks there is a mistake.
How does she know?

- Calculate a fraction of a quantity

Keywords
Cancel   Improper
Common   fraction
  factor   Mixed
Fraction   number
        Product

- You can **cancel common factors** to simplify the **product** of a **fraction** and an integer.

- To find a fraction of an amount, when the fraction is greater than 1, change it into an **improper fraction** first.

example

a Calculate $\frac{11}{14} \times 7$.   **b** Find $2\frac{4}{9}$ of 15 km.

a $\frac{11}{14} \times 7 = \frac{11}{14_{2}} \times 7^{1}$ Cancel by dividing by 7.

    $= \frac{11}{2}$ Convert your answer to a **mixed number** using division.

    $= 5\frac{1}{2}$

b $2\frac{4}{9} = 2 + \frac{4}{9} = \frac{18}{9} + \frac{4}{9} = \frac{22}{9}$ Change the mixed number into an improper fraction.

    $\frac{22}{9}$ of $15 = \frac{22}{9_{3}} \times 15^{5}$ Cancel by dividing by 3.

    $= \frac{110}{3}$ Convert your answer to a mixed number using division.

    $= 36\frac{2}{3}$ km

- To divide by a **unit fraction**, turn the fraction upside down and multiply.

A unit fraction has 1 as its numerator.

- You can think of other fractions as a unit fraction multiplied by an integer.

example

Calculate **a** $2 \div \frac{1}{4}$ **b** $8 \div \frac{2}{3}$

a $2 \div \frac{1}{4} = 2 \times \frac{4}{1}$ **b** $8 \div \frac{2}{3} = 8 \div 2 \div \frac{1}{3}$

    $= 2 \times 4$ $= 4 \div \frac{1}{3}$

    $= 8$ $= 4 \times 3$

                  $= 12$

p. 54

Exercise 15g

1 Change these mixed numbers into improper fractions.

   a $2\frac{2}{3}$ **b** $2\frac{4}{7}$ **c** $3\frac{3}{8}$ **d** $4\frac{1}{2}$ **e** $5\frac{2}{7}$ **f** $8\frac{3}{7}$

2 Change these improper fractions into mixed numbers

   a $\frac{20}{3}$ **b** $\frac{31}{7}$ **c** $\frac{53}{8}$ **d** $\frac{77}{2}$ **e** $\frac{98}{5}$ **f** $\frac{206}{4}$

3 Work out these, giving your answer as a mixed number where appropriate.

   a $8 \times \frac{5}{6}$ **b** $6 \times \frac{7}{9}$ **c** $14 \times \frac{13}{21}$ **d** $15 \times \frac{11}{12}$

   e $7 \times \frac{12}{35}$ **f** $10 \times \frac{7}{5}$ **g** $95 \times \frac{27}{57}$ **h** $44 \times \frac{17}{28}$

   i $45 \times \frac{19}{20}$ **j** $\frac{31}{48} \times 16$ **k** $\frac{24}{55} \times 65$ **l** $\frac{16}{27} \times 18$

4 Calculate

   a $1\frac{3}{8}$ of $14\,\text{MB}$ **b** $1\frac{3}{5}$ of £60   **c** $1\frac{2}{15}$ of \$40   **d** $1\frac{3}{4}$ of $22\,\text{m}$

   e $2\frac{5}{9}$ of $30\,\text{m}$ **f** $2\frac{2}{21}$ of $42\,\text{kg}$ **g** $3\frac{4}{7}$ of $56\,\text{m}$ **h** $1\frac{5}{14}$ of $154\,\text{m}$

5 Calculate

   a $6 \div \frac{1}{3}$ **b** $9 \div \frac{1}{10}$ **c** $6 \div \frac{1}{5}$ **d** $8 \div \frac{1}{4}$

   e $4 \div \frac{1}{7}$ **f** $5 \div \frac{1}{8}$ **g** $12 \div \frac{1}{9}$ **h** $23 \div \frac{1}{8}$

6 Calculate each of these. Give your answer in its simplest form.

   a $6 \div \frac{2}{3}$ **b** $9 \div \frac{9}{10}$ **c** $6 \div \frac{3}{5}$ **d** $8 \div \frac{3}{4}$

   e $4 \div \frac{5}{6}$ **f** $7 \div \frac{3}{8}$ **g** $15 \div \frac{6}{7}$ **h** $12 \div \frac{8}{11}$

   i $10 \div \frac{5}{8}$ **j** $2 \div \frac{5}{13}$ **k** $14 \div \frac{7}{9}$ **l** $8 \div \frac{3}{13}$

7 **a** Lolita the flea can jump $2\frac{3}{8}$ inches in a single leap.

   How far will she travel if she makes six identical leaps?

   b A box of biscuits weighs $3\frac{2}{5}\,\text{kg}$.

   What is the mass of 15 boxes of biscuits?

---

a A file takes $\frac{3}{4}$ of a minute to download.

   How many files can you download in 6 minutes?

b A bag of sweets weighs $\frac{7}{8}\,\text{kg}$.

   How many bags can you fill with 35 kg of sweets?

- Find the outcome of a percentage increase or decrease

- You should know how to convert between **fractions, decimals** and **percentages**.

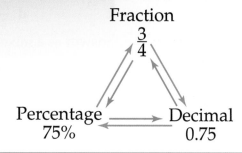

Fraction
$\frac{3}{4}$

Percentage
75%

Decimal
0.75

---

example

Convert   **a** 115% into a decimal   **b** 85% into a fraction

. . . .

a $115\% = 115 \div 100$

      $= 1.15$

b $85\% = 85 \div 100$

      $= \frac{85}{100}$

      $= \frac{17}{20}$ in its simplest form

- You can calculate a percentage **increase** or **decrease** in a single calculation.

---

example

a In a sale, all prices are reduced by 15%.
A pair of trousers normally costs £20.
What is the sale price of the pair of trousers?

b After the sale all the prices are increased by 15%.
What is the new price of a dress that cost £30 in the sale?

. . . .

a In the sale the prices decrease by 15%.
Sale price $= (100 - 15)\%$ of the old price

           $= 85\%$ of £20

           $= 0.85 \times 20$

           $= £17$

b After the sale, the prices increase by 15%.
New price $= (100 + 15)\%$ of the sale price

           $= 115\%$ of £30

           $= 1.15 \times £30$

           $= £34.50$

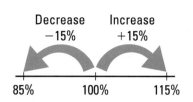

Decrease   Increase
−15%   +15%

85%   100%   115%

Exercise 15h

1 Calculate these percentage changes.

  a Increase £70 by 15%

  b Decrease £70 by 15%

  c Increase 18 m by 25%

  d Decrease 18 m by 25%

  e Increase 85 kg by 48%

  f Decrease £1400 by 11%

  g Increase £12 by 5%

  h Decrease 6700 MB by 16%

2 Mandy sells school uniforms.
She has a sale and reduces all her prices by 12%.
Calculate the sale price of each of these items.

Item	Original Price	Sales price
a Trousers	£25.00	
b Blazer	£35.00	
c Tie	£3.99	
d Shoes	£45.00	
e Shirt	£12.99	

3 a A packet of biscuits weighs 220 g. In a special offer it is increased in mass by 11%. What is the new mass of the packet of biscuits?

  b In a sale DVDs are sold with 35% off. What is the sale price of a DVD normally costing £9.50?

  c Frank buys a new car for £18 900. A year later the car has dropped in value by 9%. What is the new value of the car?

problem solving

In each case explain and justify your answer.

a Vincent owns a shop. In November he increases his prices by 10%.
In the January sales he reduces all his prices by 10%.
Is the January sale price the same as the price before the November increase?

b In a sale a shop took 15% off its normal prices.
On Wicked Wednesday it reduced the sale prices by another 25%.
Mary says that the original price has been reduced by 40%. Is she correct?

15a

1 Use divisibility tests to answer each of these questions.
Explain your answers.
 a Is 5 a factor of 432?
 b Is 639 a multiple of 3?
 c Are 6 and 9 factors of 396?
 d Is 432 a multiple of 18?

2 Write all the factors of
 a 360 b 144 c 225 d 500 e 576 f 1296

3 Use divisibility tests to see which of these numbers are prime.
Explain your answers.
 a 131 b 175 c 147 d 137 e 169 f 187

15b

4 Find the HCF and LCM of
 a 18 and 24 b 45 and 60 c 30 and 95
 d 880 and 480 e 10, 15 and 25 f 32, 48 and 64

5 Write each of these fractions in its simplest form.

 a $\frac{144}{216}$ b $\frac{175}{210}$ c $\frac{192}{256}$

 d $\frac{243}{405}$ e $\frac{930}{1488}$

6 Work out each of these, giving your answer as a fraction in its simplest form.

 a $\frac{3}{8} + \frac{7}{24}$ b $\frac{15}{28} + \frac{11}{21}$

 c $\frac{13}{40} + \frac{21}{50}$ d $\frac{33}{70} + \frac{42}{75}$

15c

7 Calculate these mentally.
 a 300×70 b $3200 \div 40$ c 5×0.1
 d $15 \div 0.01$ e 3800×0.01 f $0.28 \div 0.01$
 g $168 \div 6$ h 0.05×19 i 2.9×19
 j 7.3×12 k $175 \div 14$ l $340 \div 15$
 m 2.4×2.5 n 12×2.1 o 4.5×3.4

8 Calculate

    a 6 × 4.37   **b** 8 × 5.76   **c** 8 × 7.03   **d** 6 × 5.59

    e 12 × 3.55   **f** 14 × 4.87   **g** 19 × 5.82   **h** 37 × 4.07

    i 4.7 × 46.5   **j** 8.4 × 37.8   **k** 5.6 × 69.4   **l** 8.3 × 62.7

9 Calculate

    a 50.4 ÷ 9   **b** 74.4 ÷ 8   **c** 62.3 ÷ 7   **d** 94.5 ÷ 9

    e 47.3 ÷ 13   **f** 84.5 ÷ 14   **g** 37.2 ÷ 15   **h** 65.2 ÷ 16

10 Convert these measurements of time to the units indicated in brackets.

    a 228 minutes (hours and minutes) **b** 3780 hours (days and hours)

    c 540 days (weeks and days)   **d** 2540 seconds (minutes and seconds)

11 Dave is a baker. He sells 45 loaves of bread to eight shops. How much does he sell to each shop, assuming he sells the same amount to each shop?

12 Work out these, giving your answer as a mixed number where appropriate.

    a $12 \times \frac{3}{8}$ **b** $15 \times \frac{4}{9}$ **c** $\frac{4}{7}$ of £210   **d** $18 \times \frac{13}{27}$

    e $27 \times \frac{11}{36}$ **f** $1\frac{4}{7}$ of 14 m   **g** $2\frac{3}{9}$ of £63   **h** $2\frac{7}{8}$ of $45

    i $1\frac{3}{5}$ of 24 cm **j** $\frac{15}{11}$ of 40 m

13 Calculate

    a $9 \div \frac{1}{3}$ **b** $12 \div \frac{1}{8}$ **c** $6 \div \frac{2}{5}$ **d** $8 \div \frac{4}{5}$

    e $16 \div \frac{2}{7}$ **f** $14 \div \frac{3}{4}$ **g** $16 \div \frac{5}{8}$ **h** $18 \div \frac{3}{7}$

14 Calculate these percentage changes.

    a Increase £38 by 12%   **b** Decrease £45 by 11%

    c Increase 138 m by 2.5%   **d** Decrease 365 cm by 15%

    e Increase 374 kg by 18%   **f** Decrease £19 900 by 4.5%

15 Summary

Key indicators

- Multiply and divide whole numbers and decimals **Level 5**
- Increase or decrease an amount by a percentage **Level 6**
- Add, subtract, multiply and divide fractions **Level 6**

Level 5

1 A pair of shoes costs £30.
The price is reduced by 15% in a sale.
Calculate   **a** the saving
           b the new price

Level 6

You can find the new price in one calculation.
c Write down the missing number from the sentence

_____ % *of £30 = the new price*

Jay's answer ✔

Jay realises that 15% is the same as $\frac{15}{100}$ and 0.15

Jay checks: 85% of £30 = 0.85 × 30 = £25.50

a 15% of 30 = 0.15 × 30
            = £4.50
b £30 − £4.50 = £25.50
c 85% of £30 = the new price

Jay decides if £30 is 100% then the new price is 100% − 15% = 85% of the original price

Level 5

2 **a** I pay £16.20 to travel to work each week.
I work for 45 weeks each year.
How much do I pay to travel to work each year?
Show your working.

b I could buy one season ticket that would let me travel for all 45 weeks.
It would cost £630.
How much is that per week?

Key Stage 3 2003 3–5 Paper 1

16 Algebra

Equations and graphs

During World War II, a team of codebreakers worked at Bletchley Park, Buckinghamshire, to break the codes used by the Axis forces. Mathematicians, chess champions and crossword puzzle fanatics used their problem solving skills and a huge computer named Colossus to read the coded messages.

What's the point? The codes were set using functions. When the input and function were known, the output, or message, could be read.

✓ Check in

1 Write the next two terms in each of these sequences.

   a 10, 8, 6, 4, 2, …   **b** 2, 4, 8, 16, 32, …

   c 1, 4, 9, 16, 25, …   **d** 0.5, 0.6, 0.7, 0.8, …

2 Match the sequence with its position-to-term rule.

Add 5	1, 3, 5, 7, 9, …
Multiply it by itself	3, 6, 9, 12, 15, …
Multiply by 2 and take 1	6, 7, 8, 9, 10, …
Multiply it by 3	1, 4, 9, 16, 25, …

3 Given that $a = 3$, $b = -2$ and $c = -5$, evaluate

   a $5a - 2$ **b** $ab + 1$ **c** bc **d** $2a - b$ **e** $3b + 2c$ **f** $2a^2$

4 Solve each of these equations.

   a $3x - 2 = 13$ **b** $\dfrac{y}{3} - 1 = 3$ **c** $z^2 = 36$

   d $5a - 8 = 3a + 2$ **e** $2(b - 4) = 5(b + 7)$

5 Copy and complete the table to show values of the function $y = 3x - 1$.
From this, plot the graph of this function.

x	1	2	3
y	2		

- Solve equations which have unknowns on both sides

Keywords
Balance   Equation
Difference   Solve

- To **solve** an **equation** with the unknown on both sides, first subtract the smaller term.

Imagine that the equation $4x - 4 = 8 - 2x$ is on a set of scales.

Subtract -2x from each side, so that the scales remain **balanced**.

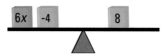

Subtracting a negative is the same as adding.

$-(-2x)$ is the same as $+2x$.

Now you need to add 4 to each side.

Finally divide each side by 6 to find the value of x.

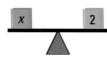

Solve these equations.
a $4x - 4 = 8 - 2x$ **b** $2(5 - 2x) = 4(4 - 2x)$

. . . .

a $4x - 4 = 8 - 2x$ Add 2x to both sides.
   $6x - 4 = 8$ Add 4 to both sides.
      $6x = 12$ Divide both sides by 6.
       $x = 2$

b $2(5 - 2x) = 4(4 - 2x)$ First expand the brackets.
   $10 - 4x = 16 - 8x$ Add 8x to both sides.
   $10 + 4x = 16$ Subtract 10 from both sides.
       $4x = 6$ Divide both sides by 4.
        $x = 1.5$

example

Exercise 16a

1 Show that all of these equations have a solution of $x = 5$.

   a $3x - 1 = 14$ **b** $2(x - 1) = 8$

   c $\dfrac{2x - 1}{3} = 3$ **d** $3x - 2 = 2x + 3$

   e $x + 12 = 4x - 3$ **f** $8x - 10 = 5(x + 1)$

2 Solve these equations. You should find each answer somewhere in the coloured panel.

p. 185

2	1	6
3	3	2

   a $8x - 35 = 25 - 2x$ **b** $13 - 4y = 6y - 7$

   c $2(2z - 6) = 4(3 - 2z)$ **d** $4 - 2a = 13 - 5a$

   e $4 - 6b = 6 - 8b$ **f** $34 - 9c = 10 - c$

3 Two equations have been solved and the steps mixed up. Unscramble them.

$x = 2$	$8x - 1 = 15$	$14 - 4x = 4x - 10$	$24 = 8x$

$x = 3$	$14 = 8x - 10$	$8x = 16$	$5x - 1 = 15 - 3x$

4 Solve these equations. You should find each answer somewhere in the coloured panel.

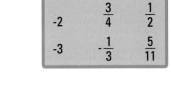

   a $11 + 5x = 15 - 3x$ **b** $20 - 8y = 15 + 3y$

   c $9 - 4z = 15 - 12z$ **d** $10 - 2a = 8 - 3a$

   e $10 - 2b = 9 - 5b$ **f** $2(12 - 2c) = 3(9 - c)$

5 For each of these situations, answer the question by writing and solving an equation.

   a I think of a number, multiply it by 4 and subtract 13. I get the same answer as when I multiply the number by 3 and subtract it from 29. What is my number?

   b What is the length of each side in this isosceles triangle?

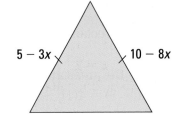

puzzle

   a Each box contains a positive algebraic term. What could be in each box?

   b What if one box contains a negative algebraic term?

   c What if both boxes contain a negative algebraic term?

$$\square + 2 = \square - 5$$
$$6x + 2 = -5$$

- Write equations to describe different situations and then solve them

Keywords
Construct
Equation
Solve

- You can often find the answer to a problem by **constructing** and **solving** an **equation**.

example

Miss Scott said, 'The sum of my current age and my age 20 years ago is equal to my age in 10 years' time. How old am I?'

. . . .

Let her current age be called x.

Her age 20 years ago is $x - 20$.

Her age in 10 years' time is $x + 10$.

So $x + (x - 20) = (x + 10)$ Remove the brackets.
$2x - 20 = x + 10$ Subtract x from both sides.
$\quad x - 20 = 10$ Add 20 to both sides.
$\quad\quad x = 30$

Miss Scott is 30 years old.

example

The areas of these rectangles are equal.
Find the dimensions of each rectangle.

. . . .

Area of rectangle Ⓐ = length × width
$\qquad\qquad\qquad = 12(x - 3)$
Area of rectangle Ⓑ = length × width
$\qquad\qquad\qquad = 4(11 - x)$

Since the areas are equal
$12(x - 3) = 4(11 - x)$ Expand the brackets.
$12x - 36 = 44 - 4x$ Add $4x$ to both sides.
$16x - 36 = 44$ Add 36 to both sides.
$\quad 16x = 80$ Divide both sides by 16.
$\quad\quad x = 5$

Dimensions of rectangle Ⓐ are 12 cm and $5 - 3 = 2$ cm.
Dimensions of rectangle Ⓑ are 4 cm and $11 - 5 = 6$ cm.

Exercise 16b

1 For each of these 'think of a number' problems, find the
  number by writing and solving an equation.
  a I think of a number, multiply it by 5 and add 20.
    The result is 10.
  b I think of a number, multiply it by 7 and subtract 4.
    This gives me the same answer as when I multiply
    the number by 2 and add 6.
  c I think of a number, double it and subtract it from 9.
    This gives me the same answer as treble my number.
  d When I treble a number and subtract it from 10, this gives
    me the same answer as when I subtract it from 15.

2 For each of these diagrams, find the unknown by writing
  and solving an equation.

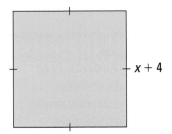

$x + 4$

The perimeter is 60 cm.

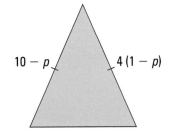

$10 - p$ $4 (1 - p)$

The triangle is isosceles.

3 a Alice, Brett and Chandni win £300 in a lottery draw. Alice
    receives twice as much as Brett, who gets £20 more than
    Chandni. How much does each person receive?
  b Jenny and Louise are identical twins. They were surprised
    to find that their monthly mobile phone bills were also
    identical. If each call costs a fixed price and Jenny made
    20 calls and spent £4 on texts and Louise made 32 calls
    but only spent £1 on texts, how much does each call cost?

> Let the amount of money
> that Brett receives be x.

puzzle

In a pyramid, two adjacent numbers are added to get the
one above.
a Find the missing numbers in this pyramid.
b Devise a pyramid of your own and swap with a partner.

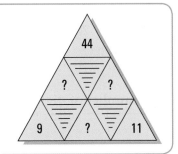

- Use formulas to find unknown quantities

Keywords
Formula   Variable
Substitute

- A **formula** describes the relationship between **variables**. If you know the values of some variables in the formula, you can find the value of the missing values.

example

The formula for the area of a trapezium is $A = \dfrac{(a + b)}{2} h$

Find the area of this trapezium.

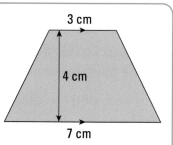

3 cm

4 cm

7 cm

$A = \dfrac{(a + b)}{2} h$ Substitute $a = 3$, $b = 7$ and $h = 4$ into the formula.

$A = \dfrac{(3 + 7)}{2} \times 4$ Work out the contents of the brackets.

$A = \dfrac{10}{2} \times 4$ Cancel the fraction.

$A = 5 \times 4$ Finally, multiply.

$A = 20$ cm²

a = length of one parallel side
b = length of second parallel side
h = distance between parallel sides

- If you know the value of the subject, you can find the value of one of the other unknowns.

example

A hotel uses the formula $C = 50 + 70n$ to charge guests, where C is the total cost in pounds and n is the number of nights spent at the hotel. Find the number of nights spent at the hotel when the total cost was £330.

$C = 50 + 70n$ Substitute $C = 330$ into the formula.

$330 = 50 + 70n$ You are left with an equation with one unknown.

$280 = 70n$ Subtract 50 from both sides.

$4 = n$ Divide both sides by 70.

The number of nights spent at the hotel was 4.

Remember to answer the question with a sentence.

Exercise 16c

1 **a** The area of a triangle is given by the formula $A = \dfrac{bh}{2}$.
Find the base length of a triangle with
area 15 cm² and height 10 cm.

b The perimeter of a rectangle is given by the formula
$P = 2l + 2w$. Find the width of a rectangle with
perimeter 34 cm and length 8 cm.

c The coordinates of a point on a graph are given by the
formula $y = x^2 - 1$. Find the missing number in the
coordinates ([?], 24) which lies on this graph.

2 A mobile phone company uses the formula $C = 10 + \dfrac{2n}{5}$
to work out its customers' monthly bills. C is the cost
in pounds and n is the number of minutes spent on the phone.

a Max spends 40 minutes on his phone one month.
How much will he be charged?

b Roan spends 2 hours on the phone one month and
receives £50 a month from his Saturday job.
Will he be able to afford his bill?

c Sinita is charged £82 one month.
How long did she spend on the phone?

d Is it possible to receive a bill of £55? Explain your answer.

3 The formula $C = \dfrac{5(F - 32)}{9}$ connects temperatures in degrees
Celsius with temperatures in degrees Fahrenheit.

Solid   Liquid   Gas

Melts at
0°C

Boils
at
100°C

Ice   Water   Steam

Find the melting point of ice and boiling point of water
in degrees Fahrenheit.

- Find and use the position-to-term rule for a sequence

p. 20

Keywords
General term
Linear
Position-to-term rule
Sequence

- You can find any term of any **sequence** using a **position-to-term rule**.

example

a Find the first five terms of the sequence defined by the rule $T(n) = 3n + 1$.

b Find the first five terms of the sequence with **general term** $T(n) = 7n - 4$.

$T(n)$ tells you that the rule is a position-to-term rule. $T(n)$ is the nth, or general term.

a $T(1) = 3 \times 1 + 1 = 4$

$T(2) = 3 \times 2 + 1 = 7$

$T(3) = 3 \times 3 + 1 = 10$

$T(4) = 3 \times 4 + 1 = 13$

$T(5) = 3 \times 5 + 1 = 16$

The first five terms are

4, 7, 10, 13 and 16.

b $T(1) = 7 \times 1 - 4 = 3$

$T(2) = 7 \times 2 - 4 = 10$

$T(3) = 7 \times 3 - 4 = 17$

$T(4) = 7 \times 4 - 4 = 24$

$T(5) = 7 \times 5 - 4 = 31$

The first five terms are

3, 10, 17, 24 and 31.

These are both linear sequences. You can work out the difference between successive terms by looking at the formula for the nth term. $T(n) = 3n + 1$ and $T(n) = 7n - 4$.

- You can find the general term of a linear sequence by looking at the difference between the terms and then comparing the sequence with the relevant times table.

example

Find the general term of the sequence 6, 9, 12, 15, 18, ...

First find the difference between the terms.

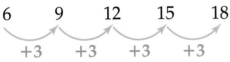

6   9   12   15   18

+3   +3   +3   +3

The difference between the terms is **3**, so compare the sequence with the **three** times table.

You need to **add 3** to the multiples of three to get the terms of the sequence.

So the rule is $T(n) = 3n + 3$.

The formula for the nth term must involve **3n**.

Position	1	2	3	4	5
3 times table	3 +3	6 +3	9 +3	12 +3	15 +3
Term, T(n)	6	9	12	15	18

Exercise 16d

1 Find the position-to-term rule for each of these linear sequences.

   a 9, 14, 19, 24, 29, …   **b** 5, 12, 19, 26, 33, …

   c 12, 23, 34, 45, 56, …   **d** 9, 8, 7, 6, 5, …

2 For each of these sequences

   i copy and complete the table of information

   ii find a formula connecting n, the diagram number, and D, the number of dots

   iii find the number of dots in the 100th pattern in the sequence.

Diagram number	1	2	3	4
Number of dots				

a

b

3 The position-to-term formulas of various linear sequences are given, some in words and others using $T(n)$. Find the first five terms of each sequence. The answers can be found in the grid, where the sequences run horizontally, vertically or diagonally.

13	2	-1	9	3	20
10	5	10	15	20	25
8	8	9	14	19	30
6	11	4	13	18	35
4	14	7	12	17	40
2	1	6	11	16	21

   a Multiply the position by 5   **e** $T(n) = 2n$

   b Multiply the position by 4 and add 1   **f** $T(n) = 5n - 4$

   c Add 10 to the position   **g** $T(n) = 3n - 1$

   d Subtract the position from 21

Hydrocarbons are chemicals containing a set number of hydrogen and carbon atoms. Here are some examples. What sequences can you find within hydrocarbons?

H   Hydrogen

C   Carbon

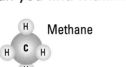

Methane

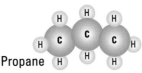

Propane

Ethane

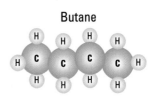

Butane

- Find an expression for the general term of a sequence of geometric patterns

Keywords
General term
Linear
Sequence

- You can find the general term of a **sequence** represented by a diagram by looking at the quantities in the diagram.

example

Find the **general term** for this sequence.

3, 5, 7, 9 is a **linear** sequence that increases in 2s. If you compare it with the beginning of the 2 times table (2, 4, 6, 8) you can see that you need to add 1 to get the terms of the sequence. So $m = 2t + 1$.

Number of triangles, t	1	2	3	4
Number of matches, m	3	5	7	9

- Sometimes you can find the general term by looking at the structure of the diagrams.

example

Find the general term for this sequence.

In each pattern, t triangles are made using **2t matches** plus **one extra match** to close the final triangle.

$m = 2t + 1$

example

Explain why $T = n + 6$, where T is the number of tiles and n is the pattern number.

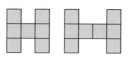 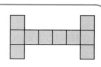

Each pattern has n tiles in a row across the middle of the H, plus six more to complete the ends of the shape.

Exercise 16e

1 Explain, by looking at the structure of the diagrams, why each of these formulas works.

  a $m = 4s$

    m = number of matches

    s = number of squares

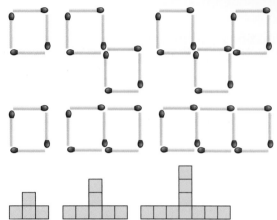

  b $m = 3s + 1$

    m = number of matches

    s = number of squares

  c $t = 3n + 1$

    t = number of tiles

    n = diagram number

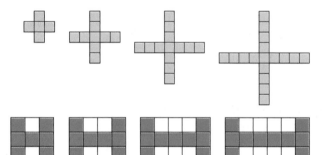

2 Look at the structure of these diagrams and generate a formula to connect the given variables for each sequence.

  a t = number of tiles

    n = diagram number

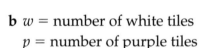

  b w = number of white tiles

    p = number of purple tiles

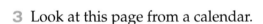

3 Look at this page from a calendar.

Pick any 'L' shape in the grid, like the one shown. Add the three numbers. Find a formula connecting the corner number (circled) with the total.
Explain your formula.

This date has an obvious sequence in it.
a What is the sequence?
b Why is this date so important in history?
c Are there any other key historical dates that can be remembered easily by the date on which they happened?

11 a.m. 11 November

• Draw graphs of functions using their equation to find points

Keywords
Equation
Function
Mapping

• **Functions** are rules that can be written using a **mapping** such as $x \rightarrow 2x$ or an **equation** such as $y = 2x$. Values that satisfy the function can be plotted to form a graph.

• The equation tells you what the graph will look like.

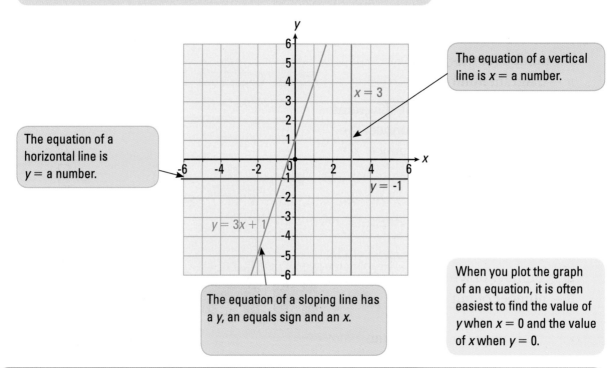

The equation of a vertical line is $x =$ a number.

The equation of a horizontal line is $y =$ a number.

The equation of a sloping line has a y, an equals sign and an x.

When you plot the graph of an equation, it is often easiest to find the value of y when $x = 0$ and the value of x when $y = 0$.

example

Plot the graphs $y = 2x - 1$ and $x + 2y = 8$ on one set of axes and write their point of intersection.

$y = 2x - 1$

x	1	2	3
y	1	3	5

$x + 2y = 8$

x	0	8
y	4	0

The graphs intersect at (2, 3).

Check: $2 + 2(3) = 8$

$8 = 8$ ✔

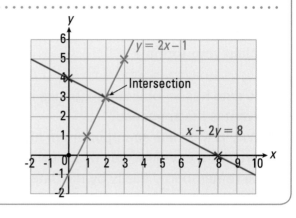

Exercise 16f

1 Write the equation of each of these lines.

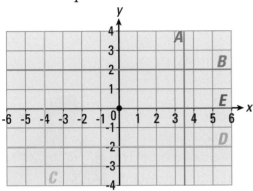

2 Plot these linear functions on the same axes.

   a $y = 3x$ **b** $y = 4x - 2$

   c $y = 2(x + 1)$ **d** $y = 10 - x$

3 Plot these linear functions on the same axes.

   a $x + y = 4$ **b** $2x + y = 10$

   c $3x + 4y = 12$ **d** $x - 2y = 4$

4 Darshan receives £100 for her birthday and wants to use the
money to buy CDs and DVDs. Each CD costs £8 and each
DVD costs £12.

   a Let the number of CDs purchased be called x and the
number of DVDs be called y. Assuming that Darshan
spends all her birthday money, write an equation to
connect the variables x and y.

   b Draw the graph of your equation.

   c Give an example of

     i a point on the line

     ii a point below the line

     iii a point above the line.

   d Explain the real-life meaning of your answers to part **c**.

Louise did an experiment
in Science.
Here are her results.

Voltage (V)	0.5	1	1.5	2	2.5	3
Current (A)	0.1	0.2	0.29	0.39	0.48	0.58

a Do voltage and current have a linear relationship?

b Find an equation that links these variables.

- Understand and read graphs which describe real-life situations

Keywords
Distance–time graph
Graph
Sketch

You can use graphs to help you answer questions about a situation.

This sketch graph shows Charlie's heart rate when he runs.

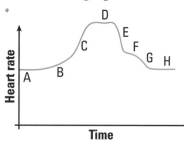

A Waiting to begin exercise
B Warm up – heart rate increases
C Fast run – heart rate increases quickly
D Keeps running – heart rate is constant
E Stops – heart rate drops
F Warms down – heart rate decreases more slowly
G Stops – heart rate drops
H Finish – heart rate returns to normal

- A **sketch graph** does not use actual data but the shape of the graph is approximately correct.

example

Karl leaves Nottingham in his car at 09:00 and drives 20 miles in half an hour. He then stops for half an hour. He then travels 40 miles in 45 minutes, before stopping for 15 minutes. He then returns to Nottingham at a speed of 30 miles per hour.

a Draw a graph to show this information.
b How far from Nottingham was Karl at 12:15?

a

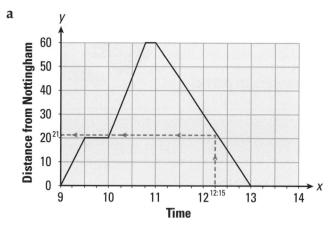

On a **distance–time** graph, flat sections of the graph represent stopping (time passes but no distance is covered).

The steeper the line, the faster the speed (more distance is covered in the same amount of time).

b At 12:15, Karl was approximately 21 miles from Nottingham.

Exercise 16g

1 Sketch a graph to illustrate each of these situations.
   Explain what is happening in each section of your graph.
   a Height of a boy from birth to 20 years old.
   b Temperature of a bath against time.
   c Cost of your mobile phone bill across one week.
   d Depth of water in this container against time (water is
      flowing in at a constant rate).
   e Volume of water in the same container against time
      (water is flowing in at a constant rate).

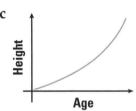

2 Explain why each of these sketch graphs is impossible.

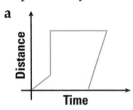 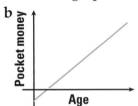 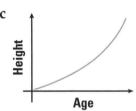

3 Margaret leaves Liverpool on her bicycle at 12 noon. She cycles
   8 miles in one hour, then stops for a 15 minute break. She then
   cycles the remaining 2 miles to her friend's house, arriving at
   a quarter to two. She stays for one hour and then cycles
   directly back to Liverpool, arriving home at 3.30 p.m.
   a Draw a graph to represent this journey.
   b How far from Liverpool was Margaret at 12.30 p.m.?
   c What was Margaret's speed at 1.30 p.m.?
   d At which two times was Margaret 5 miles from Liverpool?

discussion

Does this graph help to answer
the question 'Is there life on
planets other than Earth?'

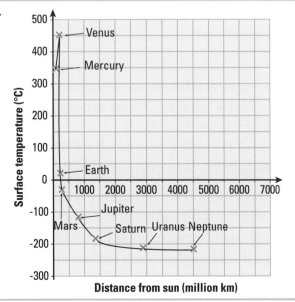

16a

1 Solve these equations.

  a $3x - 2 = 10 - 3x$ **b** $5(2y + 1) = 3(4 - 5y)$

  c $4 - 8z = 8 - 12z$ **d** $15 - x = 20 - 2x$

2 What is wrong with each of these solutions?
Write the correct solution for each.

  a $6x - 4 = 10 - 4x$ **b** $2(x + 5) = 3(10 - x)$

     $2x - 4 = 10$ $2x + 5 = 30 - x$

       $2x = 14$ $3x + 5 = 30$

        $x = 7$ $3x = 25$

                             $x = 8\frac{1}{3}$

16b

3 For each of these situations, answer the question by writing and solving an equation.

  a The areas of these rectangles are equal.
What are the dimensions of each rectangle?

3x + 2, 6, 30 − 3x, 2

  b My sister is four years younger than me.
The sum of our ages is equal to my age in 10 years time.
How old am I now?

16c

4 An internet music site charges customers according to the formula $C = 2d + 1$, where C = cost in pounds and d = number of singles downloads.

  a If I download 17 singles, how much will I be charged?

  b If I am charged £53, how many singles did I download?

5 An approximate formula for the surface area of a sphere is $A = 12r^2$, where r is the radius of the sphere.

  a Find the approximate area of a sphere with radius of 10 cm.

  b Find the radius of a sphere with surface area of 300 cm².

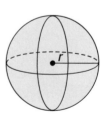

6 Find the first five terms of the sequences defined by these position-to-term rules.
   a $T(n) = 3n$ **b** $T(n) = 5n + 1$
   c $T(n) = 7n - 4$ **d** $T(n) = n^2$
   Are all the sequences linear?

7 Find a formula for $T(n)$, the general term, of each of these sequences, given that n represents the position of each term.
   a 4, 8, 12, 16, 20, ...   **b** 6, 8, 10, 12, 14, ...   **c** 1, 10, 19, 28, 37, ...

8 Find a formula connecting the number of white beads, w, with the number of green beads, g.

9 On one set of axes, plot the graphs $y = 2x + 1$ and $x + y = 4$.
   Write the coordinate of their point of intersection.

10 Describe in words what is happening in this graph.

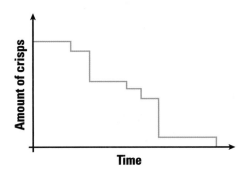

Islamic Art

Islamic architecture uses geometric patterns for decoration. The artists used maths to create these colourful patterns on walls, ceilings and floors.

Answer these questions for each of the patterns found in this room.

Green Palace Pattern Checklist

Pattern location _____

Pattern description _____

Draw the pattern:

This pattern uses (circle all that apply)

Squares   Triangles   Circles   Rectangles

Pentagons   Hexagons

Trapeziums _____

Is there symmetry in the pattern? _____

What kind of symmetry is used?   Reflection   Rotation

Look at the points where the lines in the pattern intersect.

Use a protractor to find the angles around each of these points.

What do the angles add up to? _____

Does the pattern tessellate? _____

Use shapes to create your own Islamic patterns.

Key indicators
- Recognise that $y = mx + c$ is the equation of a straight line **Level 6**
- Construct and solve linear equations **Level 6**
- Plot graphs of linear functions **Level 6**
- Construct and interpret graphs from real-life situations **Level 6**
- Find the general term (*n*th term) of a sequence **Level 6**

Level 6

1 Find the general term (*n*th term) of the sequence

5, 7, 9, 11, 13

Scott's answer ✔

The difference is 2 and so Scott compares the terms with the 2 times table

Scott finds the difference between the terms

Scott needs to add 3 to get the terms of the sequence

			5	7	9	11	13
			+2	+2	+2	+2	

Position	1	2	3	4	5
2 times table	2	4	6	8	10
Term		5	7	9	11	13

The general term (*n*th term) is $2n + 3$

Level 6

2 The diagram shows a square drawn on a square grid.

The points *A*, *B*, *C* and *D* are at the vertices of the square. Match the correct line to each equation.
One is done for you.

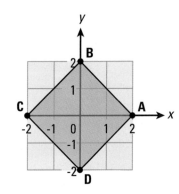

$y = 0$ ———→ Line through *C* and *D*

$x = 0$ Line through *A* and *C*

$x + y = 2$ Line through *A* and *D*

$x + y = -2$ Line through *B* and *D*

Line through *B* and *C*

Line through *A* and *B*

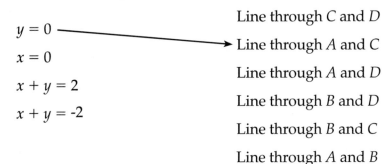

Key Stage 3 2003 4–6 Paper 1

17 Shape

3-D shapes and construction

This is almost the bird's-eye view of Oxford University Press where this book was made. The inner courtyard is called a quadrangle because four buildings surround the yard.

What's the point? The bird's-eye view of an object is called the plan view.

✓ Check in

Level 5

1 Construct these triangles using a protractor and a ruler.

a   **b**

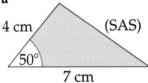
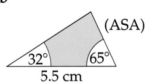

2 **a** Draw these angles accurately with a protractor.
   i 60°   **ii** 52°
  b Use a ruler and compasses to construct the bisector of each of the angles in part **a**.

3 **a** Accurately draw the line AB where $AB = 6$ cm.
  b Use a ruler and compasses to construct the perpendicular bisector of AB.

• Know some of the properties of polygons

Keywords
Interior   Regular
Polygon   Rotation
Reflection   symmetry

• A **polygon** is a 2-D shape with three or more straight sides.

You should know the names of these polygons.

Number of sides	Name	Number of sides	Name
3	Triangle	7	Heptagon
4	Quadrilateral	8	Octagon
5	Pentagon	9	Nonagon
6	Hexagon	10	Decagon

• The **interior** angles of a polygon are the angles inside the polygon.

The interior angles of a triangle add to 180°.

3 sides
3 angles

The interior angles of a quadrilateral add to 360°.

4 sides
4 angles

A **regular** shape has equal sides and equal angles.

A regular octagon
8 sides, 8 angles

A regular polygon is shown.
a State the mathematical name of the polygon.
b Draw the lines of **reflection symmetry**.
c State the order of **rotation symmetry**.

a The polygon has 7 sides and so it is a heptagon.
b There are 7 lines of reflection symmetry.
c The polygon has rotation symmetry of order 7. The shape looks exactly like itself 7 times in a complete turn.

Exercise 17a

1 Use isometric paper to tessellate
   a an equilateral triangle **b** a rhombus
   c a parallelogram **d** a regular hexagon.

2 Decide whether these quadrilaterals are regular.
   a a rectangle
   b a square
   c a rhombus

3 A regular octagon does not tessellate.
   A square is needed to fill the gaps.
   Calculate the interior angle of a regular octagon.

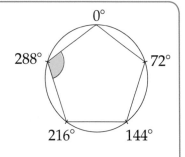

4 Calculate the angles marked with letters.

a

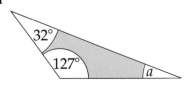

b

c

d

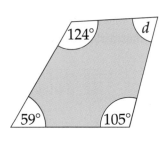

e

f

---

a Draw a regular pentagon.
  i Draw a circle.
  ii Use a protractor to mark off points at 72° intervals – at 0°, 72°, 144°, 216°, 288° and 360° (same as 0°).
  iii Join up the points with straight lines.
b Measure one of the interior angles of the pentagon.
c Draw the lines of reflection symmetry on your diagram.
d State the order of rotation symmetry of the regular pentagon.

$360° \div 5 = 72$

- Use ruler and compasses to draw triangles accurately when all three sides are known

Keywords
Compasses   Ruler
Construct   Triangle
Protractor

You can **construct triangles** when you know

- two angles and the included side (ASA)

or

- two sides and the included angle (SAS).

It is only possible to draw one triangle in each case.

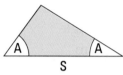

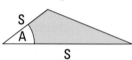

- If you know the length of all three sides (SSS), you can construct a triangle using a **ruler** and **compasses**. It is only possible to draw one triangle.

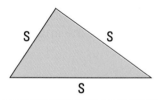

Construct triangle *DEF* (SSS).

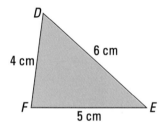

Diagrams are not accurately drawn.

Do not rub out your construction lines.

Draw the base line of 5 cm using a ruler.

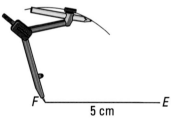

Draw an arc 4 cm from *F* using compasses.

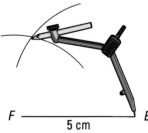

Draw an arc 6 cm from *E* using compasses.

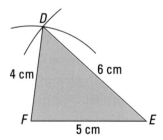

Draw the lines *FD* and *ED* to complete the triangle.

Exercise 17b

1 i Construct each of these triangles (SSS).

ii Give the mathematical name of each triangle.

a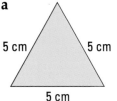
5 cm 5 cm
5 cm

b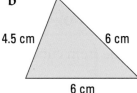
4.5 cm 6 cm
6 cm

c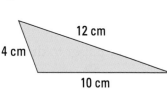
12 cm
4 cm
10 cm

2 i Use ruler and compasses to construct each quadrilateral.

ii Give the mathematical name for each quadrilateral.

iii Use a protractor to measure the shaded angle.

a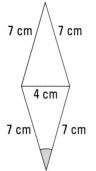
7 cm 7 cm
4 cm
7 cm 7 cm

b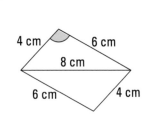
4 cm 6 cm
8 cm
6 cm 4 cm

c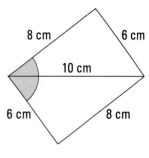
8 cm 6 cm
10 cm
6 cm 8 cm

3 Tracey and Peter were asked to construct a triangle with angles 30°, 60° and 90°. Both their triangles are correct.

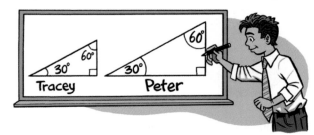
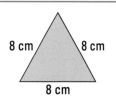

194

202

a Are the triangles similar or congruent?
  Give a reason for your choice.

b What information needs to be given so that Peter and Tracey draw identical triangles?

Use ruler and compasses to construct

a an equilateral triangle of length 8 cm

b the angle bisector of each interior angle

c the three lines of reflection symmetry of the triangle.

8 cm 8 cm
8 cm

- Draw plans and elevations of 3-D solids

Keywords
Dimensions   Solid
Elevation   Three-
Isometric   dimensions
Plan   (3-D)

- A **solid** is a shape formed in **three-dimensions (3-D)**.

You can use **isometric** paper to draw solids made from cubes.

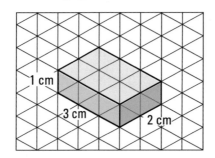

Notice the vertical lines. The isometric paper must be this way up.

The **dimensions** of the cuboid are 3 cm by 2 cm by 1 cm.

- You can use diagrams to show what an object looks like from several different directions.
  - A **front elevation** shows the view from the front.
  - A **side elevation** shows the view from the side.
  - A **plan** shows the view from above.

This is what a Dalek looks like from different directions.

Front elevation   Side elevation   Plan

example

This shape is made from four cubes.
Draw
    a the front elevation (from F)
    b the side elevation (from S)
    c the plan (from P).

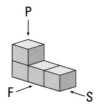

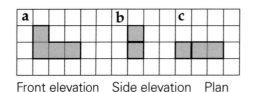

The bold lines show when the level of cubes changes.

Front elevation   Side elevation   Plan

Exercise 17c

1 i Match each of these solids with its plan view.
  ii Give the mathematical name of each solid.

a   **b**   **c**   **d**   **e**

A   **B** **C** **D**   **E**

2 On square grid paper draw
  i   the front elevation (from F)
  ii the side elevation (from S)
  iii the plan (from P)
  for each of these shapes.

a P

F   S

b P

F   S

c P

F   S

d P

F   S

e P

F   S

f P

F   S

3 A 3-D shape is made from some cubes.

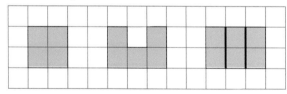

Front elevation   Side elevation   Plan

  a Draw the solid on isometric paper.
  b How many cubes are needed to make the shape?

activity

Here are the letters L and I, drawn on isometric paper.
  a Use isometric paper to write your name.
  b On square grid paper draw the front elevation, side elevation and plan of your name.

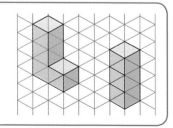

- Recognise 3-D solids from their nets

Keywords
Base
Cross-section
Net
Solid
Three-dimensions
(3-D)

- A **solid** is a shape formed in **three-dimensions (3-D)**.

These are all solids.

Cube

All the faces are squares.

Cuboid

All the faces are rectangles.

Prism

The **cross-section** is the same throughout the length.

Pyramid

The **base** tapers to a point.

- A **net** is a 2-D shape that can be folded to form a solid.
  This is the net of a square-based pyramid.

example

a On square grid paper, draw the net of this cuboid.
b Calculate **i** the surface area **ii** the volume of the cuboid.

a

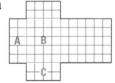

Work out the area of all six rectangular faces, and add them together to find the surface area.

b Area of A $= 5 \times 2 = 10$ cm²
   Area of B $= 5 \times 4 = 20$ cm²
   Area of C $= 4 \times 2 = 8$ cm²
   Surface area $= 10 + 10 + 20 + 20 + 8 + 8$
                  $= 76$ cm²

The units of area are square centimetres (cm²).

c Volume $=$ length $\times$ width $\times$ height
          $= 5 \times 4 \times 2$
          $= 40$ cm³

The units of volume are cubic centimetres (cm³).

Exercise 17d

1 Give the mathematical name of the solid formed by each of these nets.

a
b
c
d

e
f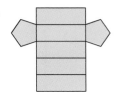
g
h

2 Copy the net of this solid.
   a Give the mathematical name of the solid formed by the net.
   b Mark on your diagram the edge that meets the red line when the net is folded.
   c Mark on your diagram the vertices that meet the red dot when the net is folded.

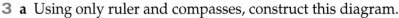

3 a Using only ruler and compasses, construct this diagram.
   b Name the solid that is formed by this net.

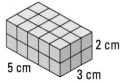

4 a On square grid paper, draw a net of a 2 cm by 3 cm by 5 cm cuboid.
   b Calculate
      i the surface area   ii the volume of the cuboid.

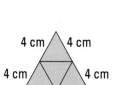

5 a On square grid paper, draw a net of this solid.
   b Give the mathematical name of the solid.
   c Calculate the surface area of the solid.

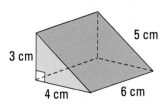

On square grid paper, find and draw 11 different nets that would form a cube.

• Describe a locus of a moving point and draw it accurately

Keywords
Arc   Path
Equidistant Perpendicular
Locus   bisector

• The **locus** of an object is its **path**.

example

Emma decided to go on the swing. Draw the locus of her foot as she swings.

The locus is an **arc**.

An arc is part of a curve.

• A point that moves according to a rule can form a locus.

example

Draw the locus of the point that is 1.5 centimetres from a fixed point, O.

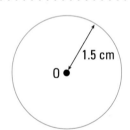

The locus is a circle with radius 1.5 centimetres.

Each point on the circle is 1.5 cm from the centre, O.

example

Draw the locus of the point that is **equidistant** from two fixed points, A and B.

Equidistant means 'equal distance'.

The locus is the **perpendicular bisector** of the (imaginary) line AB.

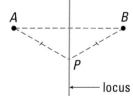

Length AP is the same as length BP. P could be anywhere on the locus and this would still be true.

Exercise 17e

1 Draw and describe in words the locus of
   a a ball bouncing along a level path
   b the tip of the hour hand on a clock
   c the bell on a bicycle travelling on a level road
   d the tip of a car windscreen wiper
   e someone's foot as they do a cartwheel.

2 Give an example of a practical situation when the locus is
   a an arc   b a straight line   c a circle.

3 Copy the diagrams on square grid paper. Draw the locus of
   the point that is equidistant from *A* and *B*.

   a
   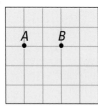

   b
   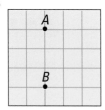

   c
   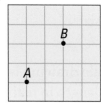

4 a Use a protractor to draw an angle of 70°.

   b Draw the locus of the point that is equidistant from
      OA and *OB*.

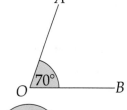

5 a A white dot is painted at the centre of a circular
     counter and the counter is rolled along a
     horizontal surface. Draw the locus of the
     white dot.
   b A white dot is painted at the rim of a circular
     counter and the counter is rolled along a
     horizontal surface. Draw the locus of the
     white dot.

A snooker table measures 7 squares by 4 squares
and only has 4 corner pockets. A ball starts from
the corner as shown.
a Draw the locus of the ball as it rebounds around
   the table until it finishes in a pocket.
b Investigate other sizes of snooker tables.

• Use a scale when a life-sized object is shown as a scale drawing

Keywords
Represent
Scale
Scale drawing

• You can use **scale drawings** to **represent** real-life objects.

• Real-life distances are reduced or enlarged using a **scale**.

• The scale allows you to interpret the scale drawing.

This scale drawing represents a domino.

Scale: 1 cm represents 2 cm

This is the real-life domino.

Each length on the scale drawing is half as long as the corresponding length in real-life.

example

The scale drawing of a door is shown.
1 cm represents 50 cm.
Calculate the dimensions of the door.

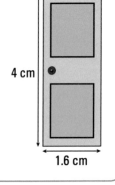

4 cm

1.6 cm

Height = 4 × 50
        = 200 cm
Width = 1.6 × 50
       = 80 cm

The real-life lengths are 50 times larger than in the scale drawing.

example

A rectangular lawn measures 10 metres by 20 metres.
a Draw a scale drawing of the lawn using a scale of 1 cm
   to represent 5 metres.
b Measure the diagonal of the rectangle.
c Calculate the length of the diagonal of the lawn.

a
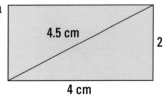
4.5 cm
2 cm
4 cm
Scale: 1 cm represents 5 m

20 ÷ 5 = 4 cm
10 ÷ 5 = 2 cm

Always put the scale on
your diagram.

b Measuring gives 4.5 cm.
c 4.5 × 5 = 22.5 m

Exercise 17f

1 On a scale drawing, 1 centimetre represents 5 centimetres.
Calculate the real-life distance represented by
  a 4 cm   **b** 9 cm   **c** 0.5 cm   **d** 2.5 cm

2 This is a scale drawing of a post box.
Calculate the height and width of the post box.
Scale: 1 cm represents 40 cm

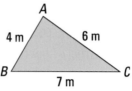

3 A triangular plot of land has lengths $AB = 4$ metres,
$AC = 6$ metres and $BC = 7$ metres as shown.
Using only ruler and compasses, construct
a scale drawing of the plot of land. Use a scale of
1 centimetre to represent 1 metre.

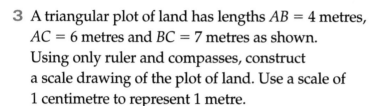

4 The audio players are shown at real-life size. Using a scale of
1 cm to represent 2 cm, draw scale drawings of the players.

  a

  b

A ladder is positioned 2 metres from the wall and
6 metres up the wall.
  a Draw a scale drawing, using a scale of 1
    centimetre to represent 1 metre.
  b Use a protractor to measure the unknown angle.
  c If the angle is more than 75°, the ladder is too
    steep and is dangerous.
    Is the ladder safe?

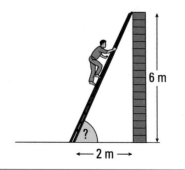

1 Each interior angle of a regular pentagon is 108°.
A regular pentagon does not tessellate.

   a State the mathematical name of the quadrilateral that is
   needed to fill the gaps.

   b Calculate each interior angle of this quadrilateral.

2 i Using ruler and compasses, construct these triangles (SSS).
   ii Calculate the area of each triangle.

a

4 cm   7.5 cm

8.5 cm

b

4 cm   3 cm

5 cm

c

2.5 cm   6 cm

6.5 cm

3 On square grid paper, draw
   i   the front elevation (from F)
   ii the side elevation (from S)
   iii the plan (from P)
        for each solid.

a P

F   S

b P

F   S

c P

F   S

4 A 3-D shape is made from cubes.

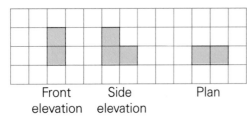

Front   Side   Plan
elevation   elevation

   a Draw the 3-D shape on isometric paper.
   b How many cubes are needed to make the solid?

5 a Draw the nets of these cuboids on square grid paper.
  b Calculate **i** the surface area **ii** the volume of each cuboid.

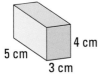 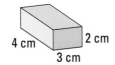

6 a Construct this net using compasses, a protractor and a ruler.
  b Give the mathematical name of the solid formed by the net.

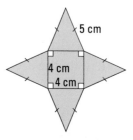

7 Draw and describe in words the locus of
  a a lawn mower cutting a rectangular lawn
  b someone's left foot as they climb the stairs
  c a ball being thrown to another person
  d a ball being thrown up and being caught by the same person
  e a shot putt being thrown.

8 Draw two points, *A* and *B*, that are 5 cm apart. Using only compasses and ruler, construct the locus of the point that is equidistant from *A* and *B*.

9 A matador moves around a stationary bull.
He is always exactly 3 metres from the bull.
Using a scale of 1 centimetre to represent 1 metre,
draw the locus of the matador.

Bull

10 The scale of a scale drawing is 1 centimetre to represent 20 centimetres.
Calculate the real-life distance represented by
  a 5 cm   **b** 10 cm   **c** 25 cm   **d** 0.5 cm   **e** 4.5 cm

11 The Blackpool Tower is 160 metres tall.
A wind turbine can be 100 metres tall.
Draw a scale drawing to show the heights of the Blackpool
Tower and a wind turbine. Use a scale of 1 centimetre to represent 40 metres.

17 Summary

Key indicators

- Identify all the symmetries of 2-D shapes **Level 5**
- Use plans and elevations to analyse 3-D shapes **Level 6**

Level 5

1   A regular hexagon is shown.

   a Draw all the lines of symmetry of a regular hexagon.
   b State the order of rotation symmetry of the regular hexagon.

Ben's answer ✔

Ben knows that a regular 6 sided polygon has 6 lines of symmetry and has rotation symmetry of order 6

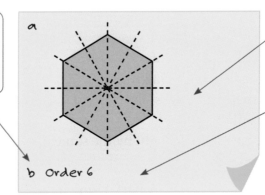

a

b Order 6

Ben realises the shape can be folded in half 6 times

Ben notices the shape looks the same 6 times in a full turn

Level 6

2   Each shape below is made from five cubes that are joined together.

   Complete the missing diagrams below.

Shape drawn on an isometric grid	View from above of the shape drawn on a square grid

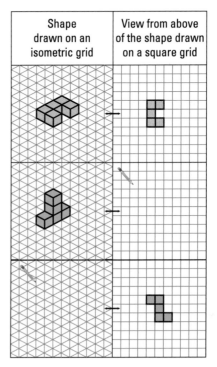

Key Stage 3 2006 4–6 Paper 2

Check in and Summary answers

Check in

1 **a** 526 **b** 504 **c** 1040   **d** 267

2 **a** $5\frac{28}{100}$ **b** 52 080   **c** 5 028 000

   d $502\frac{8}{10}$ **e** 520 0085

3 **a** 170 **b** 3500 **c** 4.8 **d** 1.3

4 **a** -6°C, -1°C, 0°C, 4°C, 8°C

Summary

2 **a** 0.455, 0.5, 0.45, 0.0055, 0.045

   b 0.0055, 0.045, 0.45, 0.455, 0.5

Check in

1 **a** 8, 15, 22, 29, 36, 43, 50

   b 13, 22, 31, 40, 49, 58, 67, 76, 85, 94, 103

   c 80, 72, 64, 56, 48, 40, 32, 24, 16, 8, 0

2 **a** 1, 3, 5, 7, 9   **b** 3, 6, 9, 12, 15

   c 7, 14, 21, 28, 35 **d** 9, 18, 27, 36, 45

3 **a** 28 **b** 54 **c** 110 **d** 8

   e 7 **f** 9 **g** 5 **h** 7

4 **a** **Input** 5, 10; **Output** 16, 19

   b **Input** 2, 5; **Output** 24, 48

Summary

2 **a** 6, 18   **b** 8, 10   **c** e.g. $-20, \div 5$

Check in

1 **a** m **b** mm   **c** cm   **d** km

2 **a** 15 **b** 16 **c** 27 **d** $10\frac{1}{2}$

3 **a** 16 **b** 40

Summary

2 **a** 8   **b** 3

Check in

1 **a** $\frac{4}{8} = \frac{1}{2}$ **b** $\frac{3}{10}$ **c** $\frac{3}{9} = \frac{1}{3}$

2 **a** $\frac{2}{3} = \frac{4}{6}$ **b** $\frac{1}{4} = \frac{4}{16}$ **c** $\frac{3}{4} = \frac{48}{64}$

3

Fraction	Decimal	Percentage
$\frac{1}{10}$	0.1	10%
$\frac{1}{4}$	0.25	25%
$\frac{1}{2}$	0.5	50%
$\frac{3}{4}$	0.75	75%

Summary

2 **a** 8.4, 4.2, 2.1 **b** £98.70

Check in

1 **a** 9, 10, 10, 10, 11, 12, 12, 15

   b 94, 98, 98, 99, 100, 101, 101, 103, 104, 110

   c 234, 243, 324, 342, 423, 432

2 **a** 14 **b** 24 **c** 110

3 **a** $\frac{1}{4}$ **b** $\frac{3}{8}$ **c** 8

Summary

2 June, 19 hours, December, 5 hours

Check in

1 **a** 49, 16, 1, 9, 25 **b** 4, 36, 64 or 81

   c 169 or 196

2 **a** 5 **b** -11 **c** 8 **d** -13

   e -12 **f** 5 **g** -21 **h** 9

3 $\frac{n}{3}, 2(n-2), 2n-1, n^2, 4n, n+10$

Summary

2 5 ml

Check in

1 **a**

	Length	Mass	Capacity
metric	millimetre	gram	litre
	centimetre	tonne	centilitre
	kilometre	kilogram	
	millimetre		
	metre		
imperial	foot	pound	gallon
	inch	ounce	

2 **a** 99 **b** 16 **c** 60 **d** 10

3 **a** 15 **b** 32 **c** 3 **d** 5

   e 7 **f** 9 **g** 48 **h** 9

4

×	50	7
30	1500	210
8	400	56

= 2166

Summary

2

×	100	40	3
30	3000	1200	90
6	600	240	18

= 5148

Check in

1 0.1, 0.4, 0.75, 0.98
2 **a** 10, 20 **b** 14, 28
  c 6, 10, 30 **d** 13, 17, 23
3 **a** $\frac{1}{3}$ **b** $\frac{5}{7}$ **c** $\frac{1}{2}$ **d** $\frac{1}{3}$
  e $\frac{1}{6}$ **f** $\frac{7}{8}$ **g** $\frac{4}{9}$ **h** $\frac{11}{20}$

Summary 2 **a** B **b** A, D

Check in

1 **a** Cuboid **b** Cylinder
  c Sphere **d** Cube
2 **b i** right **ii** obtuse
    iii acute **iv** reflex

Summary

2 **a** No, the sides are not all the same.
  b Yes, two pairs of equal and adjacent sides.
  c Yes, four equal sides and angles.

Check in

1 **a** 11, 23, 7, 9 **b** 4, 3, 31, 10
2 **a** (1, 4), (4, 4), (5, 2), (2, 2)
  b (0, 2), (1, 4), (4, 4), (4, 2)
  c (1, 3), (3, 5), (5, 3), (3, 0)
  d Parallelogram, trapezium, kite
3 2, 3, 5, 7, 11, 13, 17, 19, 23, 29
4 A house with a garage.

Summary 2 **b** $x + y = 4$

Check in

1 **a** 400 g **b** 100 g **c** 20 g **d** 240 g
2 9 boys
3 **a** 75% **b** 90, 90% **c** 40, 40%
  d $\frac{55}{100}$, 55% **e** $\frac{28}{100}$, 28% **f** $\frac{105}{100}$, 105%

Summary 2 **a** 25% **b** 3:2

Check in

1 **a** 8 **b** -12 **c** 13 **d** -13
  e -24 **f** -12 **g** -16 **h** 14
2 **a** $2x + 5$ **b** $x^2 + 5$ **c** $(5x)^2$
  d $2(x + 5)$ **e** $5x^2$
3 **a** $6x - 8y$ **b** $3x^2 + 12x$
  c $12ab$ **d** Doesn't simplify
  e $4t$ **f** $2x^2$
4 **a** $3x + 27$ **b** $5y - 20$ **c** $m^2 + 3m$
  d $xy + xz$ **e** $6x + 10$

Summary 2 $54x^2$

Check in

1 **a** anticlockwise 90° **b** clockwise 90°
  c either way 180°
2 **a** parallelogram **b** trapezium
  c rhombus **d** kite
3 **b i** $y = 1$ **ii** $x = -2$
  c i $y = 0$ **ii** $x = 0$

Summary 2 34°

Check in

1 **a** 5 **b** 20, 21 **c** 9
2 **a** £24 500 **b** Median is unchanged.
3 235 g
4 150.5 cm

Summary

2 **a** Design 1, too much writing involved.
  b Design 3, quick to fill in a tally chart.

Check in

1 **a** 28 676
2 **a i** $\frac{4}{3}$ **ii** $\frac{13}{9}$ **iii** $\frac{21}{8}$ **iv** $\frac{19}{4}$
  b i $1\frac{3}{8}$ **ii** $3\frac{1}{2}$ **iii** $3\frac{3}{5}$ **iv** $7\frac{7}{10}$
3 **a** $2 \times 2 \times 7 = 2^2 \times 7$
  b $2 \times 3 \times 3 \times 7 = 2 \times 3^2 \times 7$

Summary 2 **a** £729 **b** £14

16

Check in

1 **a** 0, -2 **b** 64, 128 **c** 36, 49 **d** 0.9, 1.0
2 **a** 6, 7, 8, 9, 10, ... **b** 1, 4, 9, 16, 25, ...
  c 1, 3, 5, 7, 9, ... **d** 3, 6, 9, 12, 15, ...
3 **a** 13 **b** -5 **c** 10
  d 8 **e** -16 **f** 18
4 **a** $x = 5$ **b** $y = 12$ **c** $z = 6$ or -6
  d $a = 5$ **e** $b = -14\frac{1}{3}$
5 $y = 5, 8$

Summary

2 $x = 0$ is the line through B and D;
  $x + y = 2$ is the line though A and B;
  $x + y = -2$ is the line though C and D

17

Check in

1, 2, 3 Check your drawings
Summary 2 Check your drawings

Index